MECHANICAL PROPERTIES OF POLYMERS

LAWRENCE E. NIELSEN

Senior Scientist
Monsanto Chemical Company
Springfield, Massachusetts

New York
REINHOLD PUBLISHING CORPORATION
CHAPMAN & HALL, LTD., LONDON

Library of Congress Catalog Card Number 62–18939

Printed in the United States of America

TO
DEANNE AND LINDA

PREFACE

It is the purpose of this book to present a concise review of a wide variety of mechanical properties of high polymers from both the theoretical and experimental viewpoints. Emphasis is placed upon general principles and useful empirical generalizations. This is the first time that many of these generalizations on mechanical behavior and structure have been collected in one place. Certainly some of the theoretical advances of the future will be based upon these empirical generalizations and rules of thumb; in the meantime, practical use may be made of them. These rules are not always strictly correct or extremely accurate, but they are of great practical value, and they enable one to readily understand many of the mechanical properties of polymers and to bring order out of the chaotic mass of data on mechanical behavior.

This book differs from most other books on mechanical behavior in that it covers a much wider field of mechanical tests. In addition to the usual tests discussed in connection with viscoelastic theory such as creep, stress relaxation, and dynamic behavior, this book also devotes considerable space to stress-strain behavior, impact strength, hardness tests, heat distortion tests, fatigue behavior, and frictional properties. In addition, a chapter is devoted to orientation phenomena and to heat and solvent treatments which are so important in the processing of polymers and which have a tremendous effect on the use properties of plastics and fibers.

Extensive references to published literature enable the reader to find important sources of information on numerous topics easily and quickly. Emphasis is placed on the most important articles on the various fields of mechanical properties and polymeric transitions. Mathematical derivations are avoided for the most part; only the final practical equations are listed, and numerous illustrative examples are given.

It is apparent, therefore, that this book is not primarily for the specialist in the field of mechanical properties of high polymers. Rather, it is written at an elementary or intermediate level to fit the needs of:

(1) The industrial polymer research scientist who should have some back-

ground information on mechanical properties and their relation to molecular structure.

(2) The design engineer who needs to know the significance of the various mechanical tests and how plastics and rubbers differ from other structural materials.

(3) The fabricator of polymeric materials who is interested in knowing how processing variables affect mechanical behavior and who wants to choose the correct polymer to fulfill the mechanical requirements of a given finished product.

(4) Those students who have an interest in high polymers and who wish to learn something of the physics and mechanical properties of such materials.

I am especially indebted to Drs. R. L. Miller, S. Newman, and F. D. Stockton who painstakingly studied the manuscript and offered numerous suggestions for its improvement. Many other of my colleagues, too numerous to mention individually here, have also read the manuscript and have been kind enough to point out mistakes and to make helpful suggestions. I also wish to acknowledge the help of my wife in arranging the literature references and in proofreading the manuscript several times during the various stages of this book. I am also indebted to the typists, headed by Mrs. Janet Webster, who had to decipher my handwriting and convert it to a legible form. Many of the graphs were made for me by Mr. R. Keeney. Finally, I wish to acknowledge the help and encouragement given me by the management of the Monsanto Chemical Company during the months required to write this book.

LAWRENCE E. NIELSEN

Springfield, Mass.
June, 1962

24

CONTENTS

Chapter 1

INTRODUCTION TO MECHANICAL BEHAVIOR

Importance of Mechanical Properties

High polymers are important to all of us. High polymeric molecules make up synthetic plastics, rubbers, films, and fibers. Natural polymers include proteins and cellulose. All of these substances have very high molecular weights, and the molecules are generally in the form of long chains. For instance, polyethylene, a typical high polymer, consists of molecules made up of long chains of CH_2 groups:

$$-\left(\begin{array}{ccccccccccc} H & & H & & H & & H & & H & & H \\ | & & | & & | & & | & & | & & | \\ C & - & C & - & C & - & C & - & C & - & C \\ | & & | & & | & & | & & | & & | \\ H & & H & & H & & H & & H & & H \end{array}\right)-.$$

Similarly, polystyrene has the structure

$$\left(\begin{array}{ccc} H & & H \\ | & & | \\ -C & - & C- \\ | & & | \\ H & & C_6H_5 \end{array}\right)_n$$

where n is of the order of several thousand.

The mechanical properties of high polymers are of interest in any application where they are used as a structural material. The use of plastics, rubbers, and fibers is determined primarily by their mechanical properties rather than by their chemical behavior. Will a plastic object be strong enough to serve its purpose? Will it be tough enough to withstand being dropped? These are the types of questions important to the design engineer and the fabricator of plastic parts. The research man is interested in knowing why one polymer is tough while another is brittle, or why one polymer is rigid while another one is a rubber. The synthetic polymer chemist wants to know how mechanical behavior is related to chemical structure in order that he can tailor-make materials with any desired properties. This book will describe the mechanical behavior of polymers and will show how such materials differ from the more conventional structural materials such as metals and glasses. The tremendous variations in properties of polymers could lead to confusion. However, the application of a few general principles makes this variation easily understood. In addition, when it is possible, it will be shown how the mechanical behavior is related to chemical or molecular structure of the polymer.

Definition of Mechanical Terms

Mechanical behavior involves the deformation of a material by applied forces. An homogeneous, isotropic, elastic material has the simplest mechanical properties; its mechanical response can be defined by only two constants. Anisotropic or crystalline materials require more constants to describe their mechanical behavior.

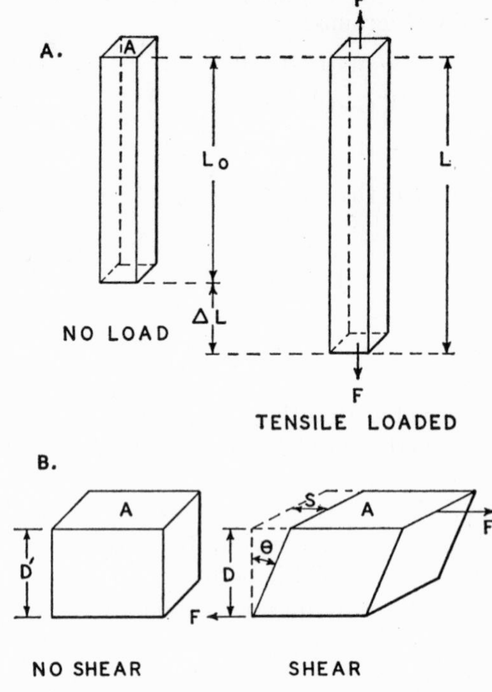

Figure 1.1. A. Tensile stretching of a bar. B. Shear of a rectangular block.

Figure 1.1A illustrates the stretching of a bar by a tensile load. The original bar has a length L_0 and a cross-sectional area A. A tensile force F increases the length of the bar by an amount ΔL to give a stretched length of L. Young's modulus E, for a material which obeys Hooke's law, is defined as the ratio of tensile stress to tensile strain, or

$$E = \frac{\text{Tensile stress } \sigma}{\text{Tensile strain } \epsilon} = \frac{\text{Force per unit area}}{\text{Stretch per unit length}} \tag{1.1}$$

therefore,

$$E = \frac{F/A}{\Delta L/L_0} = \frac{\sigma}{\epsilon}; \qquad \text{or} \qquad \sigma = \epsilon E \tag{1.2}$$

The stress is defined as the force per unit area of cross section. The elongation or strain ϵ is generally defined as

$$\epsilon = \frac{\Delta L}{L_0} \tag{1.3}$$

for small elongations; for large elongations other definitions are sometimes more convenient.

Other definitions of strain are: (1) $\Delta L/L$; (2) $\ln(L/L_0)$; (3) $\frac{1}{3}[L/L_0 - (L_0/L)^2]$. The second of the definitions, $\ln(L/L_0)$, is sometimes called true strain. The third definition is important with rubbers and comes from the kinetic theory of rubber elasticity[2, 6]. In most of the discussion in this book strain will be defined as $\Delta L/L_0$. A comparison of the different definitions of strain for various elongations is given in Table 1.1. All of the definitions give essentially the same values at very small extensions, but they differ considerably at high elongations.

In the above example it was shown how Young's modulus determines the response of an elastic material to a tensile force. The same equations apply where the bar is decreased in length by a compressive force. Young's

TABLE 1.1. COMPARISONS OF DEFINITIONS OF STRAIN.

$\Delta L/L_0$	$\Delta L/L$	$\ln (L/L_0)$	$\frac{1}{3}[L/L_0 - (L_0/L)^2]$
0	0	0	0
.010	.0099	.00995	.00990
.050	.0476	.0488	.0477
.100	.0909	.0953	.0912
.200	.167	.1823	.1685
.500	.333	.4055	.3518
1.000	.500	.6932	.583

TABLE 1.2. YOUNG'S MODULUS AND DEFORMATION OF BEAMS.

Beam	Deformation Due to Applied Force	Dimensions (original)	Young's Modulus (E)
	$\Delta L = L - L_0$	Length L_0 Cross section A	$E = \dfrac{F/A}{\Delta L/L_0}$
	Y	Length L_0 width C thickness D	$E = \dfrac{4FL^3}{CD^3Y}$
	Y	Length L_0 Radius r	$E = \dfrac{4FL_0^3}{3\pi r^4 Y}$
	Y	Length L_0 width C thickness D	$E = \dfrac{FL_0^3}{4CD^3Y}$
	Y	Length L_0 Radius r	$E = \dfrac{FL_0^3}{12\pi r^4 Y}$

modulus determined from compressive experiments should be the same as Young's modulus determined from tensile experiments. In actual practice, compressive tests give moduli equal to or slightly greater than tensile tests.

Young's modulus can also be determined from flexural deformations of beams or bars. Table 1.2 lists equations for calculating the Young's modulus of various types of cantilever and end-supported beams.

The shearing of a rectangular block is illustrated in Figure 1.1B. The rigidity or shear modulus G is defined as the ratio of shearing stress to shearing strain.

$$G = \frac{\text{shear stress } \sigma_s}{\text{shear strain } \epsilon_s} = \frac{\text{shear force per unit area}}{\text{shear per unit distance between shearing surfaces}} \tag{1.4}$$

or

$$G = \frac{F/A}{S/D} = \frac{F}{A \tan \theta} = \frac{\sigma_s}{\epsilon_s} \tag{1.5}$$

Shear is involved also in the deformation of beams under torsion. For a solid cylindrical beam which is twisted through an angle ϕ, the shear modulus is given by

$$G = \frac{2LT}{\pi r^4 \phi} \tag{1.6}$$

The beam has a length L and a radius r. A torque T is required to twist the beam through the angle ϕ. If the beam has a rectangular cross section, the shear modulus is given by

$$G = \frac{16LT}{CD^3\mu\phi} \tag{1.7}$$

The beam has a width C and a thickness D in this case; for a square beam C equals D. The shape factor μ is a function of C/D and is given in Table 1.3.

A third type of modulus is the bulk modulus B. It is defined as the ratio of the hydrostatic pressure P to the volume strain.

$$B = \frac{\text{Hydrostatic pressure } P}{\text{Volume strain}} = \frac{\text{Hydrostatic pressure}}{\text{Volume change per unit volume}} \tag{1.8}$$

$$B = \frac{P}{\Delta V/V_0} = \frac{PV_0}{\Delta V} \tag{1.9}$$

TABLE 1.3. VALUES OF SHAPE FACTOR μ.*

Ratio of Specimen Width to Thickness C/D	Shape Factor μ
1.00	2.249
1.20	2.658
1.40	2.990
1.60	3.250
1.80	3.479
2.00	3.659
2.25	3.842
2.50	3.990
2.75	4.111
3.00	4.213
3.50	4.373
4.00	4.493
4.50	4.586
5.00	4.662
6.00	4.773
7.00	4.853
8.00	4.913
10.00	4.997
20.00	5.165
50.00	5.266
100.00	5.300
∞	5.333

* Trayer, G. W., and March, H. W., *Nat. Advisory Comm. Aeronaut.*, Report No. 334.

where V_0 is the original volume of the material, and ΔV is the change in volume brought about by the application of the pressure.

It is sometimes more convenient to work with the reciprocals of the moduli rather than with the moduli themselves. The reciprocal of the bulk modulus is called the compressibility. The reciprocals of the shear modulus and Young's modulus are called the shear compliance and the tensile compliance; they are denoted by the symbol J.

When a material is stretched, its cross-sectional area changes as well as its length. Poisson's ratio ν is the constant relating these changes in dimensions, and it is defined as

$$\nu = \frac{\text{Change in width per unit of width}}{\text{Change in length per unit length}} = \frac{\Delta C/C}{\Delta L/L_0} \tag{1.10}$$

It can be shown that if the volume of a material remains constant when stretched, Poisson's ratio is 0.50. Generally materials increase their volume when subjected to a tensile stress, so Poisson's ratio is less than 0.50. For most materials, Poisson's ratio lies between 0.20 and 0.50; the ratio approaches 0.50 for rubbers and liquids.

The moduli are not independent of one another. They are interrelated by the following equation for isotropic materials:

$$E = 2G(1 + \nu) = 3B(1 - 2\nu) \tag{1.11}$$

Table 1.4 shows how the ratio of Young's modulus to shear modulus and the ratio of bulk modulus to Young's modulus change with different values of Poisson's ratio. Young's modulus is about 2.5 to 3.0 times as great as the shear modulus for most materials; the more rigid the material, the smaller the ratio. The table also shows that as a material becomes more

TABLE 1.4. INTERRELATIONS BETWEEN THE ELASTIC CONSTANTS.

Poisson's Ratio	Young's Modulus / Shear Modulus	Bulk Modulus / Young's Modulus
0	2.00	0.333
.10	2.20	0.417
.20	2.40	0.556
.25	2.50	0.667
.30	2.60	0.833
.35	2.70	1.111
.40	2.80	1.667
.45	2.90	3.333
.50	3.00	∞

TABLE 1.5. MODULUS CONVERSION FACTORS.

To Convert From	To	Multiply By
psi	dynes/sq cm	6.895×10^4
dynes/sq cm	psi	1.450×10^{-5}
psi	kg/sq mm	7.03×10^{-4}
kg/sq mm	psi	1.422×10^3
gm/denier	dynes/sq cm	8.83×10^8 d*
gm/denier	psi	1.28×10^4 d*
dynes/sq cm	bars	1.00×10^{-6}
dynes/sq cm	kg/sq mm	1.02×10^{-8}
kg/sq mm	dynes/sq cm	9.806×10^7
dynes/cm²	atmospheres	9.869×10^{-7}
psi	atmospheres	0.0681
atmospheres	dynes/cm²	1.013×10^6

* d = density.

TABLE 1.6. COMPARISON OF MECHANICAL PROPERTIES OF VARIOUS MATERIALS.

Material	Young's Modulus (dynes/cm²)	Poisson's Ratio	Tensile Strength (psi)	Tensile Strength / Density
Aluminum	7×10^{11}	0.33	9000	3300
Copper	12×10^{11}	0.35	39000	4300
Tin	4×10^{11}		4000	700
Lead	1.5×10^{11}	0.43	2000	176
Iron (cast)	9×10^{11}	0.27	15000	1900
Steel (mild)	22×10^{11}	0.28	60000	7500
Glass	6×10^{11}	0.23	10000	4000
Vitreous silica	7×10^{11}	0.14		
Granite	3×10^{11}	0.3	19000	7000
Polystyrene	3.4×10^{10}	0.33	6000	5600
Polymethyl methacrylate	3.7×10^{10}	0.33	7000	5900
Nylon 6-6	2×10^{10}		10000	9100
Polyethylene (low density)	2.4×10^9	0.38	2000	2200
Rubber	2×10^7	0.49	2000	2200

liquidlike in nature ($\nu \to 0.5$), the bulk modulus becomes much greater than the Young's modulus.

In the c.g.s. system of units the dimensions of moduli are dynes per square centimeter. In the English system the dimensions are pounds per square inch (psi). A number of other units may be found in the literature. Table 1.5 shows how to convert from one system of units to another. For instance, a rubbery material with a modulus of 100 psi has a modulus of 6.895×10^6 dynes per square centimeter.

The moduli of polymers cover a very wide range compared to other materials. Typical values of Young's modulus go from 10^6 dynes per square centimeter for rubbers to 5×10^{10} for rigid polymers. One of the reasons why high polymers are so versatile in their application is the possibility of choosing materials with so great a variation in stiffness. Table 1.6 lists some mechanical properties of a number of common materials including metals, glass, and polymers. Metals have moduli approximately a hundred times greater than the moduli of rigid polymers such as polystyrene. Even glass is about a factor of ten more rigid than plastics. This is a limitation of plastics in many applications. However, this limitation can be overcome in many cases by making a plastic part somewhat larger than a metal part or by using ribs to stiffen the plastic. Table 1.6 also shows that the strength of plastic materials is lower than that of other structural materials. However, plastics are so much lighter than metals, that when the comparison is made on the basis of equal weights of materials rather than on the basis of equal volumes, polymers compare favorably with metals. This is shown in the last column of Table 1.6.

Behavior of Viscoelastic Materials

So far only perfectly elastic materials have been discussed. Such materials in which the strain is proportional to the stress are said to obey Hooke's law; that is, they behave as perfect springs. A given load stretches them a definite amount, and when the load is removed, they shrink back to their original length.

Polymers are not perfectly elastic. In addition to having some of the characteristics of elastic materials, they also have some of the characteristics of viscous liquids. Therefore, they are known as viscoelastic materials. A liquid will deform when a shear stress is applied to it, but when the stress is removed, it will not snap back to its original state.

The coefficient of viscosity for a Newtonian liquid is defined as the ratio of tangential shearing stress to velocity gradient. In Figure 1.1B if rigid plates of area A filled with a viscous liquid move with respect to each other with a velocity v under the action of a force F, then the viscosity η is

$$\eta = \frac{\text{tangential shearing stress}}{\text{velocity gradient}} = \frac{F/A}{v/D} = \frac{F/A}{\dfrac{\Delta S}{\Delta t} \Big/ D} \tag{1.12}$$

The rate of shear or velocity gradient is

$$\frac{d\epsilon_s}{dt} = \dot{\epsilon}_s = \frac{v}{D} = \frac{\Delta S/\Delta t}{D} \tag{1.13}$$

The velocity is defined as the time derivative of the shear displacement S. For a viscous material the force resisting deformation is proportional to the velocity gradient. None of the energy is stored as in a spring but is dissipated as heat when a viscous material is deformed.

A number of mechanical tests may be used to study viscoelastic materials. Some tests are better than others. Tests should be chosen which can be interpreted. Some tests measure such complex combinations of basic factors that it becomes nearly impossible to understand the results. The most important tests include creep, stress relaxation, stress-strain, and dynamic mechanical behavior.

Creep measurements are some of the easiest to make. A load is applied to a test specimen, and its length is measured as a function of time. In addition to the initial elongation characteristic of elastic materials, the elongation will increase with time for a viscoelastic material. The creep behavior should be investigated as a function of temperature and load to properly evaluate a material.

In stress-relaxation measurements the test specimen is rapidly stretched to a given value, and the stress required to hold the length constant is measured as a function of time. The stress will be high at first and will gradually decrease. Depending upon the material, the stress may or may not decrease to zero in a practical length of time.

Stress-strain tests are made by stretching the sample at a given rate of elongation until the specimen breaks. The stress gradually builds up until the specimen either breaks or yields. From the stress-strain curve one can calculate a modulus, the ultimate elongation, and the breaking or tensile strength of the material. The stress-strain curve also indicates whether a material is brittle or ductile in nature. If the rate of strain is very high, this type of test becomes similar to an impact test which measures toughness or energy required to break the test specimen. The area under a stress-strain curve is proportional to the energy absorbed in breaking the material. Thus, from the practical standpoint, such tests are very important.

In dynamic mechanical tests the test specimen is deformed by a stress which varies sinusoidally with time. The oscillating stress and strain are generally not in phase. Such tests enable one to calculate an elastic modulus and a mechanical damping or dissipation of energy into heat. The measurements are generally made over a wide range of frequencies or at a number of temperatures. Dynamic measurements are important in such practical applications as heat buildup in tires or the reduction of dangerous resonance vibrations in various structures. In addition, we shall see that this type of test is especially useful in studies of the chemical and molecular structure of polymers and in the relation of structure to transitions in polymers.

The theory of viscoelasticity has advanced to the state where it is possible to predict creep or stress-relaxation behavior from dynamic mechanical measurements or vice versa. These various mechanical properties are interrelated in a known manner. The theory of many other mechanical tests is not so well developed. For instance, the theory of the strength of materials is not nearly so advanced. The significance of many other tests such as brittle temperature, abrasion, fatigue, hardness, and friction is not completely understood. This is the fault of the test method itself in some cases; the test methods themselves may not be conducive to measuring scientifically meaningful quantities. However, as the test methods improve and more data are accumulated, certain empirical generalizations are beginning to develop, and a better understanding of mechanical behavior is emerging. These will be discussed in later chapters.

General References

1. Alfrey, T., "Mechanical Behavior of High Polymers," New York, Interscience Publishers, Inc., 1948.
2. Flory, P. J., "Principles of Polymer Chemistry," Ithaca, New York, Cornell University Press, 1953.
3. Houwink, R., "Elasticity, Plasticity, and Structure of Matter," Cambridge, England, University Press, 1937.
4. Stuart, H. A., "Die Physik der Hochpolymeren," Vol. 4, Berlin, Springer Verlag, 1956.
5. Tobolsky, A. V., "Properties and Structure of Polymers," New York, John Wiley & Sons, Inc., 1960.
6. Treloar, L. R. G., "The Physics of Rubber Elasticity," Oxford, Clarendon Press, 1958.

Chapter 2

TRANSITIONS IN HIGH POLYMERS

An understanding of the mechanical properties of high polymers is impossible without first learning something about the types of transitions that occur in such materials. These transitions include crystal melting, first-order crystalline transitions, glass transitions, and secondary glass transitions. Nearly all the mechanical properties of polymers are determined primarily by these transitions and the temperatures at which they occur.

Glass Transitions

Some liquids may be supercooled to form glasses without crystallization taking place as the temperature is lowered. In such materials the viscosity changes at so great a rate that over a small temperature interval the character of the material changes from a liquid to a rigid solid or glass. Many other properties of a substance also show a dramatic change in this glass-transition region[7, 26]. Some properties change in a nearly discontinuous manner at a temperature called the glass-transition temperature; other properties change more gradually over a small temperature range. The nature of the glass transition is not completely understood and possibly should not be called a transition in the thermodynamic sense[20]. Polymers have glass transitions; and from the effect of these transitions on the mechanical properties, it is convenient to treat the phenomenon as a true transition.

Glass-transition temperatures may be measured by many experimental techniques, but traditionally they are determined from the volume of the glassy material as a function of temperature. At the glass-transition temperature the volume-temperature curve has an abrupt change in slope. The top curve in Figure 2.1 shows typical results on an amorphous polymer[4]. Above the glass temperature T_g the coefficient of expansion is greater than the value below T_g. Similar results are obtained if the heat content or refractive index is plotted against temperature. The heat capacity, coeffi-

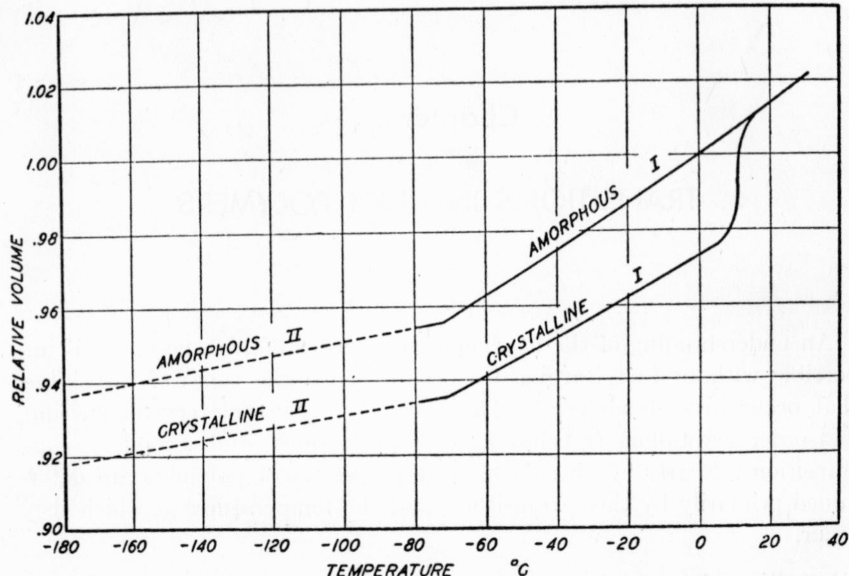

Figure 2.1. The volume-temperature characteristics of high polymers. The upper curve is for an amorphous polymer; the lower curve is for a partially crystalline polymer. Glass-transition temperature is at −71°C. Melting point is about 11°C. [*Reprinted from Bekkedahl, N., J. Research Nat. Bur. Standards*,, **13** *411* (*1934*)]

cient of expansion, diffusion coefficient, and elastic moduli all show jumps (or drops) in going through the glass transition. The mechanical damping of low-frequency oscillations goes through a sharp peak in the region of the glass transition.

A polymer above the glass temperature is a viscous liquid if the molecular weight is relatively low. If the molecular weight is very high or if the molecules are lightly crosslinked, a high polymer behaves as a rubber above the glass transition temperature T_g. In going from a rigid glass to a liquid polymer melt or rubber, Young's modulus and the shear modulus may decrease by a factor of about a thousand. The main difference between a rubber and a rigid plastic is that a rubber has a glass transition below room temperature while a plastic has a glass transition above room temperature. This is an important generalization. In other words, a rigid amorphous polymer softens to a flexible rubberlike material or to a viscous liquid in the glass-transition region.

Below the glass-transition temperature T_g, molecular motion is frozen in. At T_g the polymer has expanded to the extent that there is enough free volume available in the material for molecular motion to begin. Molecular segments occasionally have room enough to jump from one position to another with respect to their neighbors at this temperature. Because of the change in molecular mobility in the transition region, the viscosity changes by many decades within a few degrees. At T_g the viscosity is roughly 10^{13} poises.

For normal liquids well above T_g, the viscosity η may generally be represented as a function of temperature by

$$\eta = \eta_0 e^{\Delta H/RT} \tag{2.1}$$

where η_0 is a constant representing the viscosity at infinite absolute temperature, ΔH is the energy of activation for viscous flow, R is the gas constant, and T is the absolute temperature. For high polymers between T_g and 100 degrees above T_g, Williams, Landel, and Ferry[41] found that the viscosity may be more accurately approximated by

$$\log\left(\frac{\eta_T}{\eta_{T_g}}\right) = \frac{-17.44(T - T_g)}{51.6 + T - T_g} \tag{2.2}$$

In this form of the Williams-Landel-Ferry (W-L-F) equation a small correction involving density and temperature has been omitted. In this equation, temperature T and glass-transition temperature T_g are given in degrees Kelvin. The corresponding logarithm of the ratio of the viscosities at these temperatures is taken to the base 10. Equation 2.2 is plotted in Figure 2.2. Table 2.1 shows how the viscosity would be expected to change with temperature if the viscosity at the glass temperature is 10^{13} poises.

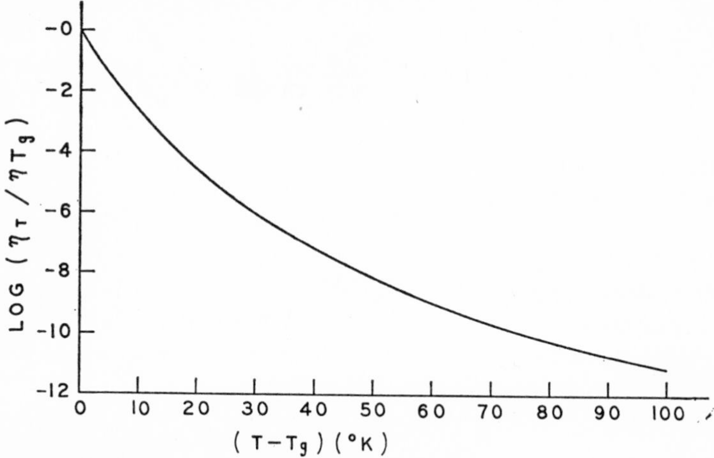

Figure 2.2. Temperature dependence of viscosity according to the W-L-F treatment.

TABLE 2.1. W-L-F PREDICTIONS OF VISCOSITY AND ITS TEMPERATURE DEPENDENCE.

$T - T_g$	$\text{Log}\left(\frac{\eta_T}{\eta_{T_g}}\right)$	η_T if $\eta_{T_g} = 10^{13}$	ΔH if $T_g = 200°K$	ΔH if $T_g = 350°K$
0	0	1.00×10^{13}	61.94	189.6
2	−0.6003	2.51×10^{12}	49.80	151.2
5	−1.4272	3.74×10^{11}	—	—
10	−2.6385	2.30×10^{10}	41.59	122.2
20	−4.5836	2.61×10^{8}	34.43	97.4
30	−6.0767	8.38×10^{6}	—	—
50	−8.2186	6.05×10^{4}	22.87	58.56
80	−10.251	5.61×10^{2}	—	—
100	−11.173	6.72×10^{1}	15.57	34.24

η in poises.
ΔH in kilocalories per mole of repeating unit.

The energy of activation ΔH for viscous flow by the W-L-F treatment is given by

$$\Delta H = \frac{Rd(\log \eta)}{d(1/T)} = \frac{4.12 \times 10^3 T^2}{(51.6 + T - T_g)^2} \tag{2.3}$$

The energy of activation ΔH is a measure of the temperature coefficient of the viscosity; the greater the energy of activation the greater is the change of viscosity with temperature. While the viscosity depends only upon the difference $(T - Tg)$, the energy of activation depends upon the absolute value of the glass temperature as well. The energy of activation of viscosity increases with T_g. This is illustrated in Table 2.1 for values of $T_g = 200°K$ and $T_g = 350°K$. The W-L-F treatment does not apply below the glass temperature. However, Bischoff, Catsiff, and Tobolsky[5] have shown that a maximum in the energy of activation occurs at T_g, and at lower temperatures the activation energy becomes much smaller.

In the above discussion it has been implied that the glass transition is the region where the viscosity reaches approximately 10^{13} poises; however, the glass transition is not an isoviscous state. The viscosity is in turn determined by the free volume of the material. The free volume may be defined in various ways, but it may be considered as the difference in volume at any temperature and the volume occupied by the liquid at absolute zero. It is an excess volume over that occupied by the molecules. Doolittle[14] has proposed that the free volume fraction f is related to the viscosity by

$$\eta = Ae^{B/f} \tag{2.4}$$

where A and B are constants. The W-L-F equation can be derived by the use of the Doolittle equation if two simple and reasonable assumptions are made. These assumptions are: (1) The free volume fraction at the glass temperature for all glassy materials is 0.025; (2) The change in volume coefficient of expansion at the glass temperature is 4.8×10^{-4} deg^{-1}. Experiments on many glass-forming liquids and polymers have shown that these assumptions are approximately correct. The glass transition should take place at a temperature where the material has expanded to the extent that its free volume is about 2.5 per cent of its total volume.

Relation of Glass Transitions to Structure

The glass-transition temperature T_g of a number of polymers is given in Tables 2.2, 2.3, and 2.4. Values of T_g vary from -123°C for a silicone to 208°C for polyvinyl carbazole. A study of these tables gives a number of clues on how the glass temperature depends upon the chemical structure of a polymer.

The most important factor in determining the value of T_g is flexibility of the polymer chain. Flexible chains such as those made up of —CH_2—CH_2— or —$Si(CH_3)_2$—O—$Si(CH_3)_2$— have low glass transitions. Stiff polymer chains such as polyvinyl formal

```
   H     H     H   H
   |     |     |   |
 —C—————C—————C———C—,
   \     |    /    |
    \    H   /     H
     O       O
      \  H  /
       \ | /
         C
         |
         H
```

polycarbonate, or polymethyl methacrylate have high transition temperatures. This is to be expected from the previous discussion.

Factors which are often difficult to separate from chain flexibility in affecting the glass transition are steric hindrance and bulkiness of the side groups attached to the backbone chain. Steric hindrance increases the glass temperature. This is illustrated by the difference in T_g of poly(*p*-methylstyrene) (101°C) and poly(*o*-methylstyrene) (125°C); methyl in the ortho position restricts the motion of the benzene ring. The difference between polymethyl acrylate and polymethyl methacrylate appears to be largely due to the steric effect of the methyl group. Bulkiness of a side group increases the glass transition. This can be illustrated by comparing the glass temperatures of the series: polyethylene, polypropylene, polystyrene, and polyvinylcarbazole in which the side groups change in the

TABLE 2.2. GLASS-TRANSITION TEMPERATURE OF POLYMERS.

Polymer	Repeat Unit	T_g (°C)
Polyethylene	H H —C—C— H H	−120
Polypropylene	H CH_3 —C—C— H H	−10, −18
Polyisobutylene	H CH_3 —C—C— H CH_3	−70, −60
Polyisoprene	H CH_3 H H —C—C═C—C— H H	−73
Polybutadiene	H H H H —C—C═C—C— H H	−90
Poly-2-isopropyl-1,3-butadiene	H $CH(CH_3)_2$ H —C—C═C—C— H H H	−47
Poly-2-*tert.* butyl-1,3-butadiene	H $C(CH_3)_3$ H —C—C═C—C— H H H	+20
Poly-2-*n*-heptyl-1,3-butadiene		−83
Poly-2-*n*-decyl-1,3-butadiene		−53
Poly-1-butene	H C_2H_5 —C—C— H H	−25

TABLE 2.2. CONTINUED

Polymer	Repeat Unit	T_g (°C)
Poly-1-pentene	$\begin{array}{cc} H & C_3H_7 \\ | & | \\ -C- & C- \\ | & | \\ H & H \end{array}$	−40, −24
Poly-1-hexene	$\begin{array}{cc} H & C_4H_9 \\ | & | \\ -C- & C- \\ | & | \\ H & H \end{array}$	−50
Poly-1-octene	$\begin{array}{cc} H & H \\ | & | \\ -C- & C- \\ | & | \\ H & C_6H_{13} \end{array}$	−65
Poly-1-dodecene	$\begin{array}{cc} H & C_{10}H_{21} \\ | & | \\ -C- & C- \\ | & | \\ H & H \end{array}$	−25 (?)
Poly-4-methyl pentene-1	$\begin{array}{cc} H & CH_2-CH(CH_3)_2 \\ | & | \\ -C- & C- \\ | & | \\ H & H \end{array}$	+18 (Cryst.) 29 (amorph.)
Polyoxymethylene	$\begin{array}{c} H \\ | \\ -C-O- \\ | \\ H \end{array}$	−50 (−85)
Polyvinyl methyl ether	$\begin{array}{cc} H & O-CH_3 \\ | & | \\ -C- & C- \\ | & | \\ H & H \end{array}$	−20, −10
Polyvinyl ethyl ether	$\begin{array}{cc} H & O-C_2H_5 \\ | & | \\ -C- & C- \\ | & | \\ H & H \end{array}$	−25
Polyvinyl-*n*-butyl ether	$\begin{array}{cc} H & O-C_4H_9 \\ | & | \\ -C- & C- \\ | & | \\ H & H \end{array}$	−52
Polyvinyl isobutyl ether	$\begin{array}{cc} H & O-CH_2-CH(CH_3)_2 \\ | & | \\ -C- & C- \\ | & | \\ H & H \end{array}$	−5, −18

TABLE 2.2. CONTINUED

Polymer	Repeat Unit	T_g (°C)
Polyvinyl tert. butyl ether	$-\overset{H}{\underset{H}{C}}-\overset{O-C(CH_3)_3}{\underset{H}{C}}-$	+88
Polydimethyl siloxane	$-\overset{CH_3}{\underset{CH_3}{Si}}-O-$	−123
Polyvinyl fluoride	$-\overset{H}{\underset{H}{C}}-\overset{F}{\underset{H}{C}}-$	−20
Polyvinyl chloride	$-\overset{H}{\underset{H}{C}}-\overset{Cl}{\underset{H}{C}}-$	87
Polyvinylidene fluoride	$-\overset{H}{\underset{H}{C}}-\overset{F}{\underset{F}{C}}-$	−35
Polyvinylidene chloride	$-\overset{H}{\underset{H}{C}}-\overset{Cl}{\underset{Cl}{C}}-$	−17
Polyperfluoropropylene	$-\overset{F}{\underset{F}{C}}-\overset{CF_3}{\underset{F}{C}}-$	11
Polychloroprene	$-\overset{H}{\underset{H}{C}}-\overset{Cl}{C}=\overset{H}{C}-\overset{H}{\underset{H}{C}}-$	−50
Polychlorotrifluoroethylene	$-\overset{Cl}{\underset{F}{C}}-\overset{F}{\underset{F}{C}}-$	45
Polytetrafluoroethylene	$-\overset{F}{\underset{F}{C}}-\overset{F}{\underset{F}{C}}-$	126

TABLE 2.2. CONTINUED

Polymer	Repeat Unit	T_g (°C)
Polyacrylonitrile	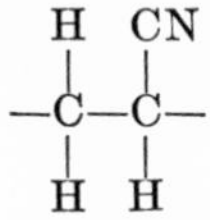 H CN —C—C— H H	104, 130
Polymethacrylonitrile	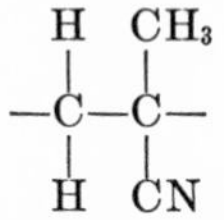 H CH_3 —C—C— H CN	120
Polyvinyl acetate	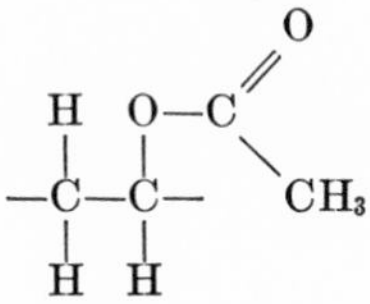 O H O—C —C—C— CH_3 H H	29
Polyvinyl carbazole	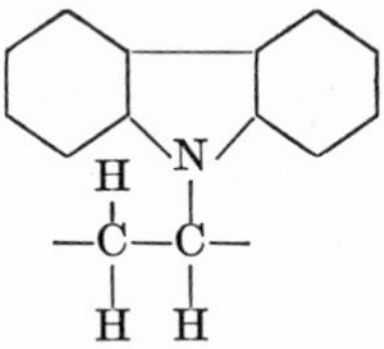 N H —C—C— H H	150, 208
Polyvinyl formal	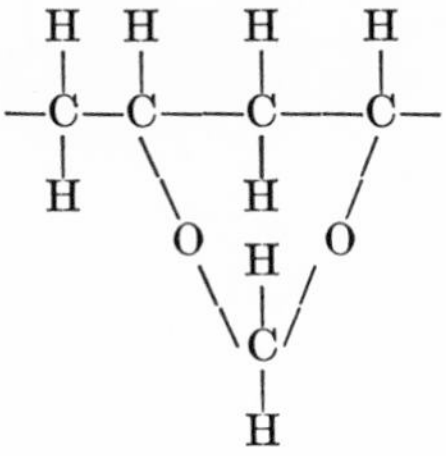 H H H H —C—C——C——C— H H O H O C H	105
Polyvinyl acetal		82
Polyvinyl proprional		72
Polyvinyl butyral	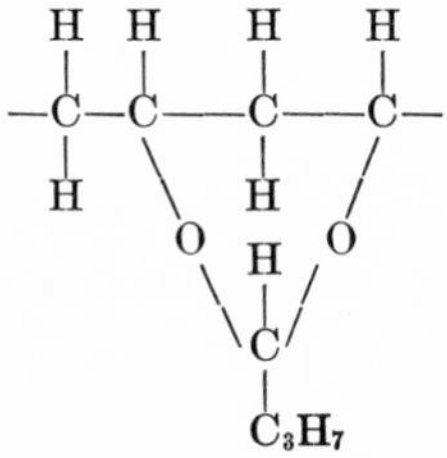 H H H H —C—C——C——C— H H O H O C C_3H_7	49

TABLE 2.2. CONTINUED

Polymer	Repeat Unit	T_g (°C)
Polyvinyl isobutyral		56
Cellulose nitrate	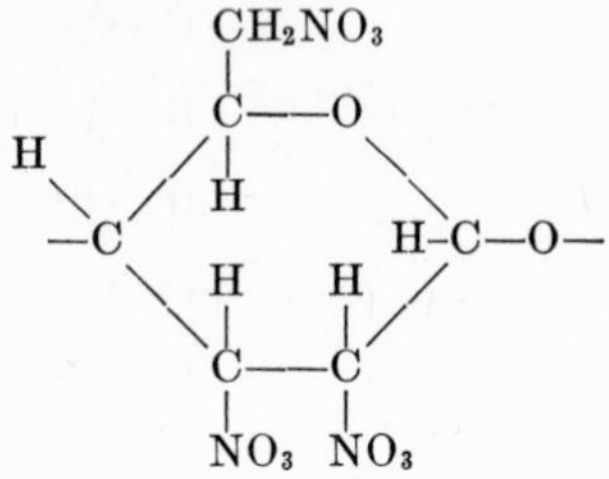 $\begin{array}{ccccc} & & CH_2NO_3 & & \\ & & \mid & & \\ & & C - O & & \\ H & / & \mid\ \ H & \backslash & \\ -C & & & & H-C-O- \\ & \backslash & H \quad H & / & \\ & & C - C & & \\ & & \mid \quad \mid & & \\ & & NO_3\ \ NO_3 & & \end{array}$	53?
Cellulose triacetate		105, 69?
Cellulose (2.3) acetate		120
Cellulose tributyrate		120
Cellulose (2.6) butyrate		125
Ethyl cellulose		43
Polyvinyl alcohol	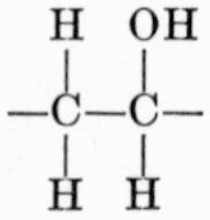 $-\underset{H}{\overset{H}{C}}-\underset{H}{\overset{OH}{C}}-$	85
Polycarbonate	$-O-C_6H_4-\underset{CH_3}{\overset{CH_3}{C}}-C_6H_4-O-\overset{O}{\overset{\|}{C}}-$	150
Polyethylene terephthalate	$-O-\underset{H}{\overset{H}{C}}-\underset{H}{\overset{H}{C}}-O-\overset{O}{\overset{\|}{C}}-C_6H_4-\overset{O}{\overset{\|}{C}}-$	69
Poly(ethylene adipate)	$-(CH_2)_2-O-\overset{O}{\overset{\|}{C}}-(CH_2)_4-\overset{O}{\overset{\|}{C}}-O-$	−70
Poly(tetramethylene sebacate)	$-(CH_2)_4-O-\overset{O}{\overset{\|}{C}}-(CH_2)_8-\overset{O}{\overset{\|}{C}}-O-$	−57
Polyhexamethylene adipamide (nylon 6-6)	$-\underset{H}{N}-(CH_2)_6-\overset{H}{N}-\overset{O}{\overset{\|}{C}}-(CH_2)_4-\overset{O}{\overset{\|}{C}}-$	50

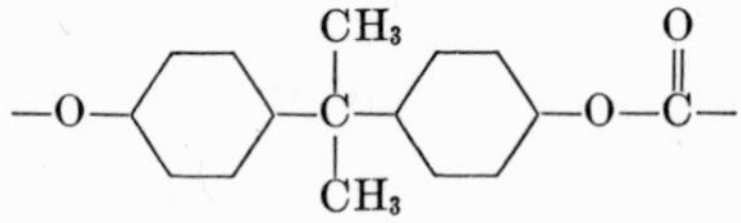

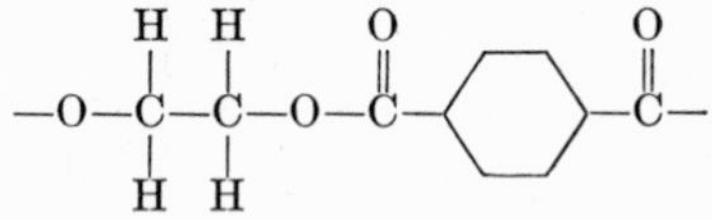

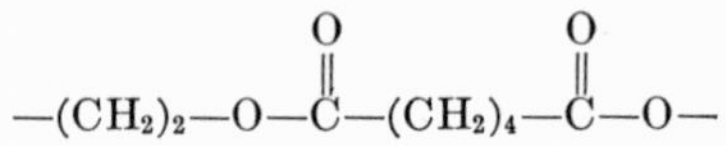

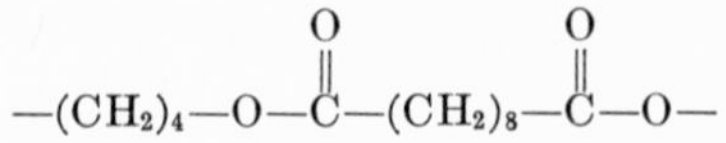

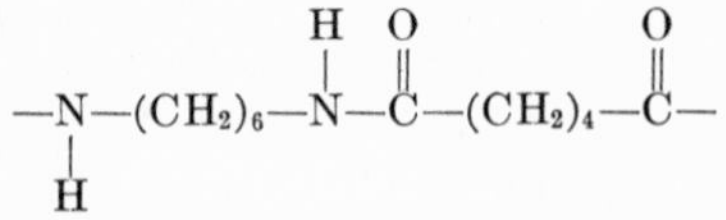

TABLE 2.2. CONTINUED

Polymer	Repeat Unit	T_g (°C)
Polyhexamethylene sebacamide (nylon 6-10)	$-\mathrm{N(H)}-(\mathrm{CH_2})_6-\mathrm{N(H)}-\mathrm{C(=O)}-(\mathrm{CH_2})_8-\mathrm{C(=O)}-$	40
Polycaprolactam (nylon 6)	$-\mathrm{N(H)}-(\mathrm{CH_2})_5-\mathrm{C(=O)}-$	50
Poly-*p*-vinyl benzyl alcohol	$-\mathrm{CH_2}-\mathrm{CH}(\mathrm{C_6H_4}-\mathrm{CH_2OH})-$	140
Poly-*o*-vinyl benzyl alcohol		160
Poly-*m*-vinyl benzyl alcohol		<125
Polyvinyl pyrrolidone	$-\mathrm{CH_2}-\mathrm{CH}(\mathrm{N}\langle\mathrm{CH_2CH_2CH_2C{=}O}\rangle)-$	175
Poly-2,2′-dichloromethyl propylene oxide	$-\mathrm{CH_2}-\mathrm{C}(\mathrm{CH_2Cl})_2-\mathrm{CH_2}-\mathrm{O}-$	10

REFERENCES TABLE 2.2.

1. Auspos, L. A., Burnam, C. W., Hall, L., Hubbard, J. K., Kirk, Jr., W., Schaefgen, J. R., and Speck, S. B., *J. Polymer Sci.*, **15**, 19 (1955).
2. BEAMAN, R. G., *J. Polymer Sci.*, **9**, 470 (1952).
3. Boyer, R. F., and Spencer, R. S., "Advances in Colloid Science," Vol. 2, p. 1, New York, Interscience Publishers, Inc., 1946.
4. Buchdahl, R., "Rheology," Vol. 2, Chapt. 4, p. 145, Eirich, F., Ed., New York, Academic Press, Inc., 1958.
5. Chapin, E., Unpublished data of Monsanto Chemical Co.
6. Dannis, M. L., *J. Appl. Polymer Sci.*, **1**, 121 (1959).
7. Fitzhugh, A. F., and Crozier, R. N., *J. Polymer Sci.*, **8**, 225 (1952).

8. Fox, T. G., Garrett, B. S., Goode, W. E., Gratch, S., Kincaid, J. F., Spell, A., and Stroupe, J. D., *J. Am. Chem. Soc.*, **80**, 1768 (1958).
9. Gaeth, R., *Kunststoffe*, **41**, 1, (1951).
10. Gerke, R. H., *J. Polymer Sci.*, **13**, 295 (1954).
11. Kolb, H. J., and Izard, E. F., *J. Appl. Phys.*, **20**, 564, 571 (1949).
12. Krigbaum, W. R. and Tokita, N., *J. Polymer Sci.*, **43**, 467 (1960).
13. Linton, W. H., and Goodman, H. H., *J. Appl. Polymer Sci.*, **1**, 179 (1959).
14. Mandelkern, L., and Flory, P. J., *J. Am. Chem. Soc.*, **73**, 3206 (1951).
15. Mandelkern, L., Martin, G. M., Quinn, F. A., *J. Research Nat. Bur. Standards*, **58**, 137 (1957).
16. Overberger, C. G., Arond, L. H., Wiley, R. H., and Garrett, R. R., *J. Polymer Sci.*, **7**, 431 (1951).
17. Reding, F. P., *J. Polymer Sci.*, **21**, 547 (1956).
18. Rogers, S. S., and Mandelkern, L., *J. Phys. Chem.*, **61**, 985 (1957).
19. Schmieder, K., and Wolf, K., *Kolloid Z.*, **134**, 149 (1954).
20. Tobolsky, A. V., "Properties and Structure of Polymers," p. 70, 320, New York, John Wiley & Sons, Inc., 1960.
21. Weir, C. E., Leser, W. H., and Wood, L. A., *J. Research Nat. Bur. Standards*, **44**, 367 (1950).
22. Wiley, R. H., and Brauer, G. M., *J. Polymer Sci.*, **11**, 221 (1953).
23. Wood, L. A., *J. Polymer Sci.*, **28**, 319 (1958).
24. Würstlin, F., *Kolloid Z.*, **120**, 84 (1951).

order

$-H$, $-CH_3$, and N

In this series T_g increases from −120 to +208°C. However, the glass temperature not only depends upon the size of the side group but also upon its flexibility. For instance, in the series polymethyl acrylate, polyethyl acrylate and polybutyl acrylate, the glass temperature actually decreases as the side group gets larger. The increased flexibility of the side group more than compensates for its increased size.

Symmetry may also affect the glass transition temperature. An increase in symmetry lowers T_g. Examples are: polyvinyl chloride (87°C) and polyvinylidene chloride (−17°C); polypropylene (−10°C) and polyisobutylene (−65°C). In these cases the increased number of side groups is more than compensated for by the increased molecular symmetry.

An increase in polarity or cohesive energy density has a tendency to raise the glass temperature, but sometimes the effect is small compared to the other factors discussed. Nonpolar polypropylene has a glass temperature of −10°C, moderately polar polyvinyl chloride has a glass transition at 87°C, and the highly polar polyacrylonitrile has a transition at 103°C.

TABLE 2.3. GLASS-TRANSITION TEMPERATURE OF ACRYLATE AND METHACRYLATE POLYMERS.*

Acrylates—$\left(\begin{array}{c}H\ \ H\\ |\ \ \ |\\ C—C\\ |\ \ \ |\\ H\ \ C—O—R\\ \ \ \ \ \|\\ \ \ \ \ O\end{array}\right)_n$— ; Methacrylates—$\left(\begin{array}{c}H\ \ CH_3\\ |\ \ \ |\\ C—C\\ |\ \ \ |\\ H\ \ C—O—R\\ \ \ \ \ \|\\ \ \ \ \ O\end{array}\right)_n$—

R =	T_g (°C) of Acrylate	T_g (°C) of Methacrylate
Methyl	+3	+105, 120 (syndiotactic) +45 (isotactic)
Ethyl	−22	+65
n-Propyl	−44	+35
n-Butyl	−56	+21
n-Hexyl	—	−5
n-Octyl	—	−20
n-Dodecyl	—	−65
n-Octadecyl	—	−100
H (acid)	+106	
$—CH_2CF_3$	−10	
$—CH_2CF_2CF_3$	−26	
$—CH_2(CF_2)_2CF_3$	−30	
$—CH_2CF_2CFHCF_3$	−22	
$—CH_2(CF_2)_3CF_3$	−37	
$—CH_2(CF_2)_4CF_3$	−39	
$—CH_2(CF_2)_6CF_3$	−17	
$—(CH_2)_2—O—CH_2—CF_3$	−38	
$—(CH_2)_2—O—CF_2—CF_2H$	−22	
$—(CH_2—CH_2—O)_2—CF_2—CF_2H$	−40	
$—(CH_2)_2—O—CH_2—(CF_2)_2—CF_3$	−45	
$—CH_2—(CF_2)_2—O—CF_3$	−55	
$—CH_2—(CF_2)_2—O—CF_2—CF_3$	−49	
$—CH_2—(CF_2)_2—O—(CF_2)_2—CF_3$	−68	
$—CH_2—(CF_2)_2—O—(CF_2)_3—CF_3$	−68	
$—(CH_2)_2—O—CH_3$	−50	
$—(CH_2)_2—O—CH_2—CH_3$	−50	
$—(CH_2)_3—O—CH_3$	−75	
$—(CH_2)_3—O—CH_2—CH_3$	−68	

REFERENCES TABLE 2.3.

1. Bovey, F. A., Abere, J. F., Rathman, G. B., and Sandberg, C. L., *J. Polymer Sci.*, **15,** 520 (1955).
2. Bovey, F. A., and Abere, J. F., *J. Polymer Sci.*, **15,** 537 (1955).
3. Goode, W. E., Owens, F. H., Fellman, R. P., Snyder, W. H., and, Moore J. E, *J. Polymer Sci.*, **46,** 317 (1960).
4. Rogers, S. S., and Mandelkern, L., *J. Phys. Chem.*, **61,** 985 (1957).*
5. Wiley, R. H., and Brauer, G. M., *J. Polymer Sci.*, **3,** 647 (1948).
6. Wood, L. A., *J. Polymer Sci.*, **28,** 319 (1958).

TABLE 2.4. GLASS-TRANSITION TEMPERATURE OF SUBSTITUTED POLYSTYRENES.*†

Polymer	T_g (°C)
Polystyrene $-(CH_2-CH(C_6H_5))_n-$	100, 105
o-Methyl	115, 125
m-Methyl	72, 82
p-Methyl	101
p-Ethyl	27, 78
p-*n*-Butyl	6
p-*n*-Hexyl	−27
p-*n*-Octyl	−45
p-*n*-Nonyl	−53
p-*n*-Decyl	−65
p-*n*-Dodecyl	−52 (?)
p-*n*-$C_{14}H_{29}$	−36 (?)
p-*n*-$C_{16}H_{33}$	+4.5 (?)
p-*n*-$C_{19}H_{39}$	+32 (?)
2,4-Dimethyl	119, 129
2,5-Dimethyl	122
3,4-Dimethyl	102, 83
p-*tert*.-Butyl	118, 131
p-Methoxy	<90
p-Phenyl	138
p-Phenoxy	100
2,5-Difluoro	101
p-Chloro	128
2,5-Dichloro	130, 115
3,4-Dichloro	138, 103
2,6-Dichloro	167, 132
α-Vinyl naphthalene	162
α-Methyl	180, 192, 150

* Reproduced with permission of the copyright owner, the American Chemical Society.

† Barb, W. G., *J. Polymer Sci.*, **37**, 515 (1959). Overberger, C., Frazier, C., Mandelman, J., and Smith, H., *J. Am. Chem. Soc.*, **75**, 3326 (1953).

In a similar manner, replacing the methyl group of polyisoprene by the polar chlorine group in chloroprene raises the glass transition about 25°C.

Barb[2] has made a detailed study of substituted polystyrenes; some of his results are shown in Table 2.4. His results agree with the principles discussed above. Groups substituted on the ortho position of the benzene ring of polystyrene produce a large increase in the glass temperature because of steric hindrance, the larger the group the greater the effect. Substitution on the para position has relatively little effect while a group on the meta position lowers the glass transition relative to the para compound. Substitution of a methyl group on the alpha position drastically stiffens the backbone chain and causes an increase of 80 to 90°C in T_g. Although a chlorine atom and a methyl group are comparable in size, a chlorine atom increases the glass temperature considerably more than a methyl group does; this may be due to the polarity of the chlorine group which decreases the free volume of the polymer because of the increased intermolecular attraction. Increasing the size of a side group raises T_g if the group itself is rigid, but if the group is flexible, the glass temperature may be lowered. This may be shown by comparing *p-tert.*-butyl polystyrene (T_g = 118°C) with *p-n*-butyl polystyrene (T_g = 6°C). In general, long alkyl chains lower the glass temperature when attached to a polymer. Both their flexibility and weak intermolecular forces contribute to this lowering. Ether linkages (—O—), such as found in silicones and poly-*p*-methoxystyrene, are extremely flexible and produce a large lowering of T_g.

In the acrylate polymers[39] shown in Table 2.3 the softening action or lowering of T_g by aliphatic groups is clearly evident. Acrylic acid, which has strong hydrogen bonds, has a glass temperature of 106°C; this is much higher than the other acrylates and indicates the effect which interatomic forces can have on T_g. Salts of acrylic acid polymers have extremely high glass temperatures; ionic bonding is thus especially effective in raising the glass temperature. Fluoroacrylates have somewhat higher glass temperatures than the corresponding alkyl acrylates[6]. It has been reported that the glass temperatures of homologous series of alkyl acrylates and similar polymers reach a minimum at about the normal octyl polymer; this probably is not true. The longer alkyl chains can crystallize, so a melting point could be mistaken for a glass temperature. Each CH_2 unit in a polymer makes a fairly constant contribution to lowering the glass transition[22].

Structure of Copolymers

Copolymers are made up of two or more types of monomers. Homopolymers are composed of long chains of monomers A or B to give —A—A—A—A—A— or —B—B—B—B—B—. Copolymers have structures something like —A—B—A—B—B—A—B—A—A—A—B—A—A—B—B—A—B—. If the distribution of the monomer units is random in the copolymer chain, then the distribution of sequence lengths of Type A can be calculated from[1]

$$N_A(n) = (1 - X_A)X_A^{(n-1)}. \tag{2.5}$$

$N_A(n)$ is the fraction of sequences of material A which have a length of n monomer units of Type A in a row, or it is the mole fraction of material A, that is in sequences of length n composed of Type A units. X_A is the mole fraction of material A in the copolymer. The weight fraction of material A which is in sequences containing n units of monomeric Type A is

$$W_A(n) = n(1 - X_A)^2 X_A^{(n-1)}. \tag{2.6}$$

Analogous equations hold for the distribution of the B sequences.

Table 2.5 shows the number and weight fractions of sequences of different lengths for copolymers containing 50, 25, and 10 mole per cent of monomeric material B. There are more sequences of length one than any other length, but in general the sequence with the greatest weight of material is of greater length. The average sequence length is $\bar{n}_A = 1/X_B$. Except in cases where the copolymers contain about the same concentration of the

TABLE 2.5. DISTRIBUTION OF SEQUENCE LENGTHS IN COPOLYMERS.

Molar Composition	Sequence Length	No. Fraction of A Sequences of Length n, $N_A(n)$	Weight Fraction of A in Sequences of Length n, $W_A(n)$
50A/50B	1	0.500	0.250
"	2	0.250	0.250
"	3	0.125	0.1875
"	4	0.062	0.1250
75A/25B	1	0.2500	0.0625
"	2	0.1875	0.0938
"	3	0.1407	0.1054
"	4	0.1054	0.1054
"	5	0.0791	0.0989
"	6	0.0593	0.0890
"	8	0.0333	0.0666
"	10	0.0188	0.0469
"	15	0.0044	0.0167
90A/10B	1	0.1000	0.0100
"	2	0.0900	0.0180
"	4	0.0729	0.0292
"	6	0.0590	0.0354
"	8	0.0478	0.0383
"	10	0.0388	0.0387
"	15	0.0229	0.0343
"	20	0.0135	0.0270
"	30	0.0047	0.0141
"	40	0.0017	0.0066
"	50	0.0006	0.0029

two types of monomers, considerable amounts of material are contained in long sequences. We shall see later that these long sequences are important in cases where crystallization can occur.

Glass Transitions in Copolymers

Copolymers have glass transitions at temperatures intermediate between those of the pure homopolymers. The relation between glass temperature and copolymer composition can generally be described by one of two simple relations. These are:

$$T_g = v_1 T_{g1} + v_2 T_{g2} \tag{2.7}$$

$$\frac{1}{T_g} = \frac{W_1}{T_{g1}} + \frac{W_2}{T_{g2}} \tag{2.8}$$

T_{g_1} and T_{g_2} are the glass temperatures in degrees Kelvin of pure homopolymers 1 and 2, respectively. The corresponding volume fractions of components 1 and 2 are v_1 and v_2, while the weight fractions are W_1 and W_2. A detailed discussion of these equations along with more complicated relations has been given by Wood[42]. Use of these copolymer equations is illustrated in Figure 2.3 in which one homopolymer has a glass temperature of 100°C (373°K) and a density of 1.1 while the other homopolymer has a glass temperature of −70°C (203°K) and a density of 0.90. This illustration corresponds roughly to the system styrene-butadiene.

Glass Transitions in Plasticized Systems

Plasticizers are liquids added to plastics to soften them. Plasticizers bring about this softening action by dissolving in the high polymer and lowering its glass-transition temperature. Plasticizers may also serve another purpose. They lower the melt viscosity, thus making the material process or fabricate more easily and at a lower temperature. For practical reasons plasticizers must be relatively nonvolatile, so they are usually limited to liquids with molecular weights of at least several hundred.

Most plasticizers have glass-transition temperatures in the range from −50 to −150°C[38]. The lower the transition temperature of the plasticizer the more efficient it is in lowering T_g of the polymer-plasticizer mixture. Efficient plasticizers generally have low viscosities and low temperature coefficients of viscosity. This is expected from theories of T_g based on free volume concepts since free volume and viscosity are related.

The lowering of T_g by plasticizers follows the same type of relations as equations 2.7 and 2.8 for copolymers. The plasticizer takes the place of the component with the lower T_g. The glass temperature of many polymer-plasticizer systems is a linear function of the volume fraction of the two

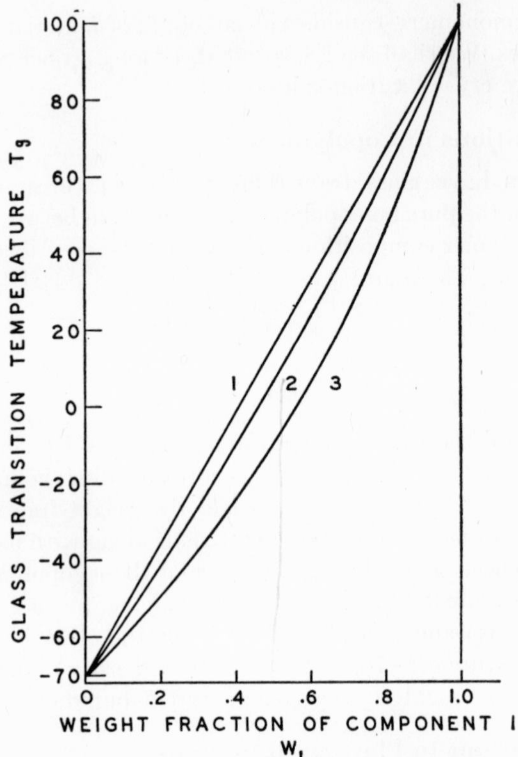

Figure 2.3. Glass-transition temperatures of copolymers as a function of composition. Curve 2 is a plot of equation 2.7. Curve 3 is a plot of equation 2.8. Homopolymer 1—T_g = 100°C, d_1 = 1.1; homopolymer 2—T_g = −70°C, d_2 = 0.90.

components. However, it is often observed that the first few per cent of plasticizer are somewhat more effective in lowering T_g than equal amounts of plasticizer at higher concentrations. In some systems the plasticizer has a solubility limit, so higher concentrations of plasticizer separate out as a second dispersed phase. Above the solubility limit, additional plasticizer is ineffective in further reduction of T_g[34]. Plasticizers are only effective as long as they are in solution.

Crystalline Polymers

Not all polymers are amorphous rubbers or glasses; many are semicrystalline. Examples of crystalline polymers are polyethylene, isotactic polypropylene, nylon 6-6, and polyvinylidene chloride. Such polymers behave as though they were a mixture of amorphous and crystalline material. The over-all degree of crystallinity may vary from a few per cent to over eighty per cent, the degree of crystallinity being defined as that fraction of the total polymer that is in the crystalline state. The remainder of the material is in the amorphous state, and it will have a glass transition as discussed in the first part of this chapter.

The volume-temperature curve of a crystalline polymer is shown in the lower curve of Figure 2.1. A change in slope occurs at T_g, and in the neighborhood of the melting point there is a fairly sharp increase in volume. Crystalline polymers melt over a temperature range, so there is not a discontinuous jump in volume at the melting point as there is with low molecular weight substances. The melting point of a polymer is taken as the highest temperature at which crystallinity can be detected in the material. The melting point may be determined from volume-temperature (dilatometric) measurements, x-ray diffraction as a function of temperature, calorimetric measurements, or from the disappearance of birefringence at the melting point. In later chapters it will be shown how the melting point can be determined from mechanical measurements.

There are two very useful empirical rules of thumb regarding crystalline polymers. The first relates the glass-transition temperature T_g to the melting point T_m. For unsymmetrical polymers the glass temperature is approximately two thirds of the melting point, both expressed in degrees Kelvin. For symmetrical polymers the ratio is roughly one half[3, 8].

$$T_g/T_m \doteq \tfrac{2}{3} \qquad \text{(Unsymmetrical)} \tag{2.9}$$

$$T_g/T_m \doteq 0.5 \qquad \text{(Symmetrical)} \tag{2.10}$$

For instance, polyethylene terephthalate has a melting point of 267°C. The rule predicts a glass temperature of 87°C; the experimental value is about 80°C. The symmetrical crystalline polymer polyvinylidene chloride has a glass transition at −17°C. The predicted melting point at 239°C is near the measured value. The second rule states that a molten polymer will crystallize at its maximum rate at a temperature equal to about nine-tenths of its melting point on the absolute temperature scale. With difficultly crystallizable polymers, it is convenient to be able to estimate the temperature at which the material will crystallize. For instance, crystallizable (isotactic) polystyrene melts at 235°C. The rule indicates maximum rate of crystallization should occur near 184°C. This is known to be about the correct value[30].

The degree of crystallinity may be measured by a number of techniques.

The crystalline portion of polymers produces sharp x-ray diffraction peaks while the amorphous phase gives rise to a very broad x-ray diffraction peak. The degree of crystallinity can be estimated from the relative areas under these two types of peaks.

The density of a polymer may be used to calculate a degree of crystallinity. If the specific volume (reciprocal of the density) is known for both the pure crystalline and amorphous phases at a given temperature, the degree of crystallinity W_c may be calculated from

$$W_c = \frac{\bar{v}_A - \bar{v}}{\bar{v}_A - \bar{v}_c} \tag{2.11}$$

where

$\bar{v}$ is the observed specific volume.

$\bar{v}_A$ is the specific volume of the amorphous phase at the same temperature.

$\bar{v}_c$ is the specific volume of the pure crystalline phase.

Crystalline polymers often show different infrared absorption bands than amorphous ones. The relative intensity of such absorption bands may be used to calculate the degree of crystallinity. If the heat of fusion of the pure polymer crystal is known, the degree of crystallinity may be calculated from calorimetric data.

In ideal cases, the degree of crystallinity as determined by these various methods will be the same. More often the different techniques give somewhat different values for the degree of crystallinity. In extreme cases one method (such as the density method) will give a moderately high crystallinity while another method (such as the x-ray method) shows no crystallinity. Obviously, the different methods do not always measure the same thing. Voids in a material can introduce errors in the density method. Extremely small crystallites can give such broad x-ray diffraction peaks that they may be interpreted as amorphous peaks. These are only two of the many factors which may introduce errors into calculations of crystallinity. Imperfections in the crystalline phase or variable degrees of ordering in both the amorphous and crystalline phases are additional factors which can not generally be evaluated. In fact, the whole concept of distinct amorphous and crystalline phases appears to be of limited validity as shown by recent morphological studies. However, from the practical standpoint, the concept of a degree of crystallinity is very useful.

Melting Point of Crystalline Polymers

Although the crystallites in a polymer melt over a temperature range, there is a temperature above which the crystals can not exist; this is the melting point. For a carefully annealed homopolymer most of the crystals melt within about five degrees of the melting point.

The longer the sequences of polymer chains in the crystals the higher the melting point. For a homopolymer, the sequence length can not be greater than the extended chain length. Therefore, the melting point depends upon the molecular weight. Flory[17, 18] has shown that the melting point is related to the number average molecular weight $\bar{M}_n$ for polymers with the most probable distribution of molecular weights by

$$\frac{1}{T_m} - \frac{1}{T_m^0} = \frac{2RM_0}{\Delta H_u \bar{M}_n} \tag{2.12}$$

The melting point T_m of a material with a given molecular weight is lower than the melting point T_m^0 of the pure homopolymer of infinite molecular weight. The temperatures must be expressed in degrees Kelvin. The molecular weight of the monomeric unit is M_0. The gas constant is R, and ΔH_u is the heat of fusion per mole of crystalline polymer repeating units. Instead of equation 2.12, the melting point as a function of molecular weight can be approximated by the equation

$$T_m = \frac{T_m^0(\bar{M}_n/M_0)}{B + \bar{M}_n/M_0} \tag{2.13}$$

where B is an empirical constant.

Copolymerization also lowers the melting point except in rare instances where the different types of monomeric units are capable of replacing one another in their crystal lattices. For a random copolymer the lowering of the melting point is given by the equation

$$\frac{1}{T_m} - \frac{1}{T_m^0} = \frac{-R}{\Delta H_u} \ln X_A \tag{2.14}$$

where X_A is the mole fraction of comonomer A (the crystallizable monomeric unit) in the copolymer. Table 2.6 gives the melting point expected for copolymers with heats of fusion of 1850 and 925 calories per mole of repeat unit and a melting point of 410°K. Ethylene copolymers should have a heat of fusion of 1850 cal/mole of ethylene but in practice they have lower values. This is characteristic of most copolymer systems.

If the copolymer is not random but is more like a block copolymer in which the A units and B units tend to form long sequences, the above equation will predict too low a melting point. This is because the long sequences are the ones important in determining the final melting point. Copolymerization lowers the maximum attainable degree of crystallinity as well as the melting point. In addition, the melting range is broadened, and the

TABLE 2.6. MELTING POINT OF RANDOM COPOLYMERS.

Mole Fraction of Crystallizable Monomer	Melting Point °K if ΔH_u = 1850 cal/mole	Melting Point °K if ΔH_u = 925 cal/mole
1.00	410	410
.95	401	392
.90	392	375
.85	383	359
.80	373	343
.75	364	327
.70	354	312
.65	345	297
.60	335	283

melting point becomes less sharp as the concentration of monomer A decreases. The equilibrium theory of crystallizable copolymers has been discussed by Flory[16].

The melting point of a polymer may also be lowered by solvents or plasticizers. The lowering is given by[16, 31]

$$\frac{1}{T_m} - \frac{1}{T_m^0} = \frac{R}{\Delta H_u} \frac{V_u}{V_1} (v_1 - \chi_1 v_1^2) \tag{2.15}$$

V_u is the molar volume of the polymer repeat unit. V_1 is the molar volume of the solvent. v_1 is the volume fraction of solvent. χ_1 is a first neighbor interaction parameter; it may be assumed to be a constant independent of composition in some cases. The term χ_1 is zero for an ideal solution, that is, molecules of one type "like" molecules of the other type as well as they "like" their own type. If the solvent has a weak attraction for the polymer (that is, it is a poor solvent), χ_1 takes on a positive value. The above equation shows that good solvents are more effective in lowering the melting point than are poor solvents. The melting points T_m^0 and heats of fusion ΔH_u of a number of polymers are given in Table 2.7.

In general, copolymerization is more effective in lowering the melting point than is plasticization. On the other hand, a plasticizer is usually more efficient in lowering the glass-transition temperature than an equal amount of a comonomer in a copolymer. These generalizations are important in plastic applications. For instance, in applications such as plastic raincoats it is important to have flexibility without excess creep, so plasticized polyvinyl chloride is used. In applications such as floor tile, creep is less detrimental but ease of processing is important, so a copolymer of polyvinyl chloride is used to destroy crystallinity. An example is shown in Figure 2.4 in which a plasticizer is compared with equal weights of a comonomer in a

TABLE 2.7. MELTING POINTS AND HEATS OF FUSION OF POLYMERS.

Polymer	Melting Point (°C)	ΔH_u(Cal/mole of repeat unit)
Polyethylene	137	925
Polypropylene	176	2370
Polybutene-1	126	3330
Polypentene-1	75	
Polyhexene-1	−55	
Polyheptene-1	−40	
Polyoctene-1	−38	
Polydodecene-1	45	
Polyoctadecene-1	76	
Poly-3-methyl butene-1	310	
Poly-4-methyl pentene-1	250	
Poly-4-methyl hexene-1	188	
Poly-5-methyl hexene-1	130	
Polyisoprene, cis (natural rubber)	28 (36)	1050
Polyisoprene, trans (gutta percha)	74	3040
Polyvinyl *tert.* butane	>350	
1,2-polybutadiene (syndiotactic)	154	
1,2-polybutadiene (isotactic)	120	
1,4-trans-polybutadiene	148 (92)	1430 (1000)
1,4-trans-poly-2,3-dimethyl butadiene	260	
Polyisobutylene	128 (1.5)	2870
Polyvinyl cyclohexane	305	
Polystyrene (isotactic)	240	2150
Poly-*o*-methyl styrene	>360	
Poly-*m*-methyl styrene	215	
Poly-2,4-dimethyl styrene	310 (350)	
Poly-2,5-dimethyl styrene	340	
Poly-3,5-dimethyl styrene	290	
Poly-3,4-dimethyl styrene	240	
Poly-*o*-fluorostyrene	270	
Poly-*p*-fluorostyrene	265	
Poly-2-methyl-4-fluorostyrene	360	
Poly-alpha-vinyl naphthalene	360	
Poly-*p*-xylene	375	7200
Polyoxymethylene	181	890
Polyethylene oxide	66	1980
Polypropylene oxide	75	
Poly-1-methoxybutadiene	118	
Polyvinyl methyl ether	144	
Polyvinyl ethyl ether	86	
Polyvinyl-*n*-propyl ether	76	
Polyvinyl isopropyl ether	190	
Polyvinyl-*n*-butyl ether	64	
Polyvinyl isobutyl ether	115 (165)	
Polyvinyl *tert.* butyl ether	260	
Polyvinyl neopentyl ether	216	

TABLE 2.7. CONTINUED

Polymer	Melting Point (°C)	ΔH_u(Cal/mole of repeat unit)
Polyvinyl benzyl ether	162	
Polyvinyl-2-chloroethyl ether	150	
Polyvinyl-2-methoxyethyl ether	73	
Polyisopropyl acrylate (isotactic)	162	
Polytertiary butyl acrylate	193	
Polymethyl methacrylate (isotactic)	160	
Polymethyl methacrylate (syndiotactic)	>200	
Poly(lauryl acrylate)†	2	
Poly(tetradecyl acrylate)†	22	
Poly(hexadecyl acrylate)†	33	
Poly(octadecyl acrylate)†	42	
Poly(lauryl methacrylate)†	−34	
Poly(tetradecyl methacrylate)†	−2	
Poly(hexadecyl methacrylate)†	20	
Poly(octadecyl methacrylate)†	34	
Polyethylene terephthalate	267	5820
Polytrimethylene terephthalate	233	
Polytetramethylene terephthalate	232	7600
Polypentamethylene terephthalate	134	
Polyhexamethylene terephthalate	160	8300
Polyoctamethylene terephthalate	132	
Polynonamethylene terephthalate	85	
Polydecamethylene terephthalate	138	11,000
Polyethylene isophthalate	240	
Polytrimethylene isophthalate	132	
Polytetramethylene isophthalate	152	10,000
Polyhexamethylene isophthalate	140	
Polyethylene sebacate	76	6950
Polytetramethylene sebacate	64	
Polydecamethylene sebacate	80	4700 (12,000)
Polyethylene adipate	50	
Polytrimethylene adipate	38	
Polydecamethylene adipate	80	3800 (10,200)
Polytrimethylene succinate	47	
Polytrimethylene glutarate	39	
Polytrimethylene pimelate	37	
Polytrimethylene suberate	41	
Polytrimethylene azelate	50	
Polydecamethylene azelate	69	10,000
Polycaproamide (nylon 6)	225 (215)	
Nylon 11	194	
Polyhexamethylene adipamide (nylon 6-6)	265	11,100
Polyhexamethylene sebacamide (nylon 6-10)	227	7300
Nylon 9-9	175	
Nylon 10-9	214	

TABLE 2.7. CONTINUED

Polymer	Melting Point (°C)	ΔH_u(Cal/mole of repeat unit)
Polydecamethylene sebacamide (nylon 10-10)	210 (216)	7800
Cellulose triacetate	306	
Cellulose triproprionate	234	
Cellulose tributyrate	183 (207)	3000
Cellulose trivalerate	122	
Cellulose tricaproate	94	
Cellulose triheptylate	88	
Cellulose tricaprylate	86 (116)	3100
Cellulose tricaprate	88	
Cellulose trilaurate	91	
Cellulose trimyristate	106	
Cellulose tripalmitate	105	
Cellulose trinitrate	>725	<1500
Polyvinyl chloride	212	3040
Polyvinylidene chloride	198	3780
Polychloroprene	80	2000
Polyvinyl fluoride	200	1800
Polytetrafluoroallene	126	
Polychlorotrifluoroethylene	220	1200
Polytetrafluoroethylene	327	685 (760)
Polyacrylonitrile	317	1160
Polycarbonate (Bis Phenol-A)	220 (267)	
Poly-N-isopropyl acrylamide	200	
Poly-3,3′-bischloromethyl oxacyclobutane	180	

† Alkyl side chain only crystallizes.

REFERENCES TABLE 2.7

1. Auspos, L. A., Burnam, C. W., Hall, L., Hubbard, J. K., Kirk, W., Schaefgen, J. R., and Speck, S. B., *J. Polymer Sci.*, **15**, 19 (1955).
2. Bunn, C. W., *J. Polymer Sci.*, **16**, 323 (1955).
3. Campbell, T. W., and Haven, Jr., A. C., *J. Appl. Polymer Sci.*, **1**, 73 (1959).
4. Dole, M., *Kolloid Z.*, **165**, 40 (1959).
5. Dole, M., and Wunderlich, B., *Makromol. Chem.*, **34**, 29 (1959).
6. Edgar, O. B., and Hill, R., *J. Polymer Sci.*, **8**, 1 (1952).
7. Evans, R. D., Mighton, H. R., and Flory, P. J., *J. Am. Chem. Soc.*, **72**, 2018 (1950).*
8. Flory, P. J., Garrett, R. R., Newman, S., and Mandelkern, L., *J. Polymer Sci.*, **12**, 97 (1954).
9. Greenberg, S. A., and Alfrey, T., *J. Am. Chem. Soc.*, **76**, 6280 (1954).
10. Izard, E. F., *J. Polymer Sci.*, **8**, 503 (1952).
11. Krigbaum, W. R., and Tokita, N., *J. Polymer Sci.*, **43**, 467 (1960).

12. Malm, C. J., Mench, J. W., Kendall, D. L., and Hiatt, G. D., *Ind. Eng. Chem.*, **43**, 688 (1951).
13. Mandelkern, L., *Chem. Rev.*, **59**, 903 (1956).
14. Mandelkern, L., Tryon, M., and Quinn, Jr., F. A., *J. Polymer Sci.*, **19**, 77 (1956).
15. Miller, R. L., and Nielsen, L. E., *J. Polymer Sci.*, **44**, 391 (1960).
16. Reding, F. P., *J. Polymer Sci.*, **21**, 547 (1956).
17. Sapper, D. I., *J. Polymer Sci.*, **43**, 383 (1960).
18. Schaefgen, J. R., *J. Polymer Sci.*, **38**, 549 (1959).
19. Starkweather, H. W., and Boyd, R. H., *J. Phys. Chem.*, **64**, 410 (1960).
20. Tobolsky, A. V., "Properties and Structure of Polymers," p. 55, New York, John Wiley & Sons, Inc., 1960.

copolymer. The actual values are similar to what would be expected if vinyl chloride were copolymerized with vinyl acetate or if polyvinyl chloride were plasticized with a liquid such as dioctyl phthalate. The following values were assumed:

ΔH_u = 2000 cal/mole of repeat unit
Molar volume of polymer repeat unit = 45 ml/mole
Melting point of polymer = 450°K (177°C)
Molar volume of the plasticizer V_1 = 400 ml/mole.

The plasticizer is inefficient in lowering the melting point because of its large molar volume compared to that of the monomeric unit. The reason the comonomer is inefficient in lowering the glass temperature is that it has a high T_g compared to that of the plasticizer.

Relation of Crystallinity and Melting Point to Structure

Some of the relationships between structure and the glass temperature also hold for melting points. The melting points of polymers have been discussed by Bunn[10], Dole and Wunderlich[13], and Campbell and Haven[11]. The melting points of a number of polymers are listed in Table 2.7.

Rigid molecules such as:

polycarbonate—$\left(\text{O}-\langle\bigcirc\rangle-\underset{\text{CH}_3}{\overset{\text{CH}_3}{\text{C}}}-\langle\bigcirc\rangle-\text{O}-\overset{\text{O}}{\overset{\|}{\text{C}}} \right)_n$— ($T_m$ = 267°C),

poly-*p*-xylene, —$\left(\text{CH}_2-\langle\bigcirc\rangle-\text{CH}_2 \right)_n$— ($T_m$ = 375°C),

polyvinyl tertiary butane—$(\text{CH}_2-\underset{\text{C(CH}_3)_3}{\text{CH}})_n$— ($Tm$ > 350°C),

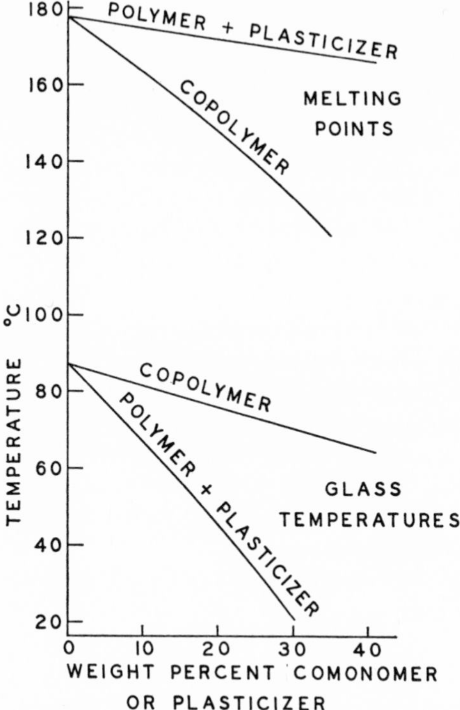

Figure 2.4. Relative lowering of melting point and glass-transition temperature by copolymerization and plasticization.

and cellulose triacetate ($T_m = 306°C$) have much higher melting points than flexible molecules such as:

polybutadiene (*trans* 1, 4) ($T_m = 92°$ C),

polyvinyl ethyl ether $-(CH_2-\underset{\underset{O-C_2H_5}{|}}{CH})_n-$ ($T_m = 86°C$),

polyethylene adipate $-\left[(CH_2)_2-O-\overset{\overset{O}{\|}}{C}-(CH_2)_4-\overset{\overset{O}{\|}}{C}-O\right]_m-$, ($T_m = 50°C$),

polyoxymethylene $-(CH_2-O)_n-$ ($T_m = 181°C$), and

polyethylene $-(CH_2-CH_2)_n-$ ($T_m = 137°C$).

Aromatic polymers, such as aromatic polyesters, have higher melting points than the corresponding alkyl polymers. The phenylene unit (—⟨⟩—) in the backbone of a polymer chain is especially effective in stiffening it and in raising the melting point[15]. Although it might appear that a double bond in the backbone of a polymer would stiffen it, the double bond actually seems to make the units attached to it more flexible than normal. Therefore, polymers such as polyisoprene melt at lower temperatures than the corresponding saturated polymers[10]. Conjugated double bonds, however, have a large stiffening effect.

Substitution of a flexible nonpolar side group such as an alkyl or ethoxy group onto a polymer lowers its melting point. Numerous examples may be found in Table 2.7, including the cellulose triester series and the polyvinyl ether series. The melting point goes through a minimum as the length of the side chain increases. This is because of side-chain crystallization[21] in which the melting point of the side chain increases as its length increases. Bulky and rigid side groups increase the melting point. For instance, isotactic polystyrene with its rigid phenyl group melts at 240°C while polyoctene-1 with its flexible normal hexyl side chain melts at −38°C. The tertiary butyl group is a fairly large and rigid unit which can introduce enough steric hindrance to stiffen the backbone of a polymer chain. For instance, poly-*tertiary*-butyl ether melts at 260°C; poly-*n*-butyl ether has a melting point of only 64°C. In general, branching of an alkyl chain raises the melting point when compared to the normal straight chain. Spherically shaped molecules tend to have abnormally high melting points; branched groups such as tertiary butyl tend to make a molecule more spherical or symmetrical in shape than a straight chain. Symmetry effects may also be important in explaining why para aromatic polymers melt at a higher temperature than the corresponding meta aromatic polymers. A para group looks the same when it rotates 180° around its axis; however, a meta group has a different appearance when it flops over. Thus, a meta compound can gain more entropy by becoming free to move and thereby tends to melt at a lower temperature.

Polyethers and polyesters are low melting polymers. The reason may be because of the very great flexibility of these groups. However, Dole and Wunderlich[13] believe their low melting points are due to low heats of fusion; the heats of fusion of polyesters is only about half that of polyethylene. The melting point of a substance is determined by the ratio of its molar heat of fusion and molar entropy of fusion, that is, $T_m = \Delta H_u/\Delta S_u$. Thus, a low melting point can result from either a low heat of fusion or a large entropy of fusion. The unexpectedly high melting point of isotactic polypropylene (176°C) appears to be due to a small entropy of fusion. The polypropylene chains are in a helical configuration in the crystal lattice, and they seem to retain much of this helical configuration even in the liquid state. Thus, the entropy of fusion is much less than what would be expected if the chains had a random configuration in the liquid.

The melting point of a polymer can often be correlated with the melting point of the monomer. If the monomer has a high melting point, the polymer will tend to have a high melting point also. For instance, ethylene and polyethylene melt at −181°C and +137°C, respectively, while acrylonitrile and polyacrylonitrile melt at −82 and +317°C, respectively.

High cohesive energies and intermolecular forces tend to raise the melting point. The high melting points of some of the polyamides (nylons) may be due to their strong hydrogen bonding.

The factors affecting the degree of crystallinity are not the same ones that determine the melting point. A degree of crystallinity much greater than 80 per cent is rare, and most crystalline polymers are more nearly 50 per cent crystalline. For a given polymer a low molecular weight fraction is usually more crystalline than a high molecular weight fraction[37]. Apparently the greater number of entanglements in the high molecular weight material hinder many sections of chains from moving so that they can fit into a crystal lattice; the parts of chains near entanglement points must remain in the amorphous phase. A second factor is the higher viscosity of the higher molecular weight polymer. Viscosity slows up the sorting of chain segments and the disengagement of chain entanglements so that they can fit into the crystal lattice. Thus, high molecular weight polymer requires a more prolonged heat treatment or annealing process than does a lower molecular weight polymer in order to attain the same degree of crystallinity.

In the case of copolymers, one of the comonomer units generally cannot fit into a crystal lattice. Therefore, copolymerization decreases the maximum attainable degree of crystallinity. Flory[16] has proposed an equilibrium theory of the crystallinity of copolymers. Under equilibrium conditions the longest chain sequences crystallize out at temperatures just below the maximum melting point. At a slightly lower temperature somewhat shorter sequence lengths are capable of crystallizing. Thus, there is a sorting of the sequences so that the longer sequence lengths crystallize out before the short ones; a given sequence length might be considered as having a fairly definite melting point. In this manner it is easily seen why copolymers melt over a broad temperature range.

Wunderlich[43] has developed a nonequilibrium theory of the crystallinity of copolymers. In this theory it is assumed that the molten polymer is cooled so rapidly that there is no time for chain segments to sort themselves out into aggregates of similar lengths. A chain segment can crystallize only if its neighbors happen to be above a minimum length and of the same type of monomeric unit. These quenched copolymers have much smaller degrees of crystallinity than what they would have if they were crystallized under equilibrium conditions. If a quenched polymer is warmed up, a recrystallization process may take place in which the total crystallinity may actually increase with temperature for awhile. If a quenched polymer is heated up fairly rapidly, its apparent melting point is considerably below the equilibrium melting point.

The tacticity or the degree of stereoregularity of a polymer can also affect its degree of crystallinity. If a polymer chain polymerizes so that the substituent on a vinyl monomer is always in the same stereoconfiguration relative to the monomeric unit behind it, the chain is said to be isotactic. If the stereoconfiguration alters from one monomer unit to the next, the polymer chain is said to be syndiotactic. If the polymer molecule is made up of a mixture of isotactic and syndiotactic units in a random manner, the polymer is called atactic[33]. Figure 2.5 illustrates schematically the differences between isotactic, syndiotactic, and atactic molecules; the short vertical lines indicate the stereo placement of the substituent group on the vinyl monomeric units. The isotactic and the syndiotactic polymers should be capable of crystallization. The atactic polymer should be amor-

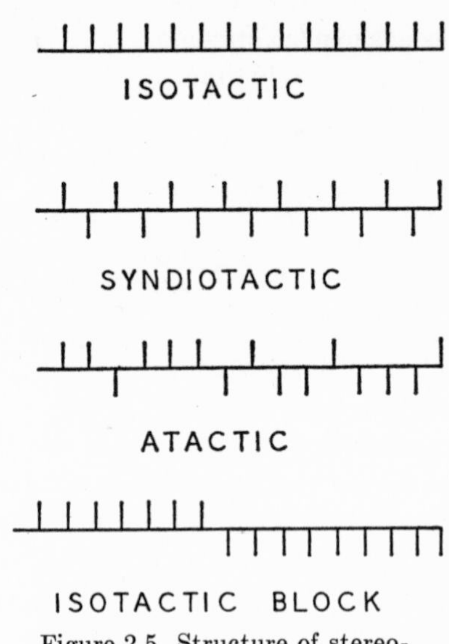

Figure 2.5. Structure of stereo-regulated polymers (schematic).

phous. Of course, the degree of stereoregularity is capable of varying over the range from pure isotactic through atactic to pure syndiotactic materials.

Some polymers such as polyvinyl chloride and polyacrylonitrile never attain very high crystallinity, and the crystallites are usually small or very imperfect. The reason for this can either be: (1) The polymers have low degrees of tacticity and are, therefore, capable of crystallizing only to a small extent. (2) The polymers are capable of attaining a high degree of crystallinity, but the polymers are very slow to crystallize and never approach anything like an equilibrium condition under the type of heat treatment given them. Seldom does one know which of these explanations is the correct one, but with some polymers the second explanation is the more probable one. In cases where the polymer is reluctant to crystallize, the crystallization process can often be speeded up by the addition of a small amount of plasticizer or even a small amount of a comonomer to increase the ease with which segmental motion can take place.

Morphology of Crystalline Polymers

When crystallizable polymers are cooled from the melt or from solutions, spherulites often develop as crystallization takes place[27, 28, 29, 35]. Spherulites such as those shown in Figure 2.6 are large enough to be seen under a microscope. Spherulites are made up of small crystallites, but they also contain amorphous material. They grow from a nucleus at their center. As crystallization proceeds, the growing spherulites impinge upon one another so that boundaries made up of straight line sections are formed between them.

The more crystalline polymers, such as high density polyethylene, can form single crystals when carefully grown from very dilute solutions[27, 28, 36]. The single crystals are thin plates or hollow pyramids, and steps of about a hundred Angstrom units in thickness may be observed on their surfaces. Keller[27, 28, 29] has shown that the polymer chain axis is perpendicular to the surface of the plates. Since the extended length of the chains is many times greater than a hundred Angstrom units, he postulated that the polymer chains are folded in the single crystals in layers of uniform thickness in a manner similar to that shown in Figure 2.7. Small angle x-ray scattering and electron microscope studies have substantiated the theory that single crystals are made up of lamellae built up of folded polymer chains.

Evidence is piling up which indicates that bulk polymers and spherulites are also made up of lamellae of folded chains. This is a great shift from the concepts of the old fringe-micelle theory[19] where crystalline polymers were considered as being made up of distinct regions of crystalline and

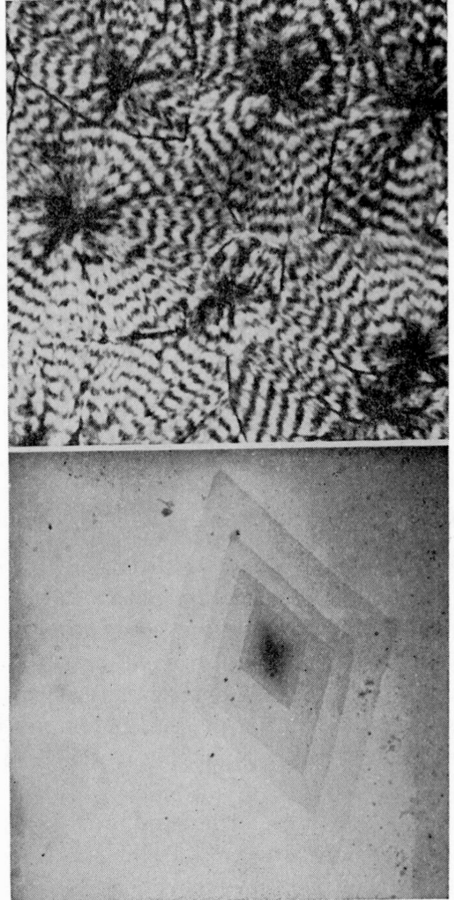

Figure 2.6. Top—spherulites of polyethylene. Bottom—A single crystal of polyethylene. (*Courtesy of G. Claver and R. Clark, Monsanto Chemical Co.*)

amorphous phases with sharp boundaries between the phases such as shown in the bottom half of Figure 2.7. A single polymer chain would generally run through several crystallites connected by amorphous regions. In the theory of folded chain crystallization, the concept of an amorphous phase becomes somewhat indefinite. Possibly the material corresponding to the amorphous phase is found in the chain folds and the region between lamellae.

A. FOLDED CHAIN THEORY

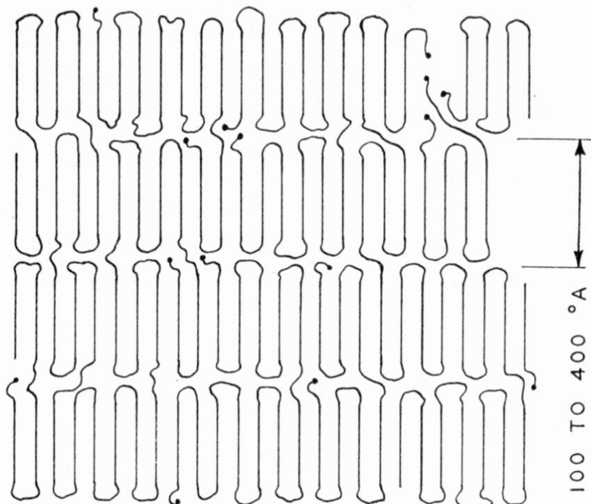

B. FRINGE-MICELLE THEORY

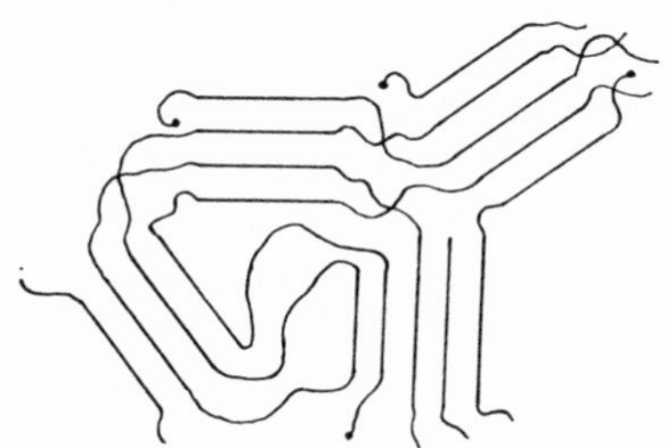

Figure 2.7. Morphology of crystalline polymers: A. Schematic diagram of a polymer crystallite made up of folded chains. B. Crystallites and amorphous regions according to the fringe-micelle theory.

The morphology of crystalline polymers may be changed by heat treatments. The more rapidly a polymer is cooled through the crystallization zone, the smaller are the spherulites. The spacing between chain folds also depends upon the temperature at which the single crystals are grown. The higher the crystallization temperature the greater the distance between chain folds or lamellae. For high density polyethylene the spacing between folds varies from 100Å for crystals grown at 60°C to several hundred Angstrom units for crystals grown at 135°C.

Secondary Transitions

Many polymers have secondary glass transitions in addition to the main glass transition discussed in the first part of this chapter[9, 12, 23, 24, 25, 32, 40]. These secondary transitions may be detected by volume-temperature measurements, studies of mechanical damping, nuclear magnetic resonance measurements, or electrical loss or power factor measurements made over a range of temperature or frequencies.

The main glass transition occurs in the temperature range where large segments of the polymer backbone chain become free to move. Secondary transitions often occur at temperatures where subgroups or side chains on the main polymer chain become free to move or oscillate. Side groups, being small compared to molecular segments, require less free volume than polymer chains for movement. Thus, secondary transitions occur at lower temperatures than main glass transitions.

The glass transition of polymethyl methacrylate occurs at about 115°C. This polymer has a side group consisting of

$$-\overset{\overset{\displaystyle O}{\|}}{C}-O-CH_3$$

which has some mode of motion that gives rise to a secondary transition near room temperature. Polypropylene has a methyl group on every other carbon atom of the backbone chain. A secondary transition due to the methyl groups has been reported at −260°C[32]; its main transition is at −10°C. Polymers with a cyclohexyl side chain have a transition at about −80°C when the frequency of measurement is one cycle per second[23]. This transition is due to the cyclohexyl group changing from one chair configuration to another chair configuration. Such motion is practically independent of the nature of the remainder of the polymer molecule.

Semicrystalline polymers often have secondary transitions in the amorphous phase; the exact nature of these transitions is not completely understood. Although these transitions occur in the amorphous phase, they seem to be influenced by the restrictions imposed on the amorphous material by the crystalline phase. Linear amorphous polyethylene has its T_g at −120°C. There is another transition in the amorphous phase of semicrystalline polyethylene at about −25°C.

Secondary transitions can also occur in the crystalline phase. For instance, polytetrafluoroethylene has a first order transition near room temperature where the material transforms from one type of crystal to another. Polybutene-1 also has two crystalline forms. Another type of transition is connected with the crystalline phase of some polymers. For instance, polyethylene has a transition in mechanical damping between 0° and 110°C, depending upon the nature of the polymer and its heat treatment. The temperature at which this transition occurs can be correlated with the expected size of the crystallites in the polymer. The smaller the crystals, the lower the transition temperature. This transition may be related to the recently discovered folding of polymer chains in crystals. The length of polymer between folds depends upon the heat treatment given the polymer. The equilibrium fold length increases with increase of temperature of crystallization. The transition takes place at temperatures where recrystallization can occur at a measurable rate. Similar transitions occur in other crystalline polymers, but the nature of these transitions is not yet clarified.

In later chapters it will be shown how the mechanical properties of polymers are determined primarily by the glass transition. However, secondary transitions play an important part in modifying mechanical behavior. For instance, a secondary transition may be responsible for a rigid material being tough rather than brittle.

References

1. Alfrey, T., Bohrer, J. J., and Mark, H., "Copolymerization," New York, Interscience Publishers, Inc., 1952.
2. Barb, W. G., *J. Polymer Sci.*, **37,** 515 (1959).
3. Beaman, R. G., *J. Polymer Sci.*, **9,** 470 (1952).
4. Bekkedahl, N., *J. Research, Nat. Bur. Standards*, **13,** 411 (1934).
5. Bischoff, J., Catsiff, E., and Tobolsky, A. V., *J. Am. Chem. Soc.*, **74,** 3378 (1952).
6. Bovey, F. A., Abere, J. F., Rathmann, G. B., and Sandberg, C. L., *J. Polymer Sci.*, **15,** 520 (1955).
7. Boyer, R. F., and Spencer, R. S., "Advance in Colloid Science," Vol. 2, p. 1, New York, Interscience Publishers, Inc., 1946.
8. Boyer, R. F., *J. Appl. Phys.*, **25,** 825 (1954).
9. Buchdahl, R., and Nielsen, L. E., *J. Polymer Sci.*, **15,** 1 (1955).
10. Bunn, C. W., *J. Polymer Sci.*, **16,** 323 (1955).
11. Campbell, T. W., and Haven, Jr., A. C., *J. Appl. Polymer Sci.*, **1,** 73 (1959).
12. Deutsch, K., Hoff, E. A. W., and Reddish, W., *J. Polymer Sci.*, **13,** 565 (1954).
13. Dole, M., and Wunderlich, B., *Makromol. Chem.*, **34,** 29 (1959).
14. Doolittle, A. K., *J. Appl. Phys.*, **22,** 1471 (1951).
15. Edgar, O. B., and Hill, R., *J. Polymer Sci*, **8,** 1 (1952).
16. Flory, P. J., *Trans. Faraday Soc.*, **51,** 848 (1955).
17. Flory, P. J., *J. Chem. Phys.*, **17,** 223 (1949), *ibid.*, **13,** 684 (1947).
18. Flory, P. J., "Principles of Polymer Chemistry," Chap. 13, Ithaca, Cornell University Press, 1953.
19. Gernross, O., Hermann, K., and Abitz, W., *Z. Physik. Chem.*, **10B,** 371 (1930).
20. Gibbs, J. H., and DiMarzio, E. A., *J. Chem. Phys.*, **28,** 373 (1958).
21. Greenberg, S. A., and Alfrey, T., *J. Am. Chem. Soc.*, **76,** 6280 (1954).
22. Grieveson, B. M., *Polymer*, **1,** 499 (1960).

23. Heijboer, J., *Koloid Z.*, **171,** 7 (1960).
24. Heijboer, J., Debbing, P., and Staverman, A. J., *Proc. Intern. Rheol. Congr., 2nd Congr.*, **123,** (1953).
25. Hoff, E. A. W., Robinson, D. W., and Willbourn, A. H., *J. Polymer Sci.*, **18,** 161 (1955).
26. Kauzmann, W., *Chem. Rev.*, **43,** 219 (1948).
27. Keller, A., *Makromol. Chem.*, **34,** 1 (1959).
28. Keller, A., *Phil. Mag.*, **2,** 1171 (1957).
29. Keller, A., and O'Connor, A., *Discussions Faraday Soc.*, **25,** 114 (1958).
30. Kenyon, A. S., Gross, R. C., and Wurstner, A. L., *J. Polymer Sci.*, **40,** 159 (1959).
31. Mandelkern, L., *Chem. Rev.*, **56,** 903 (1956).
32. Muus, L. T., McCrum, N. G., and McGrew, F. C., *Soc. Plastics Eng. J.*, **15,** 368 (1959).
33. Natta, G., and Corradini, P., *J. Polymer Sci.*, **39,** 29 (1959).
34. Richard, W. R., and Smith, P. A. S., *J. Chem. Phys.*, **18,** 230 (1950).
35. Schuur, G., "Some Aspects of the Crystallization of High Polymers," Commun., Nr. 276, Delft, Rubber Stichting, 1955.
36. Till, P. H., *J. Polymer Sci.*, **17,** 447 (1957).
37. Tung, L. H., and Buckser S., *J. Phys. Chem.*, **62,** 1530 (1958).
38. Warner, A. J., *ASTM Bull.* No. 165, 53 (April, 1950).
39. Wiley, R. H., and Brauer, G. M., *J. Polymer Sci.*, **3,** 647 (1948).
40. Willbourn, A. H., *Trans. Faraday Soc.*, **54,** 717 (1958).
41. Williams, M. L., Landel, R. F., and Ferry, J. D., *J. Am. Chem. Soc.*, **77,** 3701 (1955).
42. Wood, L. A., *J. Polymer Sci.*, **28,** 319 (1958).
43. Wunderlich, B., *J. Chem. Phys.*, **29,** 1395 (1958).

Chapter 3

CREEP

General Behavior and Instrumentation

The dimensional stability of polymers is important in many applications. A rigid plastic object should be capable of withstanding modest tensile or compressive loads for long periods of time without change in dimensions or shape. A plastic raincoat, even though soft and flexible, must be able to hang on a hook for weeks at a time without flowing so much that it falls to the floor. A rubber tire must not develop flat spots on its surface even though the car may not be used for some time. Fibers must not deform too easily under prolonged stress, or our clothing would take on an undesirable appearance such as baggy knees in our trousers. These are a few examples illustrating applications where it is important to know the creep behavior of polymers.

Creep tests can be carried out in tension, compression, or shear. In any case a constant load is applied to the test specimen, and its deformation is measured as a function of time. The tensile creep test such as illustrated schematically in Figure 1.1A is the most widely used. The stress can be supplied by hanging weights on the specimen, or it can be supplied by a spring mechanism. The elongation may be determined, for instance, by periodically measuring the distance between two fiducial marks on the specimen with a cathetometer, or in special cases, with a graduated ruler. With rigid materials where great accuracy is required in measuring small changes in length, strain gages attached to the surface of the specimen may be used[44, 78]. If there is no slippage in the grips holding the specimen, the device for measuring elongation may be attached to the specimen grips, and the change in length may be determined from changes in the separation of the grips. Differential transformers can be used for this purpose; they have the added advantage that the electrical voltages corresponding to changes in length may be greatly amplified and displayed on the chart of a recorder[48]. The changes in length may be measured from a fraction of a

60

second up to days or even years. The loads may be varied from very small values up to stresses approaching the breaking strength of the material.

The creep behavior of a cellulose acetate plastic is shown in Figure 3.1[36]. These curves are typical of plastic or viscoelastic materials. The specimen has an instantaneous elongation immediately after the load is first applied. This deformation is inversely proportional to the elastic modulus or stiffness. For a given load, a material with a high modulus, such as polystyrene, stretches less than a material with a low modulus, such as a rubber. The period after the initial deformation is followed by a period in which there is a rapid rate of creep. The rate of creep gradually decreases to a constant rate, which in the extreme case approaches zero, so in some cases the deformation may reach a nearly constant value at long times. Figure 3.1 also shows that the greater the load the greater is the creep elongation and creep rate.

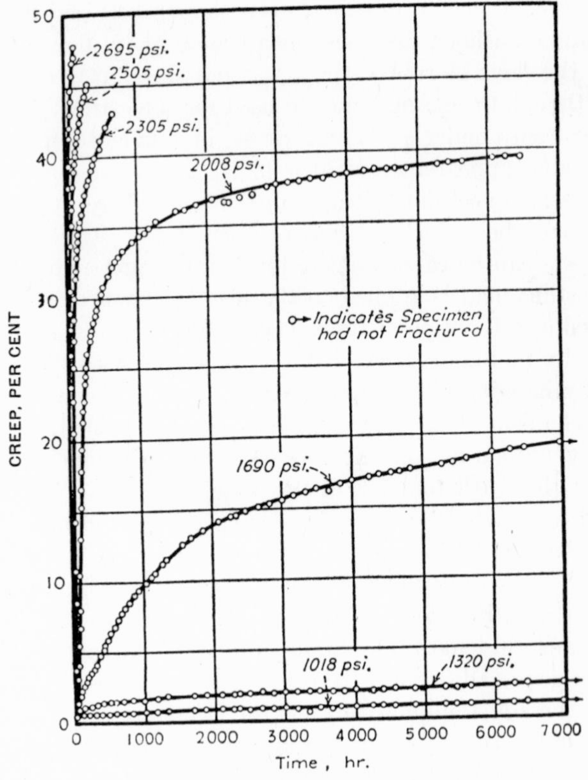

Figure 3.1. Creep of cellulose acetate at 25°C. [*Reprinted from Findley, W. N., Modern Plastics*, **19**, *71* (*Aug., 1942*)]

In Figure 3.1 the per cent elongation is plotted as a function of time. Often the creep compliance is plotted against time. The compliance is obtained by dividing the elongation at any time by the stress on the specimen. The compliance gives an apparent reciprocal modulus which changes with time. In most theoretical work it is assumed that the compliance is independent of load. For many materials this independence is true at low loads, but at higher loads the compliance changes with load. In Figure 3.1 there is a curve for each stress. For materials in which the compliance does not depend upon the stress, the creep curve is a single curve for all stresses when compliance is plotted against time.

Models

A simple model may be used to help understand the creep behavior of polymers. Such a model is shown in Figure 3.2. This four-element model is composed of a spring and dashpot in series and another spring and dashpot in parallel. A stress σ is applied to this model. Each spring is assumed to be Hookean, that is, its deformation ϵ is proportional to the stress on it and inversely proportional to its stiffness or modulus E. Each dashpot is assumed to be filled with a Newtonian liquid, so that its deformation is

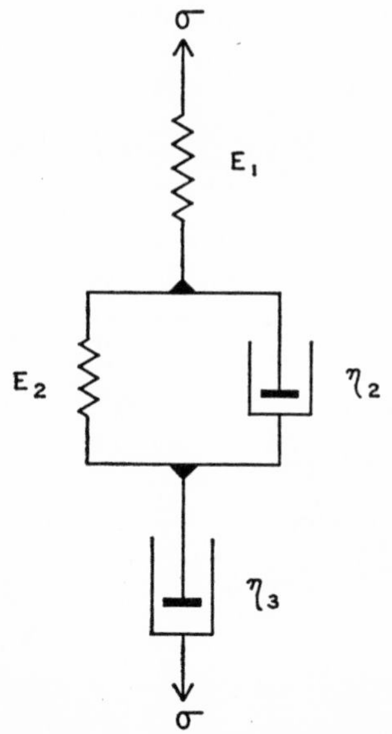

Figure 3.2. A four-element model for viscoelastic creep behavior.

proportional to the time and to stress on it and inversely proportional to the viscosity η of the liquid in the dashpot. When a constant force is applied to such a spring, it immediately stretches by an amount which does not change with time. On the other hand, when a constant force is applied to such a dashpot, its deformation increases linearly with time.

The total stress is applied to spring E, and dashpot η_3. The stress is shared by spring E_2 and dashpot η_2 when connected in parallel by amounts which vary with time; as the dashpot and spring of the parallel combination stretch, more and more of the total stress is carried by the spring. Finally all the stress is carried by E_2 and none by η_2; at this point the spring stretches no more. The elongation ϵ_2 of the parallel spring and dashpot η_2 as a function of time t is given by

$$\epsilon_2 = \frac{\sigma}{E_2}(1 - e^{-t/\tau}) \tag{3.1}$$

where τ, the retardation time, is defined by

$$\tau = \eta_2/E_2 \tag{3.2}$$

The total deformation is equal to the sum of the deformations of the spring E_1, the dashpot η_3, and the parallel combination E_2 and η_2.

$$\epsilon = \epsilon_1 + \epsilon_2 + \epsilon_3 \tag{3.3}$$

or

$$\epsilon = \frac{\sigma}{E_1} + \frac{\sigma}{E_2}(1 - e^{-t/\tau}) + \frac{\sigma}{\eta_3}t \tag{3.4}$$

The retardation time τ gives the time required for the parallel combination of E_2 and η_2 to deform to $1/e$ or 36.79 per cent of its total deformation, which is achieved at very long times compared to τ.

The creep behavior of this model is illustrated in Figures 3.3 and 3.4. In this example the following values were used:

$$\sigma = 10^9 \text{ dynes/cm}^2 \qquad E_1 = 5 \times 10^9 \text{ dynes}/cm^2$$

$$\eta_2 = 5 \times 10^9 \text{ poises} \qquad E_2 = 10^9 \text{ dynes}/cm^2$$

$$\eta_3 = 5 \times 10^{11} \text{ poises} \qquad \tau = 5 \text{ seconds}$$

The load was applied at zero time. Spring E_1 immediately stretches by an amount σ/E_1. Creep starts at a high rate but gradually tapers off to a constant rate due to dashpot η_3. At time t_1 the load is removed, and spring E_1 snaps back to its unstretched state. During the recovery time, the spring E_2 gradually forces the plunger of dashpot η_2 back to its original condition

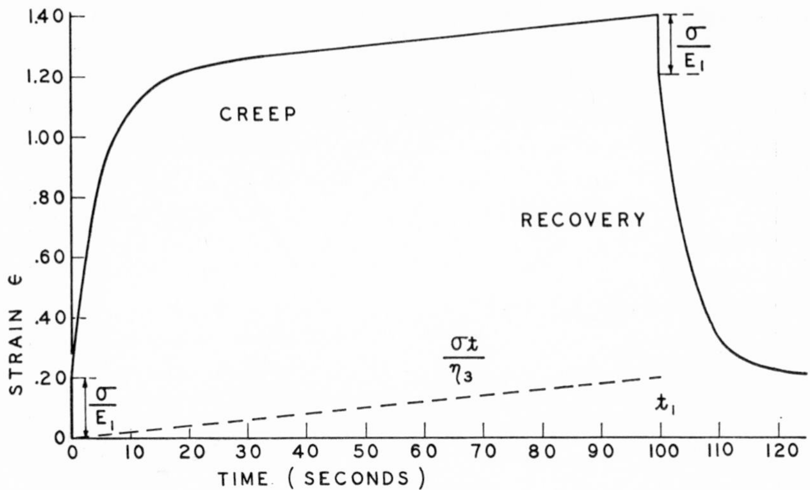

Figure 3.3. Creep of a four-element model with $E_1 = 5 \times 10^9$ dynes/cm², $E_2 = 10^9$ dynes/cm², $\eta_2 = 5 \times 10^9$ poises, $\eta_3 = 5 \times 10^{11}$ poises and $\sigma = 10^9$ dynes/cm².

also. However, dashpot η_3 does not retract to its original state as there is no force acting on it. This dashpot retains a deformation equal to $\frac{\sigma}{\eta_3} t_1$. The recovery curve obtained after the load is removed at time t_1 is given by

$$\epsilon = \epsilon_2 e^{-(t-t_1)/\tau} + \epsilon_3 \tag{3.5}$$

where

$$\epsilon_2 = \frac{\sigma}{E_2}(1 - e^{-t_1/\tau}) \tag{3.6}$$

and

$$\epsilon_3 = \frac{\sigma}{\eta_3} t_1 \tag{3.7}$$

Creep curves may be plotted in different ways. Rather than plotting elongation (or compliance) against time, it is sometimes more enlightening to plot the elongation as a function of the logarithm of the time or the logarithm of the elongation as a function of the logarithm of the time. The creep curve shown in Figure 3.3 is replotted in Figure 3.4 with the logarithm of the time as the independent variable in place of the time. The creep curve now has a sigmoidal shape with the steepest part of the curve occurring at a time equal to the retardation time. Most of the creep takes place

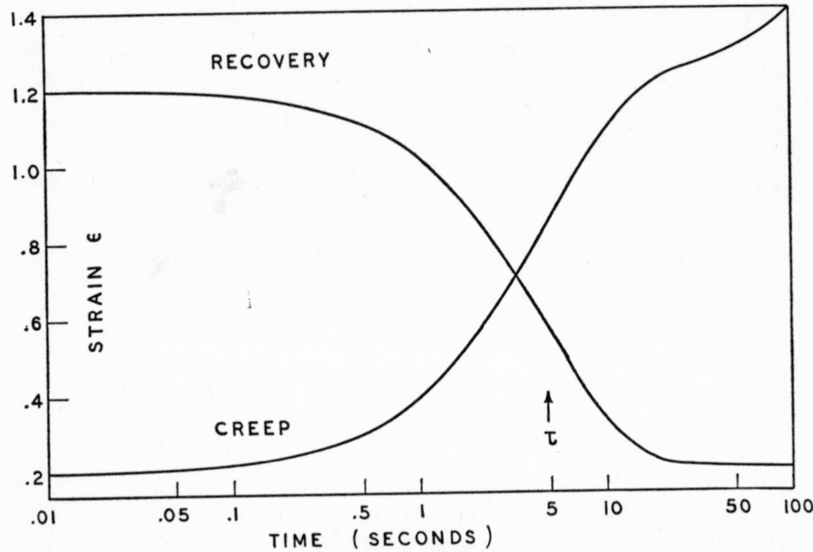

Figure 3.4. Creep of a four-element model plotted on a log time scale. Same parameters as in Figure 3.3.

within a period of time equal to one decade around the retardation time. At times much less than the retardation time, the material cannot respond very much to the stress and acts like a rigid substance. At periods much longer than the retardation time, the only response to the stress is due to the viscous flow of dashpot η_3. While the creep due to viscous flow is linear on a straight time plot, the creep curve has a definite upward curvature on a log t plot; this upward curvature can be seen from about 30 to 100 seconds in Figure 3.4.

On a log t plot the recovery curve also has a sigmoidal shape. Again, most of the recovery takes place within one decade of the retardation time τ, and the maximum rate of recovery occurs at a time equal to the retardation time. Complete recovery cannot occur because of viscous flow of dashpot η_3.

The four-element model used here illustrates most of the characteristics of creep curves, but practically no materials are so simple that their creep curves can be represented by a model which has only one retardation time. While polymeric materials generally give sigmoidal-shaped creep curves such as those in Figure 3.4, the creep takes place over many decades of time rather than during one decade for the simple model. Actual materials have many retardation times distributed over many decades of time. The accurate calculation of the distribution of retardation times can be an involved, time-consuming operation. However, a simple approximate method does exist in which the slope of the creep curve is plotted against log t. Where the creep curve is steepest, there are more retardation times than elsewhere. The function representing the distribution of retardation times is $L_1(\tau)$. It may be approximated by[59, 75]

$$L_1(\tau) = \frac{d}{d \ln t}[J(t)] = \frac{1}{2.303}\frac{d}{d \log t}[J(t)] \tag{3.8}$$

or more accurately

$$L_1(\tau) = \frac{d}{d \ln t}[J(t) - t/\eta] = \frac{1}{2.303}\frac{d}{d \log t}[J(t) - t/\eta] \tag{3.9}$$

In the use of these equations the time scale is plotted as logarithm to the base e if the derivative is with respect to $d \ln t$. The logarithmic time scale should be to the base 10 if the derivative is with respect to $d \log t$.

In these equations $J(t)$ is the compliance as a function of time, on a logarithmic scale, and t/η represents the creep due to flow. This approximation is fairly crude. Instead of giving a single retardation time for the creep curve of the four-element model shown in Figure 3.4, a curve with a peak at the most probable τ is found. However, the approximation is better for actual materials. More accurate approximation methods of calculating the distribution of retardation times are reviewed by Leaderman[59].

Effect of Glass Transitions and Temperature on Creep

The creep properties of a polymer are very dependent upon temperature. At temperatures well below the glass-transition temperature, the polymer is rigid with a high modulus or low compliance. Such materials generally have a tensile compliance of about 3×10^{-11} cm^2/dyne (2×10^{-6} sq in./lb). If the temperature is so low that segmental movement of the polymer chains cannot occur, very little creep will take place even after long periods of time. As the temperature is raised, not only does the compliance (or elongation) increase, but also the rate of creep increases since some segmental molecular motion can take place. As long as a chain segment is frozen in a fixed position, the stress on it cannot be internally relieved. However, a chain segment under stress will move so as to relieve the stress whenever possible. The stress removed from one segment is added to others, thus stretching them a little more. These other chain segments in turn move so as to relieve the stress on themselves from time to time whenever given the opportunity. The result is a gradual increase in the length of the test specimen with time. The stress on a segment of a polymer chain can be relieved if the chain can slide with respect to its neighbors. This type of motion is similar to viscous flow. Stress can also be removed from a polymer chain if the chain breaks; this occurs if chemical reactions such as oxidation are taking place during the creep test.

In the glass-transition region, the creep properties become extremely temperature dependent. Typical tensile compliance values are of the order of 10^{-9} cm^2/dyne. Thus, a given load in the transition region gives a much greater elongation than the same load at much lower temperatures. However, even more remarkable is the very great change of elongation with time in the transition region. The creep rate $\left(\frac{d \log \epsilon}{d \log t}\right)$ goes through a maximum near the glass temperature for many polymers, especially those which are lightly crosslinked or slightly crystalline or which have very high molecular weights[25, 69]. At temperatures well above the glass temperature much greater elongations may take place, but the creep rate generally decreases. At temperatures well above T_g, typical compliances are 10^{-6} to 10^{-7} cm^2/dyne.

The creep behavior of a plasticized polyvinyl chloride material in, below, and above the glass-transition region is shown in Figure 3.5[69]. The results

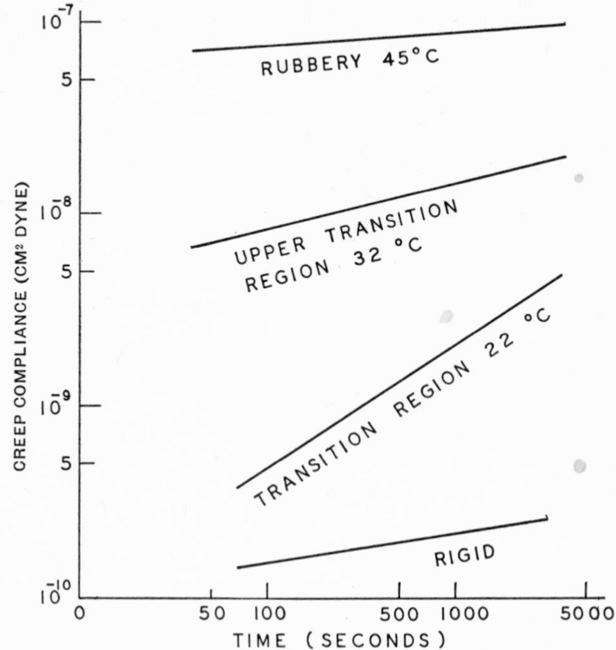

Figure 3.5. Creep of a plasticized polyvinyl chloride polymer at different temperatures. [*Data replotted from Nielsen, L. E., Buchdahl, R., and Levreault, R., J. Appl. Phys.,* **21**, *607 (1950)*]

are plotted as log J against log t as suggested by Nutting[11, 70]. In its simplest form the Nutting equation for creep is

$$\epsilon = K \sigma t^n \quad (3.10)$$

or

$$\log \epsilon = \log K + \log \sigma + n \log t \quad (3.11)$$

where K and n are constants. The constant n can vary between zero and one. If n equals zero, the material is perfectly elastic; while if n is one, the material acts like a viscous liquid. Thus, n is a measure of the relative importance of apparent elastic and viscous contributions to the creep behavior.

Materials obeying Nutting's equation give straight lines when the logarithm of the elongation (or compliance) is plotted against the logarithm of the time; the slope of the line is n. The greater the slope of the line the greater is the rate of creep. The curves in Figure 3.5 clearly show the softening (increase in compliance) as the temperature is raised through the transition region. The curves also show the maximum in creep rate in the transition region. These results are typical of many polymers.

Effects of Molecular Weight and Chain Entanglements

At temperatures well below the glass-transition region, the creep behavior of an amorphous polymer does not depend upon molecular weight. This is to be expected as long as the molecular weight is above some minimum at which good specimens can be prepared. If creep depended upon the movement of whole polymer chains relative to one another, creep should decrease as the molecular weight increases. However, polymer molecules move by chain segments[2] rather than by whole molecules; one part of a chain may change its configuration without the rest of the chain knowing about it. Although segments at the end of chains should have somewhat more freedom of movement than other segments, in high polymers there are so many segments that the effect due to end groups is small. For instance, if a segment contains twenty monomer units, a polymer with a degree of polymerization of five thousand would have two end segments and 248 other segments. Thus, for glassy materials where the total elongation in a creep experiment is very small (say of the order of 1 per cent), the creep should be nearly independent of molecular weight.

Above the glass temperature, amorphous, uncrosslinked, high polymers behave as viscous liquids or as rubbers. The creep of such materials is very dependent upon molecular weight. Most of the creep curve is nearly a straight line when elongation is plotted against time. The creep rate is determined primarily by the viscosity of the polymer. The greater the viscosity the smaller the creep rate. The viscosity of a liquid polymer increases with molecular weight; this is why the creep of such materials depends upon their molecular weights.

Figure 3.6[41, 42] shows how the viscosity of a polymer depends upon molecular weight. A plot of the logarithm of the viscosity versus the logarithm of the molecular weight gives two straight lines which meet at a critical molecular weight M_c. At molecular weights below M_c the viscosity is roughly proportional to the molecular weight.

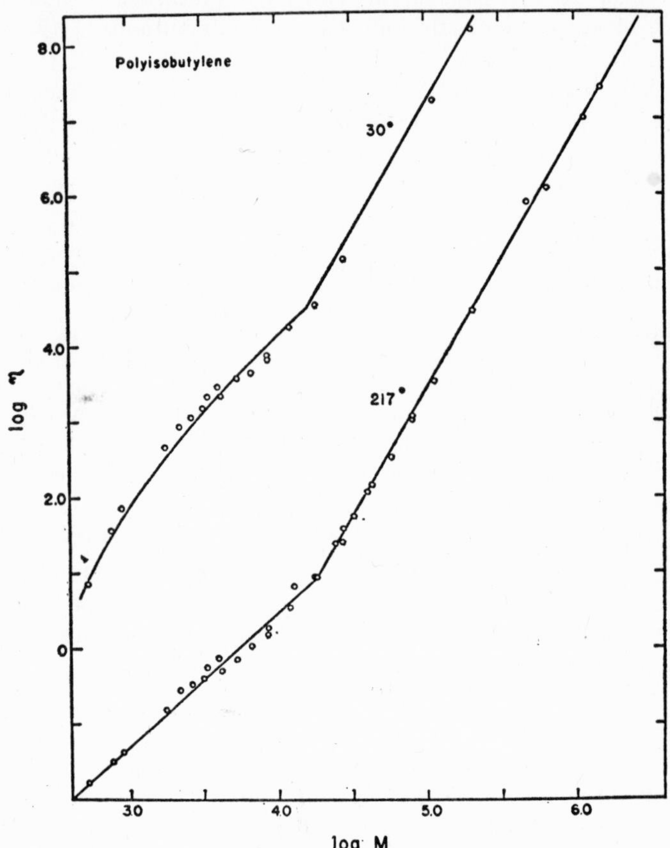

Figure 3.6. Dependence of polyisobutylene viscosity on weight average molecular weight. Data taken at 30°C and 217°C. [*Reprinted from Fox, T. G., and Flory, P. J., J. Phys. Chem.*, **55,** *221 (1951), with permission of the copyright owner, the American Chemical Society*]

$$\text{Log } \eta = \log K_1 + \log M \qquad M < M_c \quad (3.12)$$

At molecular weights greater than M_c the viscosity is proportional to the molecular weight to the 3.4 power.

$$\text{Log } \eta = \log K_2 + 3.4 \log M \qquad M > M_c \quad (3.13)$$

The constants K_1 and K_2 depend upon the temperature and the nature of the polymer. These equations hold for low rates of shear or elongation. Usually viscosity is used only with a shear deformation. However, viscosity can also be calculated from tensile deformations. It can be shown that the tensile viscosity is three times the corresponding shear viscosity[2, 41]. Viscosity can be calculated from creep data in several ways. If at long times the creep curve becomes a straight line, the viscosity can be estimated from the slope of the creep curve by the following equation:

$$\eta = \frac{\sigma}{3^{d\epsilon}/dt} \qquad (3.14)$$

The constant three arises from the conversion of tensile viscosity to the more familiar shear viscosity. The viscosity can also be measured more accurately by subtracting the inverted recovery curve from the creep curve as a function of time and substituting this difference $\Delta\epsilon$ into the equation

$$\eta = \frac{\sigma}{3d(\Delta\epsilon)/dt} \qquad (3.15)$$

A third method of calculating the viscosity by a creep test is to substitute the nonrecoverable creep into

$$\eta = \frac{\sigma t}{3\epsilon_3} \qquad (3.16)$$

as suggested by Figure 3.3.

The critical molecular weight M_c is thought to be the molecular weight at which the polymer chains become long enough for chain entanglements to occur[13, 41]. These chain entanglements are probably similar in nature to the entanglements encountered in a tangled ball of string or in a dish of cooked spaghetti. These entanglements act like temporary crosslinks which tie molecules together and greatly change their flow or creep behavior[10, 67, 68]. Like crosslinks in rubbers, chain entanglements make polymers somewhat elastic in behavior.

Table 3.1 lists the critical molecular weight and viscosity behavior of a number of polymers[41, 42]. In this table the molecular weight has been replaced by Z, the number of atoms in the backbone of a polymer chain.

TABLE 3.1. Polymer Viscosity and Chain Entanglements.

Polymer	Z_c	Viscosity Equation Above Z_c
Polyisobutylene	610	$\log \eta = 3.4 \log Z + 5.5 \times 10^5/T^2 - 10.93$
Polystyrene	730	$\log \eta = 3.4 \log Z + 2.7 \times 10^{16}/T^6 - 9.51$
Poly(dimethyl siloxane)	~950	$\log \eta = 3.4 \log Z - 9.0$ (stokes at 25°C)
Polymethyl methacrylate	208	$\log \eta = 3.4 \log Z + 4.5 \times 10^{34}/T^{13} - 7.4$
Polyvinyl Acetate	—	$\log \eta = 3.4 \log Z + 9.77 \times 10^{10}/T^4 - 10.05$
Decamethylene sebacate	290	$\log \eta = 3.4 \log Z - 8.2$ (at 109°C)
Decamethylene adipate	280	$\log \eta = 3.4 \log Z + 3.4 \times 10^5/T^2 - 11.2$
Diethyl adipate	290	$\log \eta = 3.4 \log Z + 2.1 \times 10^{10}/T^4 - 9.1$
Poly(ε-caprolactam) linear	340	$\log \eta = 3.4 \log Z - 8.0$ (at 253°C)
Poly(ε-caprolactam) branched, octachain	550	$\log \eta = 3.4 \log Z - 8.7$ (at 253°C)

Fox, T. G., and Loshaek, S., *J. Appl. Phys.*, **26,** 1080 (1955).

Fox, T. G., Gratch, S., and Loshaek, S., "Rheology," Eirich, F. R., Ed., Vol. 1, Chap. 12, p. 431, New York, Academic Press, Inc., 1956.

The chain length Z is related to the molecular weight M for polymers which have two atoms in the backbone chain per monomer unit by

$$Z = 2M/M_0 \tag{3.17}$$

where M_0 is the molecular weight of the monomeric unit. In any sample of high polymeric material there is a distribution of molecular weights. In viscosity equations the proper molecular weight to use is the weight average molecular weight, generally denoted by $\bar{M}_w$. Likewise the proper chain length is the weight average chain length. Table 3.1 illustrates a number of interesting features about chain entanglements and viscosity. Flexible polymers such as polyisobutylene and polydimethyl siloxane have longer chain lengths between entanglements Z_c than more polar or less flexible polymers such as polymethyl methacrylate and decamethylene sebacate. Linear polymers have shorter chain lengths between entanglements than branched polymers. Also, for a given molecular weight, the viscosity of linear polymers is greater than the viscosity of a branched polymer.

If a solvent or plasticizer is added to a polymer, the chain length between entanglements increases, and the number of entanglements per unit volume decreases. Bueche[13, 41] finds that the product of the critical chain length Z_c and the volume fraction of polymer in the solution remains nearly constant. In addition to reducing the viscosity by cutting down the number of entanglements, solvents markedly decrease the absolute viscosity at any temperature, since low molecular liquids have viscosities which are much smaller than the viscosities of higher molecular weight materials.

In the above discussion only the effect of molecular weight on the viscosity has been considered. However, in most creep tests there is a measurable recovery when the load is removed. This indicates that the creep must have both a viscous and an elastic component. In most uncrosslinked polymers the elastic component of creep comes from chain entanglements. Therefore, as the molecular weight of a polymer increases, the number of entanglements increases, so the elasticity and amount of recoverable creep should increase. The fact that the relative amount of recovery is greater after a short creep test than after a long one is an indication that the number of entanglements decreases on stretching the sample. The decrease in number of entanglements on stretching may also be observed, in some cases by carrying out a creep test, and then after a short recovery period repeating the creep test. If the number of entanglements has decreased, the elongation at any time will be greater during the second creep test[67]. If the rest period between tests is long enough, the number of entanglements builds up to the equilibrium concentration, and the second test will be just like the first when corrected for the change in length due to the small amount of nonrecoverable deformation after the first test.

The effects of time and temperature on the creep behavior of uncrosslinked amorphous polymers may be summarized as follows: All such materials have creep curves similar to the one shown in Figure 3.4 except the complete curve is spread over a much wider time scale. If the temperature is well below the glass temperature, only the first part of the curve will be observed; it might require years or centuries to observe the complete curve as shown in Figure 3.4. If the temperature is well above the glass temperature, only the upswing in the extreme right part of the curve of Figure 3.4 will be observed unless measurements can be made in a fraction of a second. In the transition region, nearly the complete curve can be observed in a period of time from a few seconds to a few hours. These results suggest that time and temperature are in some respects somehow equivalent; the log t scale can be replaced by a distorted temperature scale. We shall see how this can be done in the chapter on stress relaxation.

How does molecular weight change the general shape of the curve in Figure 3.4? Between 20 and 50 seconds there is a suggestion of a plateau on this curve. As the molecular weight of the polymer increases, this plateau becomes much more pronounced and may extend over several decades of time before the upswing at the extreme right of the curve takes place. This plateau, which is found before viscous flow starts to dominate the creep behavior, is due to chain entanglements[15]. Chain entanglements slow up creep for a period of time. Bueche[14, 15] has discussed the nature of the creep curve when entanglements are important. His theory predicts a viscosity depending upon the 3.5 power of the molecular weight above the critical entanglement molecular weight; this 3.5 power dependence is close to the observed 3.4 power dependence on molecular weight.

Creep of Crosslinked Polymers

Below the glass temperature so little chain motion can occur that crosslinking has very little effect on creep properties unless there is a very high degree of crosslinking as in thermosetting phenol-formaldehyde polymers. However, crosslinks have a very dramatic effect on creep at temperatures above T_g. Crosslinking, or the tying together of polymer chains by chemical bonds, changes a polymer from a viscous liquid to an elastic rubber. An ideal crosslinked rubber should instantaneously stretch a given amount when a load is applied to it, and the amount of elongation should not change with time. When the load is removed, the specimen should snap back to its original length. Actual rubbers, however, do not quite fulfill these conditions.

Figure 3.7 shows how the creep of a butyl rubber changes in going from a linear uncrosslinked polymer to rubbers crosslinked to various degrees[65]. Although only a very small degree of crosslinking is required to greatly reduce the creep, a high degree of crosslinking is required to even approach anything like the case of an ideal rubber. Experiments on natural rubber reported by Wood[83] show that creep even on the best rubbers never completely stops. In practice, the crosslink network in polymers is always imperfect in that chain ends are not tied into the network, and there is always a small amount of soluble polymer.

The network structure in crosslinked polymers may be investigated by a number of techniques. One of the best of these techniques involves swelling of the polymer in a solvent. If a crosslinked polymer is soaked in a liquid which is a solvent for the uncrosslinked material, the crosslinked material will swell, but it will not all dissolve. Any uncrosslinked material will dissolve and diffuse out of the swollen material; this soluble part is called the sol fraction. The crosslinked part will swell until the osmotic forces trying to dissolve the polymer are balanced by the elastic forces due to the stretched segments of polymer chains. These elastic retractive forces are inversely proportional to the molecular weight of polymer between points of crosslinking. A highly crosslinked polymer will not swell as much as a

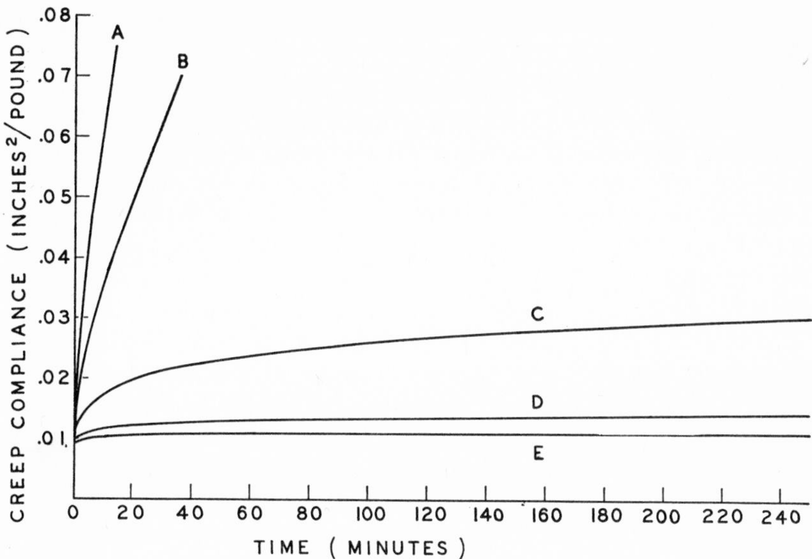

Figure 3.7. Creep of butyl rubbers of different molecular weights and degrees of crosslinking. A. Uncrosslinked, molecular weight = 315,000. B. Uncrosslinked, molecular weight = 480,000. C, D, E. Increasing degree of crosslinking. (*Unpublished data of Monsanto Chemical Co.*)

lightly crosslinked one. The theory of the swelling of crosslinked polymers has been discussed in detail by Flory[40]. The important equation relating the extent of swelling to the concentration of crosslinks is

$$-[\ln (1 - v_2) + v_2 + \chi_1 v_2^2] = \left(\frac{V_1}{\bar{v}_2 M_c}\right)\left(1 - \frac{2M_c}{M}\right)\left(v_2^{\frac{1}{3}} - \frac{v_2}{2}\right) \tag{3.18}$$

v_2 = volume fraction of polymer in swollen gel
V_1 = molar volume of solvent
$\bar{v}_2$ = specific volume of polymer
χ_1 = a solvent-polymer interaction term
M = molecular weight of polymer before crosslinking
M_c = molecular weight of polymer chain between points of crosslinking.

Swelling is usually expressed as the swelling ratio q; this is equal to the ratio of the volumes of the swollen to unswollen gel. Swelling ratio q is equal to the reciprocal of v_2.

Table 3.2 gives the sol fraction, swelling ratio, and approximate M_c values for the same butyl rubbers whose creep curves are shown in Figure 3.7. The measurements were made in cyclohexane at 24°C. As expected,

TABLE 3.2. SWELLING OF CROSSLINKED POLYISOBUTYLENE RUBBERS IN CYCLOHEXANE.

Rubber Number	Swelling Ratio	Sol Fraction	M_c
A	—	1.00	Uncrosslinked, M = 315,000
B	—	1.00	Uncrosslinked, M = 480,000
C	88.5	0.49	140,000
D	10.1	0.048	31,000
E	6.8	0.024	14,000

lightly crosslinked polymers have more soluble material which can be extracted than have the highly crosslinked polymers. Only a few crosslinks per molecule are required to drastically reduce the creep from that found with uncrosslinked rubbers. The highly crosslinked rubbers in Figure 3.7 have quite flat creep curves; however, measurements continued for periods of time much longer than those shown in the figure clearly indicate that the creep continues at a slow rate.

In crosslinked rubbers the molecular weight between crosslinks M_c is from about a thousand on up to many thousand. In highly crosslinked polymers such as ebonite and phenol-formaldehyde resins there may be crosslinks every few atoms along the polymer chains. These materials can never have the properties of rubbers as they have extremely high glass temperatures, often at temperatures so high that the polymers decompose before softening. Such polymers show relatively little creep and can sustain large loads for many years without appreciable changes in dimensions.

Creep of Crystalline Polymers

In slightly crystalline polymers the crystallites act like crosslinks in modifying the creep behavior of polymers above their glass-transition temperatures. A good example is plasticized polyvinyl chloride used in applications such as plastic raincoats. This material is rubbery in nature but does not flow under prolonged loads even though it is not crosslinked by a chemical reaction as is vulcanized rubber. In materials such as plasticized polyvinyl chloride, crystallites act as crosslinks; a number of polymer chains become firmly bound together where they go through the crystallite[62]. A single polymer chain can transverse several crystallites and the amorphous material between.

Up to about fifteen per cent crystallinity a polymer behaves as a crosslinked rubber[66]. In the region around 20 per cent crystallinity the material becomes considerably more rigid than a rubber. At least part of this stiffening appears to come about because the amorphous chain sequences become so short that normal rubberlike motion of the chains cannot take place. Above approximately 40 per cent crystallinity the crystallites impinge upon one another and form a continuous crystaline phase throughout the material[52]. At this point much of the stress is carried by the crystalline phase rather than by the amorphous phase. The stiffening action of the crystalline phase greatly reduces the compliance of the polymer.

The compliance (or modulus) of crystalline polymers is generally very temperature-sensitive compared to either chemically crosslinked rubbers or rigid amorphous polymers at temperatures well below the glass temperature. Several factors may contribute to this high temperature sensitivity of the creep properties. First, the degree of crystallinity changes with temperature. Secondly, in some polymers recrystallization can occur, and the rate of recrystallization depends upon the temperature. A strained crystal or an imperfect crystal melts at a lower temperature than an unstrained or perfect one. If not properly oriented so that the stress and chain axis are parallel, a crystallite under stress will melt and then recrystallize in an unstrained state. This process can account for part of the creep of crystalline polymers.

The creep properties of crystalline polymers not only change rapidly with temperature, but in some cases at a given temperature crystalline polymers creep more with time than crosslinked polymers or rigid amorphous polymers. This extensive creep may be partly due to recrystallization phenomena. It can also be due to the rotation of some crystallites in such a manner as to relieve the stress on them. Stress on crystallites may be relieved by motion along slip planes as in metal crystals, or if the stress concentrates too much on part of a crystal, the crystal may break. All of these factors make the creep greater than what would be expected if the crystallites were truly rigid and permanent in nature. However, a crystalline polymer above its glass temperature creeps very little when compared to the same material in the amorphous rubbery state. Thus, crystalline polymers tend to have even broader distributions of retardation times than amorphous polymers. The creep behavior of typical crystalline polymers (polyethylene and polytetrafluoroethylene "Teflon" is compared with an amorphous polymer (polystyrene) and with slightly crystalline polymers (polyvinyl chloride and polychlorotrifluoroethylene "Kel-F" in Figure 3.8. These curves were obtained at 25°C; this temperature is well below the glass temperature of polystyrene, so this material creeps only slightly even at high stresses. Polyethylene is far above its glass temperature, and although it is highly crystalline, it has a large elongation and a fairly high rate of creep. Polychlorotrifluoroethylene is not far from its

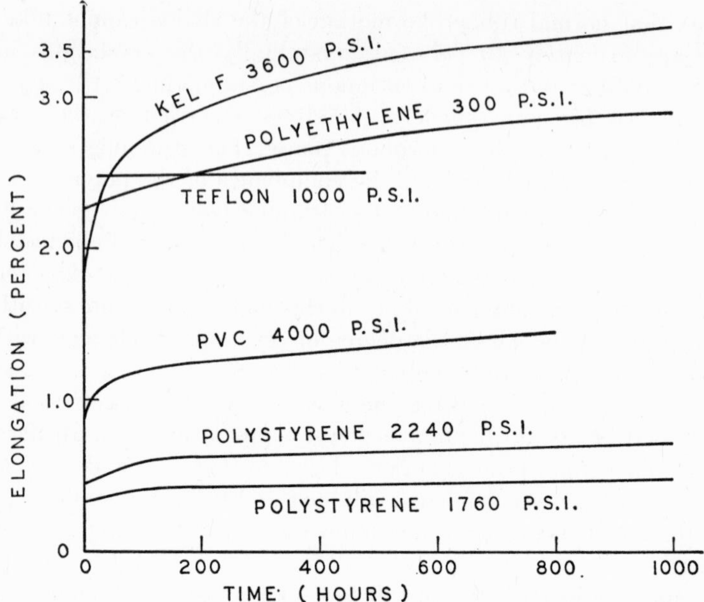

Figure 3.8. Creep of crystalline and amorphous polymers. [*After Sauer, J. A., Marin, J., and Hsiao, C. C., J. Appl. Phys.*, **20,** *507 (1949); Findley, W. N., and Khosla, G., J. Appl. Phys.*, **26,** *821 (1955); Findley, W. N., Modern Plastics*, **32,** *150 (Nov., 1954); and Doban, R. C., Sperati, C. A., and Sandt, B. W., Soc. Plastics Eng. J.*, **11,** *17 (Nov., 1955)*]

glass transition of 45°C so it has a high creep rate. Polytetrafluoroethylene has a large initial elongation, but its subsequent length remains nearly constant. This small creep rate may be due to the fact that 25°C is so far removed from the melting point that very little recrystallization can take place.

Effect of Stress

At small loads the compliance at a given time of most materials is independent of stress; for example, doubling the load doubles the deformation. At higher loads, especially those approaching the load required to break the polymer, the compliance at any given time increases with the load. This effect is generally quite pronounced with crystalline polymers, tough polyblend materials, and amorphous polymers in the transition region or above. However, rigid polymers such as polystyrene and highly crosslinked phenol-formaldehyde resins also show creep elongation which increases at a rate greater than the first power of the stress at very high loads. As a result, doubling the stress more than doubles the elongation. Apparently factors which eventually cause the polymer to break start operating to weaken the material long before the final fracture takes place.

Leaderman[58] found that the initial elastic deformation, which takes place when a load is first applied, is nearly exactly proportional to the applied stress. The creep which occurs afterwards, however, is not proportional to the stress. Such behavior appears to be quite general for many types of polymers.

Table 3.3 contains data on polyethylene at different loads at 85°F. This table gives an example of a material where creep compliance is nearly proportional to the first power of the stress at low loads, but at high loads the creep increases more rapidly than the first power of the stress. The reference compliance J_{50} is taken at a stress of 50 psi. The ratio of the compliance J at any load to the reference compliance J_{50} begins at approximately 1.0, but at higher stresses this ratio more than doubles.

Stress has another effect on the creep behavior of most polymers. The volume of an isotropic material increases when it is stretched unless it has a Poisson's ratio of 0.50. At least part of this increase in volume manifests itself as an increase in free volume[33]. From the discussion on glass transitions we know that molecular motion becomes easier when the free volume increases, and at the same time there is a decrease in viscosity. The decrease in viscosity in turn shifts the retardation times to shorter times. For instance, in the four-element model shown in Figure 3.3 the retardation time τ is given by η_2/E_2. In the example of a creep curve shown in Figure 3.4 the retardation time is five seconds. If the effect of a much larger stress were to reduce the retardation time to a value less than five seconds, the result would be similar to shifting the sigmoidal curve of Figure 3.4 to the left on the log time scale.

TABLE 3.3. STRESS DEPENDENCE OF CREEP OF POLYETHYLENE.

Stress psi	Elongation After 2000 hr (%)	J/J_{50}
50	0.30	1.00
100	0.65	1.08
150	1.08	1.20
200	1.50	1.25
300	2.40	1.33
400	3.75	1.57
600	8.0	2.25

Gohn, G. R., and Cummings, J. D., *ASTM Bull.*, No. 247, 64–68 (July, 1960).

The Superposition Principle

Suppose a creep test is carried out with an imposed stress of σ_1, and then after a time, the stress is suddenly changed to a new value of σ_2 and the test continued. Can the shape of the creep curve be predicted after the stress is changed? Fortunately, a simple law, known as the Boltzmann superposition principle, holds for most materials so that the creep curve can be predicted.

The first assumption involved in using the superposition principle is that the elongation is proportional to the stress, that is, the compliance is independent of the stress. The second assumption is that the elongation due to a given load is independent of the elongation due to any previous load[2, 58]. Therefore, the deformation due to a complex loading history is the sum of the deformations due to each separate load. This is illustrated in Figure 3.9. A stress σ_0 is applied at time t_0. At time t_1 the load is increased to σ_1 by adding an additional load equal to $(\sigma_1 - \sigma_0)$. In this case $\sigma_1 = 1.5\sigma_0$. The creep curve after t_1 is the sum of the continued creep due to load σ_0 plus the creep due to a load $(\sigma_1 - \sigma_0)$ applied at time t_1. Zero reference time for the additional load $(\sigma_1 - \sigma_0)$ is t_1, so the time scale for the added creep is $(t - t_1)$. After time t_2, all the load is removed. Removal of

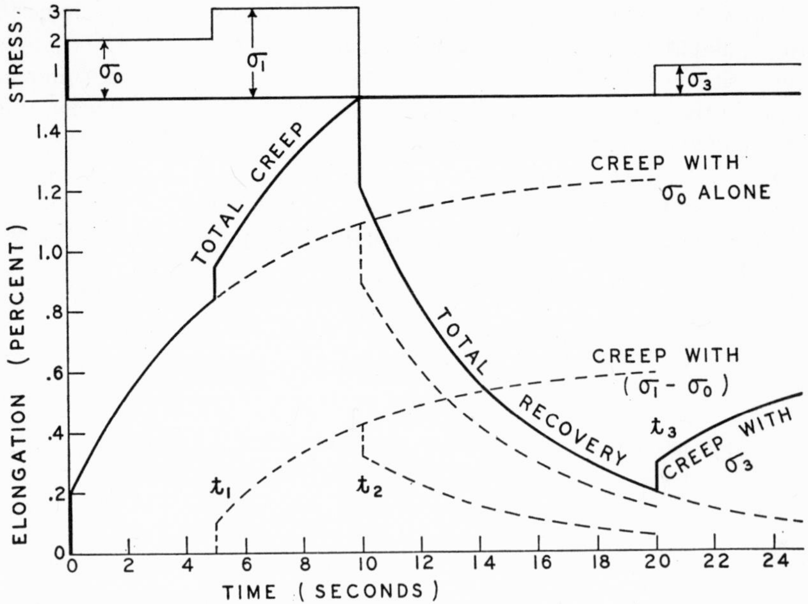

Figure 3.9. The Boltzmann superposition principle applied to creep behavior.

a load is equivalent to adding a negative load. Finally after a time t_3, a load σ_3 is added to the specimen. The creep due to σ_3 is superimposed upon the recovery curve. Mathematically, the creep resulting from a series of load changes may be represented by

$$\epsilon(t) = \sigma_0 J(t) + (\sigma_1 - \sigma_0) J(t - t_1) \cdots + (\sigma_i - \sigma_{i-1}) J(t - t_i) \tag{3.19}$$

The creep $\epsilon(t)$ is here written as an implicit function of the time t.

Creep Rupture Tests

Most creep tests are carried out with such small loads that the specimens never break. However, if the loads approach the breaking strength or the usual tensile strength of the polymer, the creep test will be terminated after a time by the breaking of the specimen. The time for this creep rupture to occur depends upon the load; the greater the load the shorter the time for the specimen to break. Examples of creep rupture are shown in Figure 3.1 where the specimens with the highest loads broke before the completion of the creep experiment.

Both theory and experiment suggest that the stress on the specimen and the time for the specimen to break should be related by an equation of the form[17, 20, 24, 77]

$$\log t_B = \log A - B\sigma \tag{3.20}$$

The time required for the specimen to break is t_B; σ is the stress; and A and B are constants which depend upon the temperature.

An equation of the above form is to be expected if creep rupture is considered as a rate process. The rate of rupture is inversely proportional to the time to break, therefore,

$$1/t_B = A'e^{-\Delta H/RT} \tag{3.21}$$

or

$$\ln t_B = -\ln A' + \Delta H/RT \tag{3.22}$$

The energy of activation of the fracture process is ΔH; it is a measure of the difficulty for the process causing fracture to occur. This elementary process bringing about fracture can be the jumping of stressed chain segments to positions where the stress on them is less, or it may involve the orientation of microscopic volumes within the material and their elongation to a critical value. In any case, when a stress is applied to the specimen, it will be easier for the process bringing about fracture to occur since it is aided by the stress. Thus, the stress lowers the energy of activation to an amount $(\Delta H - B'\sigma)$. Substitution of this quantity in place of ΔH in equation 3.22 gives

$$\ln t_B = \left(-\ln A' + \frac{\Delta H}{RT} - \frac{B'\sigma}{RT}\right) \tag{3.23}$$

This is essentially the same form as equation 3.20. A plot of stress against log t should give a straight line.

Both Taylor[77] and Bueche[17] emphasize that some stress relaxation process is the primary cause of the time dependence of the strength of a material. Bueche believes this relaxation process is the movement of chain segments so as to relieve the stress on them. Taylor visualizes the relaxation process as the orientation of small elements of the material; when any portion of these elements reaches a critical elongation, they break. Taylor's theory predicts that the elongation to break will increase as the stress increases even though the time to break will decrease; however, this is generally not true.

Creep rupture should be speeded up by an increase in temperature. For nylon 66 Coleman[24] found that t_B decreased with increasing temperature according to the following equation with an applied stress of 5.5×10^9 dynes/cm^2.

$$\log t_B = -17.85 + \frac{8.45 \times 10^3}{T} \tag{3.24}$$

Data were obtained from 30°C to 125°C; t_B is in seconds, and T = °K.

The stress cracking of polyethylene[55] is an example of how the environment may change creep rupture behavior. Polyethylene may be able to carry a certain load indefinitely when exposed to the atmosphere. However, if the polyethylene is placed in contact with certain vapors or liquids, the material will break in a short time. Some liquids have little effect on the time to break, but others drastically decrease t_B. Liquids especially detrimental to the strength of polyethylene include aqueous solutions of some surface active substances and propyl alcohol.

Creep Studies on Polymers

There are only a few articles which review the extensive work on the creep properties of polymers. The classic work of Leaderman[58] should be read by everyone who is interested in creep behavior. This book not only explains the theory in a simple and beautiful style, but it also contains many creep curves on a number of polymers and discusses the interpretation of the creep curves in detail. Leaderman[59] has also reviewed the viscoelastic properties, including creep, and has discussed the general effects of temperature and time. Alfrey[2] discusses some of the work on creep up until about 1948. More recently, Findley[37] has reviewed the mechanism of creep in plastics.

The creep behavior of polyethylenes has been investigated many times. Carey[18, 19] has measured the creep and creep rupture as a function of temperature, stress, and molecular weight of the polymer. Hoff, Clegg, and Sherrard-Smith[51] show many curves illustrating the effect of stress, temperature, and heat treatments on the creep of low density (highly branched) polyethylene. Gohn and Cummings[47] have looked into the effects of temperature and melt viscosity as a function of stress up to times exceeding a thousand hours on compression-molded specimens. Measurements at elevated temperatures include those of Dienes[29] and Dixon[30]. Dienes used a four-element model to explain his results. Dixon, using both high and low density polyethylenes, found that his creep results over a range of temperatures and stresses obeyed the Nutting equation. Ballentine, Dienes, Manowitz, Ander, and Mesrobian[6] investigated the effect of crosslinking polyethylene by ionizing radiation. Findley and Khosla[38, 39] use Eyring's hyperbolic sine model[53] to explain the creep behavior.

Findley[35], Findley and Khosla[38, 39], Dienes[29], and Bergen and Wolstenholme[7] measured the creep of unplasticized polyvinyl chlorides and vinyl chloride-vinyl acetate copolymers. Findley[35] found that polyvinyl chloride annealed at high temperatures had less creep than unannealed material. This effect might be due to more crystallinity or to a smaller free volume of the annealed polymer. Bergen and Wolstenholme[7] used short-time, high-temperature tests to predict the room-temperature behavior for long times.

Port, Jordan, Palm, Witnauer, Hansen, and Swern[73] measured the creep of copolymers of vinyl chloride and vinyl stearate or other vinyl esters. Creep of plasticized polyvinyl chlorides as a function of temperature, type of plasticizer, and concentration of plasticizer has been studied by Aiken, Alfrey, Janssen, and Mark[1], Alfrey, Wiederhorn, Stein, and Tobolsky[3, 4] and Alfrey[2]. Their work showed that polyvinyl chloride is not completely amorphous but must be somewhat crystalline. Different plasticizers give creep curves of different shapes. On a log time scale, trioctyl phosphate gives a much flatter creep curve than tricresyl phosphate. In general, plasticizers with cyclic groups such as the cresyl group have steeper creep curves than plasticizers with alkyl groups similar to the octyl group. Dyson[32] measured creep with various concentrations and types of plasticizers. Nielsen, Buchdahl, and Levreault[69] and Buchdahl and Nielsen[11] found that the creep of most plasticized compositions could be approximated by Nutting's equation with the creep rate $(d \log \epsilon)/(d \log t)$ a maximum in the transition region.

Some of the creep data on polystyrene have been reviewed by Williams and Cleereman[9]. Sauer, Marin, and Hsiao[74] measured the creep of polystyrene up to a thousand hours at stresses up to near the ultimate strength of the material. The compliance at any time increases with the stress, so the Boltzmann superposition principle does not hold at high stresses. Findley[34] has commented on the creep rate as a function of stress. Marin and Cuff[61] measured the creep of compression-molded polystyrene in tension, torsion, and bending. Cheatham and Dietz[22] have measured the creep behavior of polystyrene which had been oriented by hot stretching previous to making the creep tests. Creep experiments on polystyrene above its glass temperature were made by Buchdahl[10], Nielsen and Buchdahl[67, 68], and Buchdahl, Nielsen, and Merz[12]; their work established the importance of chain entanglements on flow properties. The effects of molecular weight, stress, and temperature were explored. Merz, Nielsen, and Buchdahl[64], found that films cast from different solvents had dramatically different creep behavior. It was assumed that the differences were due to trace amounts of residual solvents, but attempts have been made to explain the results in terms of changes in molecular configuration and entanglements arising from the nature of the solvents[50]. Polymer molecules form loose coils in good solvents and tight coils in poor solvents.

Creep data on polymethyl methacrylate have been reported by MacLeod[60], Weber, Robertson, and Bartoe[82], Fukada[43], McCrackin and Bersch[63], and Bueche[13]. Bueche studied plasticized as well as unplasticized polymers; he extended theory to show the importance of entanglements on creep.

The paper by McCrackin and Bersch[63] is especially interesting as it is one of the few cases where uniaxial creep is compared with biaxial creep. Uniaxial creep is normal creep in which the stress is applied in one direction. In biaxial creep, stresses are applied in two directions perpendicular to one another; biaxial creep tests may be made on square pieces of film by stressing them equally both lengthwise and crosswise. It was found that biaxial creep is about half as great as uniaxial creep. One would expect this as the crosswise stress prevents the width of the specimen from decreasing as in a normal creep test. Theory predicts that

$$\epsilon_2 = \frac{1}{2}\epsilon_1 + \frac{\sigma}{6B} \tag{3.25}$$

where ϵ_1 is the uniaxial strain produced by a stress σ, ϵ_2 is the biaxial strain in either direction produced by a stress σ, and B is the bulk modulus. In general, the last term containing the bulk modulus is small, so biaxial creep should be about one half the uniaxial creep for a given stress.

Only a few papers covering the extensive literature on the creep of rubbers will be mentioned here. A review article by Wood[84] on the elasticity of rubber discusses creep as well as other mechanical properties. Bueche[15, 16] discusses the theory of creep of rubbers and presents data on a number of different polymers. These papers show the effect of imperfections in the crosslinked structure of rubbers—the creep never stops. Gehman[46] measured the creep of natural rubber and GR-S as a function of cure and plasticizer concentration. The effects of molecular weight and molecular weight distribution of polyisobutylene rubbers have been studied by Van Holde and Williams[81] and Zapp and Baldwin[86]. Throdahl[79] compared the creep of rubbers as a function of aging with some conventional aging methods; creep shows up differences between antioxidants. Rubbers containing carboxylic acid groups may be cross linked by ionic bonds formed by divalent cations from materials such as calcium or zinc oxides. Such rubbers have been studied by Cunneen, Moore, and Shephard[28], Cooper and Bird[26], and by Cooper[27]. The creep of such rubbers is greater than when chemical bonds form the crosslinks. The theory of the creep of a rubber with a single retardation time is discussed by Blatz and Tobolsky[8].

The creep of cellulosic materials has been described in a number of papers including those on cellulose acetate by Findley[36] and Swanson and Williams[76]. The latter authors did not find any evidence of crystallinity, although their creep curves suggest that some crystalinity may have existed in the cellulose acetate in a paracrystalline state[54]. Gearhart and Kennedy[45] studied the efficiency of plasticizers in improving the flow of cellulose acetate butyrate plastics; they fit their data to a four-element model. Van Holde[80] and Plazek[72] found that cellulose nitrate polymers obey Andrade's creep equation[5]. Andrade's equation is similar to the Nutting equation except that the exponent of the time is limited to a value of one-third; that is, creep is proportional to $t^{\frac{1}{3}}$.

Measurements on highly crosslinked phenol-formaldehyde polymers containing various fillers have been made by Leaderman[57], Telfair, Carswell, and Nason[78], and Gailus and Telfair[44]. The creep of very slightly crosslinked phenol-formaldehyde resins as a function of crosslinking, temperature, and stress has been measured by Guzzetti, Dienes, and Alfrey[49]; the viscosity of the resins took a large jump when the crosslinking became great enough to form a gel.

Investigations on other polymers include those of Doban, Sperati, and Sandt (31) on polytetrafluoroethylene, Kistler[56] on polyvinyl acetate, and Catsiff, Alfrey, and O'Shaughnessy[21] on nylon. Cogdell and Hardesty[23] compare the creep behavior of polyoxymethylene with a number of other polymers. Rayons were studied by O'Shaughnessy[71], and polyvinyl alcohol and polyvinyl formal were studied by Yamamura and Kuramoto[85]; the creep of these materials is sensitive to water vapor, which acts as a plasticizer.

References

1. Aiken, W., Alfrey, Jr., T., Janssen, A., and Mark, H., *J. Polymer Sci.*, **2,** 178 (1947).
2. Alfrey, Jr., T., "Mechanical Behavior of High Polymers," New York, Interscience Publishers, Inc., 1948.
3. Alfrey, Jr., T., Wiederhorn, N., Stein, R., and Tobolsky, A., *J. Colloid Sci.*, **4,** 211 (1949).
4. Alfrey, Jr., T., Wiederhorn, N., Stein, R., and Tobolsky, A., *Ind. Eng. Chem.*, **41,** 701 (1949).
5. Andrade, E. N., *Proc. Roy. Soc. London*, **A84,** 1 (1910) and **A90,** 329 (1914).
6. Ballentine, D. S., Dienes, G. J., Manowitz, B., Ander, P., and Mesrobian, R. B., *J. Polymer Sci.*, **13,** 410 (1954).
7. Bergen, Jr., R. L., Wolstenholme, W. E., *Soc. Plastics Eng. J.*, **16,** 1235 (1960).
8. Blatz, P. J., and Tobolsky, A. V., *J. Chem. Phys.*, **14,** 113 (1946).
9. Boundy, R. H., and Boyer, R. F., "Styrene—Its Polymers, Copolymers, and Derivatives," New York, Reinhold Publishing Corp., 1952.
10. Buchdahl, R., *J. Colloid Sci.*, **3,** 87 (1948).
11. Buchdahl, R., and Nielsen, L. E., *J. Appl. Phys.*, **22,** 1344 (1951).
12. Buchdahl, R., Nielsen, L. E., and Merz, E. H., *J. Polymer Sci.*, **6,** 403 (1951).
13. Bueche, F., *J. Appl. Phys.*, **26,** 738 (1955).
14. Bueche, F., *J. Chem. Phys.*, **25,** 599 (1956).
15. Bueche, F., *J. Polymer Sci.*, **25,** 305 (1957).
16. Bueche, F., *J. Appl. Polymer Sci.*, **1,** 240 (1959).
17. Bueche, F., *J. Appl. Phys.*, **29,** 1231 (1958).
18. Carey, R. H., *Soc. Plastics Eng. J.*, **10,** 16 (March, 1954).
19. Carey, R. H., *Ind. Eng. Chem.*, **50,** 1045 (1958).
20. Carey, R. H., *Soc. Plastics Eng. J.*, **12,** 21 (March, 1956).
21. Catsiff, E., Alfrey, Jr., T., and O'Shaughnessy, M. T., *Textile Research J.*, **23,** 808 (1953).
22. Cheatham, R. G., and Dietz, A. G. H., *Modern Plastics*, **29,** 113 (Sept., 1951).
23. Cogdell, J. F., and Hardesty, R. H., *Soc. Plastics Eng. J.*, **14,** 25 (Apr., 1958).
24. Coleman, B., *Textile Research J.*, **27,** 393 (1957); **28,** 393 and 891 (1958).
25. Conant, F. S., and Liska, J. W., *J. Appl. Phys.*, **15,** 767 (1944).
26. Cooper, W., and Bird, T. B., *Ind. Eng. Chem.*, **50,** 771 (1958).
27. Cooper, W., *J. Polymer Sci.*, **28,** 195 (1958).
28. Cunneen, J. I., Moore, C. G., and Shephard, B. R., *J. Appl. Polymer Sci.*, **3,** 11 (1960).
29. Dienes, G. J., *J. Colloid Sci.*, **2,** 131 (1947).
30. Dixon, R. R., *Soc. Plastics Eng. J.*, **14,** 23 (Apr., 1958).
31. Doban, R. C., Sperati, C. A., and Sandt, B. W., *Soc. Plastics Eng. J.*, **11,** 17 (Nov., 1955).
32. Dyson, A., *J. Polymer Sci.*, **7,** 133 (1951).
33. Ferry, J. D., and Stratton, R. A., *Koll. Z.*, **171,** 107 (1960).
34. Findley, W. N., *J. Appl. Phys.*, **21,** 258 (1950).

35. Findley, W. N., *Modern Plastics*, **32,** 150 (Nov., 1954).
36. Findley, W. N., *Modern Plastics*, **19,** 71 (Aug., 1942).
37. Findley, W. N., *Soc. Plastics Eng. J.*, **16,** 57, 192 (1960).
38. Findley, W. N., and Khosla, G., *Soc. Plastics Eng. J.*, **12,** 20 (Dec., 1956).
39. Findley, W. N., and Khosla, G., *J. Appl. Phys.*, **26,** 821 (1955).
40. Flory, P. J., "Principles of Polymer Chemistry," Ithaca, Cornell University Press, 1953.
41. Fox, T. G., Gratch, S., and Loshaek, S., "Rheology," Vol. 1, Chap. 12, p. 431, Eirich, F. R., Ed., New York, Academic Press, Inc., 1956.
42. Fox, T. G., and Loshaek, S., *J. Appl. Phys.*, **26,** 1080 (1955).
43. Fukada, E., *J. Phys. Soc. Japan*, **6,** 254 (1951) or *Physics. Abstr.*, **55A,** 563, No. 4679 (1952).
44. Gailus, W. J., and Telfair, D., *Modern Plastics*, **22,** 149 (May, 1945).
45. Gearhart, W. M., and Kennedy, W. D., *Ind. Eng. Chem.*, **41,** 695 (1949).
46. Gehman, S. D., *J. Appl. Phys.*, **19,** 456 (1948).
47. Gohn, G. R., and Cummings, J. D., *ASTM, Bull.* No. 247, 64 (July 1960).
48. Gossick, B. R., *Rev. Sci. Instr.*, **25,** 907 (1954).
49. Guzzetti, A. J., Dienes, G. J., and Alfrey, Jr., T., *J. Colloid Sci.*, **5,** 202 (1950).
50. Haas, H. C., and Livingston, D. I., *J. Polymer Sci.*, **17,** 135 (1955).
51. Hoff, E. A. W., Clegg, P. L., and Sherrard-Smith, K., *British Plast.*, **31,** 384 (1958).
52. Hoffman, J. D., Weeks, J. J., and Murphey, W. M., *J. Research, Nat. Bur. Standards*, **63A,** 67 (1959).
53. Holland, H. D., Halsey, G., Eyring, H., *Textile Research J.*, **16,** 201 (1946).
54. Hosemann, R., *Z. Physik*, **128,** 1, 455 (1950).
55. Howard, J. B., *Soc. Plastics Eng. J.*, **15,** 397 (1959).
56. Kistler, S., *J. Appl. Phys.*, **11,** 769 (1940).
57. Leaderman, H., *J. Appl. Mechanics*, **6,** A79 (1939).
58. Leaderman, H., "Elastic and Creep Properties of Filamentous Materials and Other High Polymers," Washington, D. C. The Textile Foundation, 1943.
59. Leaderman, H., "Rheology," Vol. 1, Chap. 1, p. 1, Eirich, F. R., Ed., New York, Academic Press, Inc., 1958.
60. MacLeod, A. A., *Ind. Eng. Chem.*, **47,** 1319 (1955).
61. Marin, J., and Cuff, G., *Am. Soc. Testing Materials Proc.*, **49,** 1158 (1949).
62. Mark, H., and Tobolsky, A. V., "Physical Chemistry of High Polymeric Systems," p. 243, New York, Interscience Publishers, Inc., 1950.
63. McCrackin, F. L., and Bersch, C. F., *Soc. Plastics Eng. J.*, **15,** 791 (1959).
64. Merz, E. H., Nielsen, L. E., and Buchdahl, R., *J. Polymer Sci.*, **4,** 605 (1949).
65. Nielsen, L. E., Unpublished data of Monsanto Chemical Co.
66. Nielsen, L. E., *J. Appl. Polymer Sci.*, **2,** 351 (1959).
67. Nielsen, L. E., and Buchdahl, R., *J. Colloid Sci.*, **5,** 282 (1950).
68. Nielsen, L. E. and Buchdahl, R., *J. Chem. Phys.*, **17,** 839 (1949).
69. Nielsen, L. E., Buchdahl, R., and Levreault, R., *J. Appl. Phys.*, **21,** 607 (1950).
70. Nutting, P., *Proc. Am. Soc. Testing Materials*, **21,** 1162 (1921).
71. O'Shaughnessy, M. T., *Textile Research J.*, **18,** 263 (1948).
72. Plazek, D. J., *J. Colloid Sci.*, **15,** 50 (1960).
73. Port, W. S., Jordan, Jr., E. F., Palm, W. E., Witnauer, L. P., Hansen, J. E., and Swern, D., *Ind. Eng. Chem.*, **47,** 472 (1955).
74. Sauer, J. A., Marin, J., and Hsiao, C. C., *J. Appl. Phys.*, **20,** 507 (1949).

75. Staverman, A. J., and Schwarzl, F., "Die Physik Der Hochpolymeren," Vol. 4, pp. 1–48, Stuart, H. A., Ed., Berlin, Springer Verlag, 1956.
76. Swanson, D. L., and Williams, J. W., *J. Appl. Phys.*, **26,** 810 (1955).
77. Taylor, N. W., *J. Appl. Phys.*, **18,** 943 (1947).
78. Telfair, D., Carswell, T. S., and Nason, H. K., *Modern Plastics*, **21,** 137 (Feb., 1944).
79. Throdahl, M. C., *Ind. Eng. Chem.*, **40,** 2180 (1948).
80. Van Holde, K., *J. Polymer Sci.*, **24,** 417 (1957).
81. Van Holde, K. E., and Williams, J. W., *J. Polymer Sci.* **11,** 243 (1953).
82. Weber, C. H., Robertson, E. N., and Bartoe, W. F., *Ind. Eng. Chem.*, **47,** 1311 (1955).
83. Wood, L. A., *Nat. Bur. Standards (U.S.) Report*, 5796, (May 12, 1958).
84. Wood, L. A., *Rubber Chem. and Technol.*, **31,** 959 (1958).
85. Yamamura, H., and Kuramoto, N., *J. Appl. Polymer Sci.*, **2,** 71 (1959).
86. Zapp, R. L., and Baldwin, F. P., *Ind. Eng. Chem.*, **38,** 948 (1946).

Chapter 4

STRESS RELAXATION

General Behavior and Instrumentation

In a stress-relaxation test, the specimen is deformed a fixed amount, and the stress required to maintain this deformation is measured for a period of time. The maximum stress occurs as soon as the deformation takes place, and the stress decreases gradually with time from this maximum value.

From the practical standpoint, creep measurements are generally considered more important than stress relaxation measurement, and since creep measurements are so easily made, stress-relaxation tests have been neglected by engineers and research workers who evaluate the behavior of high polymeric materials. However, scientists who are interested in the theory of viscoelastic materials and in the relation of properties to molecular structure have concentrated more on stress relaxation than on creep measurements. Stress-relaxation data are generally more easily interpreted in terms of viscoelastic theory than are creep data. Stress-relaxation data, are, however, also of interest in a number of practical applications such as the determination of the stress holding a metal insert in some fabricated plastic pieces or the evaluation of antioxidants in polymers[20, 54].

Many types of instruments have been used to measure stress relaxation[4, 16, 23, 28, 30, 32, 33, 34, 37, 54, 73]. Relatively simple instruments may be used with rubbers and low modulus polymers, but it is a much more difficult task to build an accurate instrument for rigid polymers. The apparatus must be very rigid, otherwise the deformation of the apparatus may be comparable to that of the polymer. Also, the transducer used to measure the stress must be capable of operating with very little deformation. For instance, a rigid polymer one inch long might be stretched only 0.001 inch in a stress-relaxation experiment. In order to measure the stress to 1.0%, the stress-measuring device should not deform more than 10 microinches unless its deformation is compensated for in some manner.

A modified balance may be used with rubbery materials. One end of the test specimen is attached to the pan of a balance while the other end is attached to a stretching device. The length of the stretched specimen is held constant by changing the load on the balance. The changing load can be calculated as a stress on the specimen; this stress when plotted as a function of time gives the stress-relaxation curve.

More elaborate instruments use strain gages[16, 30] or differential transformers[28, 32, 33, 34, 37] in connection with electronic recorders to give a permanent and continuous record of the stress as a function of time. One such instrument is shown schematically in Figure 4.1. The stress is measured by a strain gage attached to a cantilever beam spring. When a stress is applied to the specimen, the beam is bent a slight amount. The deflection of the beam is in turn transmitted to the strain gage, thus changing its resistance and its electrical output; the electrical voltage is fed into the recorder to give a trace proportional to stress (or force) versus time. The elongation is applied to the specimen by quickly pulling down on the lower rod. The elongation stop allows one to impose any fixed elongation to the specimen. The elongation is held constant by tightening the lower set screw.

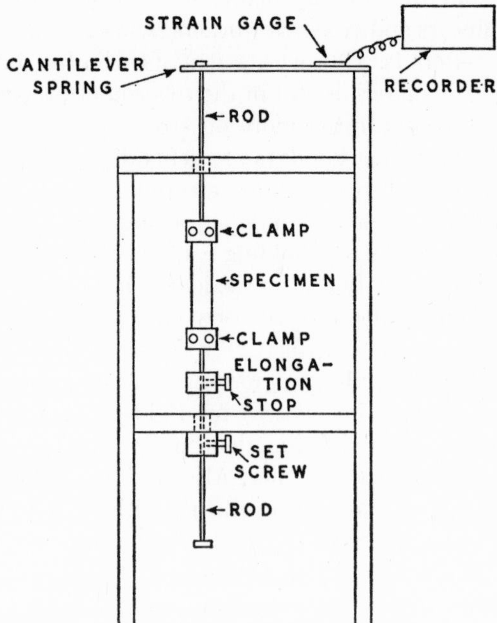

Figure 4.1. Apparatus for measuring stress relaxation.

Model of Stress Relaxation and Relaxation Times

A very simple model may be used to illustrate many of the features of a stress-relaxation experiment. All that is needed is a spring and dashpot hooked together in series. If the dashpot η_2 and spring E_2 used in the model for creep (see Figure 3.2) are made infinitely stiff or nondeformable, all the deformation will take place in spring E_1 and dashpot η_3. Such a model with a dashpot η and a spring E in series is called a Maxwell unit.

When a stress σ is applied to a Maxwell model, the equation of motion is

$$\frac{d\epsilon}{dt} = \frac{\sigma}{\eta} + \frac{1}{E}\frac{d\sigma}{dt}. \tag{4.1}$$

The same stress is applied to both the spring and the dashpot, but the total elongation is the sum of the deformations of the two elements. Since the elongation ϵ does not change with time after the initial deformation during a stress-relaxation experiment, $d\epsilon/dt = 0$. In this case the equation of motion may be integrated to give

$$\sigma = \sigma_0 \, e^{-(Et/\eta)} = \sigma_0 \, e^{-t/\tau} \tag{4.2}$$

where σ_0 is the initial stress immediately after the model (or specimen) is stretched, τ is the relaxation time defined as

$$\tau = \eta/E. \tag{4.3}$$

At the beginning of a stress-relaxation experiment the model is nearly instantaneously stretched a fixed amount. All the initial deformation goes into stretching the spring. The stretched spring immediately starts to exert a force on the piston of the dashpot so that eventually the dashpot gets stretched, the spring returns to its unstretched state, and the stress on the model decreases to zero. The relaxation time τ is the time required for the stress to decay to $1/e$ times its original value or to 36.79 per cent of its initial value. The relaxation time in a stress-relaxation experiment is analogous to the retardation time in a creep experiment.

Figures 4.2 and 4.3 illustrate the change of stress with time for a Maxwell model in which $E = 10^7$ dynes/cm^2, $\eta = 5 \times 10^7$ poises, and, consequently, $\tau = 5$ seconds. The fractional stress σ/σ_0 is plotted against time (Figure 4.2) and also against the logarithm of the time (Figure 4.3). In the sigmoidally shaped log t plot, the curve has its maximum slope when the time is equal to the relaxation time. Most of the relaxation takes place within one decade of time around the relaxation time. It is also worth noting that the relaxation curve should be independent of the elongation used in the experiment. If the stress is divided by the elongation, the relaxation

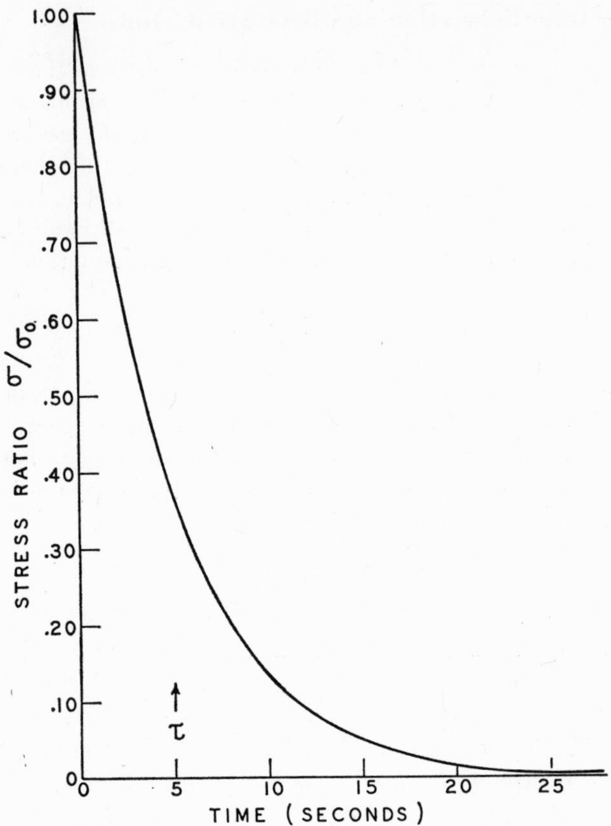

Figure 4.2. Stress relaxation of a Maxwell unit with E = 10^7 dynes/cm^2, $\eta = 5 \times 10^7$ poises, and $\tau = 5$ seconds.

curve gives the variation of the relaxation modulus $E_r(t)$ as a function of time.

$$\frac{\sigma}{\epsilon} = E_r(t) = \frac{\sigma_0}{\epsilon} e^{-t/\tau}. \tag{4.4}$$

Thus, stress-relaxation experiments give the variation of the modulus with time in the same way that creep experiments give the time dependence of the compliance.

Most polymers have more than one relaxation time. They have in general a nearly infinite number of relaxation times covering many decades of time. The effect of this distribution of relaxation times is to flatten out the sigmoidally shaped curve of Figure 4.3 so that it covers a much greater time

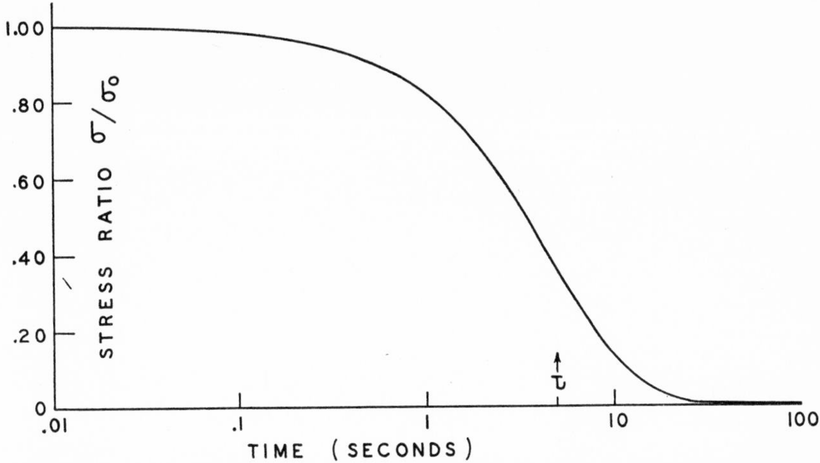

Figure 4.3. Stress relaxation of a Maxwell unit. Same constants as in Figure 4.2.

scale. The stress relaxation of a material with three relaxation times, for instance, is given by

$$E_r(t) = E_1 e^{-t/\tau_1} + E_2 e^{-t/\tau_2} + E_3 e^{-t/\tau_3}. \tag{4.5}$$

The values of E_1, E_2, and E_3 may be considered as the moduli of the three springs of three Maxwell units in parallel. A simple example is given in Table 4.1. If the relaxation times are so numerous that they can be considered as practically continuous, the stress relaxation is given by

$$E_r(t) = \lim_{n\to\infty} \sum_{i=1}^{n} E_i\, e^{-t/\tau_i} = \int_{\tau=0}^{\infty} E(\tau)\, e^{-t/\tau}\, d\tau + E_\infty \tag{4.6}$$

At zero time before any relaxation has occurred, the modulus is

$$E_r(0) = \lim_{n\to\infty} \sum_{i=1}^{n} E_i = \int_{\tau=0}^{\infty} E(\tau)\, d\tau + E_\infty . \tag{4.7}$$

Since the distribution of relaxation times is very broad, it is more convenient to represent the distribution as a function of log time rather than as a function of linear time. If

$$H(\ln \tau) = \tau E(\tau) \tag{4.8}$$

then

$$E(t) = \int_{\ln\tau=-\infty}^{\infty} \mathrm{H}(\ln \tau)\, e^{-t/\tau}\, d \ln \tau + E_\infty . \tag{4.9}$$

TABLE 4.1. STRESS RELAXATION OF A MODEL WITH THREE RELAXATION TIMES.

$$E_r(t) = E_1 e^{-t/\tau_1} + E_2 e^{-t/\tau_2} + E_3 e^{-t/\tau_3}$$

Let $E_1 = E_2 = E_3 = 1 \times 10^7$ dynes/cm²

$$\tau_1 = 0.1, \quad \tau_2 = 1.0, \quad \tau_3 = 10.0$$

$$E_r(t) = 10^7 e^{-(t/0.10)} + 10^7 e^{-t} + 10^7 e^{-(t/10)}$$

Time (sec.)	Term (1)	Term (2)	Term (3)	Stress-Relaxation Modulus
0.0	1.00×10^7	1.00×10^7	1.00×10^7	3.00×10^7
0.10	0.368 "	0.905 "	0.990 "	2.26 "
0.50	0.007 "	0.606 "	0.951 "	1.56 "
1.0	.00 "	0.368 "	0.905 "	1.27 "
5.0	.00 "	0.007 "	0.606 "	0.61 "
10.0	.00 "	.00 "	0.368 "	0.37 "
100.0	.00 "	.00 "	.00 "	0.00 "

$H(\ln \tau)$ is the distribution of relaxation times on a log scale, and E_∞ is the rubber equilibrium modulus at very long times if there is no viscous flow; $E(\tau)$ is the relaxation spectrum as a function of linear time. The stress-relaxation modulus for a given time is determined primarily by the relaxation times which are longer than that given time.

The distribution of relaxation times $H(\ln \tau)$ may be calculated in a number of ways. A very simple but crude approximation involves the measurement of the slope of the stress-relaxation modulus $E_r(t)$ vs. log t curve[1, 24, 36, 56, 63].

$$H(\ln \tau) \doteq -\frac{d[E_r(t)]}{d \ln t} \doteq \frac{-1}{2.303} \frac{d[E_r(t)]}{d \log_{10} t}. \tag{4.10}$$

A more accurate approximation of the distribution of relaxation times may be found by also measuring the second derivative of the stress-relaxation curve:

$$H(\ln \tau) = \frac{-d}{d \ln t}[E_r(t)] + \frac{d^2 [E_r(t)]}{d(\ln t)^2}. \tag{4.11}$$

These equations are evaluated under the condition $t = \tau$.

In order to get an accurate distribution of relaxation times, the experimental data should cover at least eight to fifteen decades of time. It is practically impossible to cover such a great range of times. However, in a later section it will be shown how to approximate the time range by shifting stress-relaxation curves obtained at different temperatures.

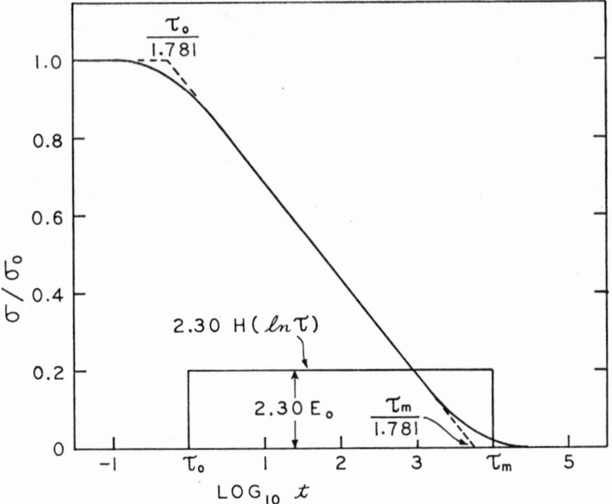

Figure 4.4. Stress relaxation of a material with a box distribution of relaxation times.

The distribution of relaxation times of many materials can be approximated over long periods of time by a box-shaped distribution[63, 66]. The box distribution is often applicable to a part of the stress relaxation curves of crystalline polymers or to rubbers at long times where flow occurs. An example of a box distribution of relaxation times and the resulting stress-relaxation curve is shown in Figure 4.4 The stress-relaxation curve is a straight line in the region of the box. Outside the box there are no relaxation times, so the relaxation curve does not change with time.

The shortest relaxation time is τ_0 and the maximum relaxation time is τ_m . The box distribution is defined as

$$H(\tau) = E_0 \quad \text{for} \quad \tau_0 < \tau < \tau_m \tag{4.12}$$

$$H(\tau) = 0 \quad \text{for} \quad \tau < \tau_0 \quad \text{and for} \quad \tau > \tau_m \tag{4.13}$$

With a box distribution, the rate of change of stress-relaxation modulus in the region of the box is

$$\frac{-d[E_r(t)]}{d \ln t} = E_0 = H(\ln \tau) \tag{4.14}$$

or

$$\frac{-d[E_r(t)]}{d \log_{10} t} = 2.303E_0 = 2.303H(\log \tau) \tag{4.15}$$

The higher the box the more rapidly the stress decays. In stress-relaxation experiments in which the stress decreases linearly on a log time scale, it can be assumed that the distribution of relaxation times must approximate a box.

At temperatures near the glass-transition temperature the stress-relaxation curve can often be approximated by assuming that the distribution of relaxation times is shaped like a wedge on a log time scale[60]. In the general case the stress-relaxation modulus $E_r(t)$ is always related to the distribution of relaxation times H ($\ln \tau$) by the equation[24, 63]

$$E_r(t) = \int_{-\infty}^{+\infty} H(\ln \tau)e^{-t/\tau}\, d \ln \tau. \tag{4.16}$$

Although the theory of viscoelasticity discussed so far has been primarily phenomenological in nature, recent molecular theories of the viscoelasticity of polymers have had some success. These theories have been developed by Rouse[55], Bueche[8, 9], and Zimm[76], and extended by others[41]. These theories were originally developed for dilute solutions, but Ferry, Landel and Williams[22] extended them to bulk polymers in the rubbery state. Molecular theories of viscoelasticity give a spectrum of discrete relaxation times rather than a continuous distribution. The long time end of the relaxation spectrum may be approximated by

$$\tau_p = \frac{6\eta M}{\pi^2\, dRTp^2}, \qquad p = 1, 2, 3 \cdots N/5 \tag{4.17}$$

where η is the steady state zero rate of shear viscosity, M is the molecular weight of the polymer, d is its density, R is the gas constant, T is the absolute temperature, and N is the number of segments in a molecule. The longest relaxation time τ_1, is obtained by letting $p = 1$.

The stress-relaxation behavior may be calculated from equations analogous to equations 4.5 or 4.6.

$$\frac{\sigma}{\sigma_0} \doteq \frac{5}{N}\sum_{p=1}^{N/5} e^{-t/\tau_p} \doteq \frac{5}{N}\sum_{p=1}^{N/5} e^{-(tp^2/\tau_1)} \tag{4.18}$$

At times somewhat smaller than the maximum relaxation time τ_1, it can be shown that the above equation may be roughly approximated by

$$\frac{\sigma}{\sigma_0} \simeq \frac{5\pi^{\frac{1}{2}}\tau_1^{\frac{1}{2}}}{2Nt^{\frac{1}{2}}}. \tag{4.19}$$

Thus, at temperatures above the glass temperature, a plot of log (σ/σ_0) against log t should give a straight line with a negative slope of one half. This prediction has been verified for a number of amorphous rubbers and polymers in the time-temperature region in which their elastic modulus is about 10^6 to 10^7 dynes/cm^2. Equation 4.19 does not hold for either very short times or for long times approaching τ_1, at which time the modulus is roughly 10^4 or 10^5 dynes/cm^2 [24, 63].

At times equal to the maximum relaxation time τ_1, or longer, the stress relaxation is determined primarily by only τ_1, and not the other relaxation times. At this point, especially for fractions with a narrow molecular weight distribution, a plot of the logarithm of the stress-relaxation modulus against time gives a straight line which has a negative slope proportional to τ_1,[68, 69]. That is, for $t > \tau_1$, $d \log E_r(t)/dt = -1/(2.303\ \tau_1)$. These conditions hold when the modulus is about 10^4 or 10^5 dynes/cm^2.

Effects of Transitions and Temperature on Stress Relaxation

The stress-relaxation behavior of polymers is extremely temperature dependent, especially in the region of the glass transition[63]. Most amorphous polymers at temperatures well below the glass temperature have a tensile (Young's) modulus of about 3.0×10^{10} dynes/cm^2 at the beginning of a stress-relaxation experiment. The modulus gradually decreases with time, but it may take years for the stress to decrease to near zero values. Rubbers have tensile moduli of about 10^7 dynes/cm^2 (145 psi) for short-time stress-relaxation experiments. Theoretically, much higher modulus values could be found if the stress could be measured at very short times, say at one millionth of a second, after the start of a stress-relaxation experiment. However, in practice these higher values are difficult to measure at temperatures well above the transition temperature. The manner in which the stress decays in a rubber depends more on its molecular weight and on its degree of crosslinking than it does on the temperature. These factors are discussed in a later section.

Not only is the stress-relaxation behavior of an amorphous polymer most sensitive to temperature in the transition region, but at a given temperature in the transition region the stress changes very rapidly with time. In the transition region a plot of the logarithm of the relaxation modulus (or $\log \sigma/\sigma_0$) against the logarithm of the time is nearly a straight line with a steep negative slope. At both higher and lower temperatures the slope of the stress-relaxation plots becomes less. These effects are illustrated in Figure 4.5. The glass temperature of the polymethyl methacrylate shown in the figure is about 112°C.

Effects of Molecular Weight and Crosslinking

The effects of molecular weight are most prominent above the glass-transition temperature. Figure 4.6 illustrates the general shape of the stress-relaxation modulus curve for a medium molecular weight polymer, a very

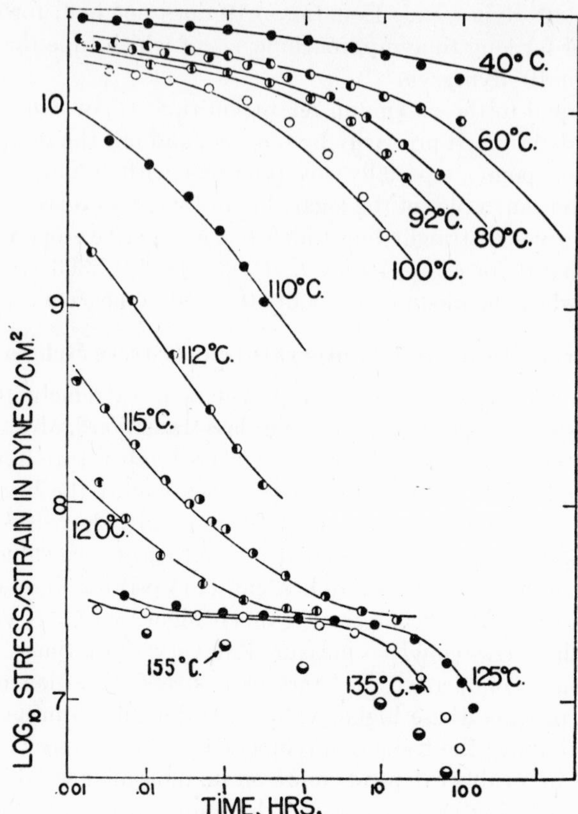

Figure 4.5. Stress-relaxation modulus curves of polymethyl methacrylate at different temperatures. [*After McLoughlin, J. R., and Tobolsky, A. V., J. Colloid Sci.*, **7**, *555* (*1952*)]

high molecular weight polymer, and a crosslinked rubber at a temperature above their glass temperature.

Crosslinks in the rubber keep the stress from decreasing to zero. The network structure prevents the stretched-out molecular segments from snapping back to their normally coiled equilibrium configuration unless the molecules become cut by a degradation reaction or unless the network structure was originally very imperfect. The kinetic theory of rubber elasticity[25, 71] enables one to estimate the value of the equilibrium stress-relaxation modulus E

$$E = \frac{3RTd}{M_c} \tag{4.20}$$

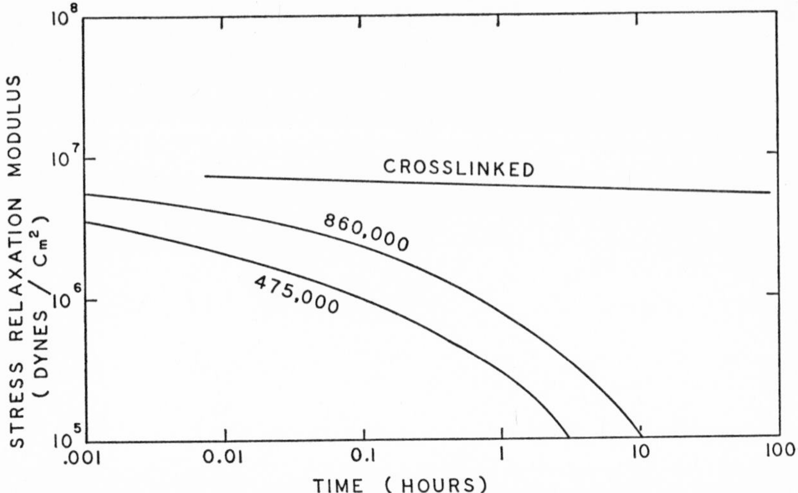

Figure 4.6. Stress relaxation of a medium molecular weight (475,000) polyisobutylene, a high molecular weight (860,000) polyisobutylene, and a crosslinked polyisobutylene rubber at 30°C. [*Uncrosslinked polymer data from Andrews, R. D., and Tobolsky, A. V., J. Polymer Sci.*, **7**, *221 (1951). Crosslinked rubber data from Fitzgerald, W., and Nielsen, L. E., unpublished*]

in which M_c is the number average molecular weight of the polymer segments between crosslinks, d is the density, T is the absolute temperature, and R is the gas constant. The equilibrium modulus E is given in dynes per square centimeter when the value of R is taken as 8.316×10^7 ergs per °C per mole. This equation shows that the modulus of a rubber should increase with temperature; this is in contrast to the normal behavior of uncrosslinked polymers in either the rigid or liquid state. The modulus increases with temperature because of the increased thermal or Brownian motion which causes the stretched molecular segments to tug at their anchor points and try to assume a more probable coiled-up shape. The equation 4.20 also shows that the modulus of a rubber increases as the degree of crosslinking increases or as M_c decreases. For rubber M_c is about 1000 to 10,000 in general.

Equation 4.20 is not very accurate for actual rubbers. A much better equation relating the tensile stress σ, calculated on the basis of the original cross section, to the elongation is[25, 71]:

$$\sigma = \frac{RTd}{M_c}(1 - 2M_c/\bar{M}_n)(\alpha - 1/\alpha^2). \tag{4.21}$$

The number average molecular weight of the polymer before it is crosslinked is $\bar{M}_n$. Therefore, the term $(1 - 2M_c/\bar{M}_n)$ can be considered as a correction factor which takes into account the imperfections in the network structure. This correction may be neglected for very high molecular weights. According to rubber theory the proper elongation to use is not $(L - L_0)/L_0$ but is $\frac{1}{3}(\alpha - 1/\alpha^2)$ where α is L/L_0, the ratio of the stretched length to the unstretched length. As shown in Table 1.1, the two definitions of elongation are nearly the same for small elongations, but they are quite different for large elongations.

From equation 4.21 the correct Young's modulus E of a rubber is

$$E = \frac{\sigma}{\frac{1}{3}(\alpha - 1/\alpha^2)} = \frac{3dRT}{M_c}(1 - 2M_c/\bar{M}_n) \tag{4.22}$$

Also from the kinetic theory of rubber, it can be shown that the shear modulus G of a rubber is given by

$$G = \frac{\sigma_s}{(\alpha - 1/\alpha)} = \frac{dRT}{M_c}(1 - 2M_c/\bar{M}_n) \tag{4.23}$$

where $(\alpha - 1/\alpha)$ is the shear strain.

For low molecular weight uncrosslinked rubbers the stress decreases constantly with time. There is only a suggestion of a plateau region where the stress-relaxation modulus remains nearly constant with time. However, with very high molecular weight polymers there is a distinct plateau where the modulus remains nearly constant for an appreciable period of time. The higher the molecular weight the more pronounced is the plateau. In the plateau region the polymer appears to be a crosslinked material, but at longer times the modulus again decreases as though the crosslinked network were being destroyed. The plateau region is assumed to be caused by chain entanglements which act as temporary crosslinks[10]. The stress on the stretched chain segments is gradually relieved as molecular motion destroys the entanglements. There can be enough entanglements to make the polymer response quite elastic. For instance, polystyrene with a molecular weight of 160,000 heated to 115°C will snap back like a rubber band when stretched rapidly and then released. Treating the entanglements as temporary crosslinks and using the equations of the kinetic theory of rubber such as equation 4.21 gives an M_c of about 20,000[46]. Thus, there are roughly 200 monomeric units between crosslinks in polystyrene. This agrees within a factor of two for the molecular weight between entanglements as determined by viscosity measurements. See Table 3.1.

Crystalline Polymers

The theory of stress relaxation in crystalline polymers is in its infancy, and there are so few experimental data that not even many empirical generalizations can be made.

The main effect of crystallinity is to broaden the distribution of relaxation times and to extend the relaxation of stress to much longer periods. This trend is true at both high and low degrees of crystallinity. A stress-relaxation experiment on a plasticized polyvinyl chloride polymer may last for many days[57]. If this material were not slightly crystalline, the stress would be expected to decay to nearly zero in a few hours at the most. Polyethylene, which is a semirigid polymer at room temperature, would be a viscous liquid if it were not crystalline. The stress decays slowly in this material at a uniform rate of about 5 to 12 per cent per decade of time when the stress ratio σ/σ_0 is plotted against log time[12, 31, 73].

Stress-relaxation data on crystalline polyethylene at different temperatures is shown in Figure 4.7[12]. The flatness of the curves may be contrasted with typical curves for an amorphous polymer such as shown in Figure 4.5.

Crystalline polymers with glass temperatures above room temperature behave in a similar manner. For instance, the stress decays very slowly in nylon 6-6[11, 29]. From the master curve of Catsiff, Alfrey, and O'Shaughnessy[11] the stress ratio σ/σ_0 decreases to 30 per cent of its initial value in ten decades of time; the last 30 per cent of the stress decreases at even a much smaller rate.

It is doubtful if the Boltzmann superposition principle or the reduced variable treatment are applicable to many crystalline polymers. This failure is especially true when the temperature is changed enough to change the degree of crystallinity. Takemura and co-workers have attempted to construct master stress-relaxation modulus curves by using a vertical shift to take care of the effect of changing crystallinity[43, 59]. This vertical shift is required in addition to the usual horizontal shift used in constructing a master curve of reduced modulus versus time.

The degree of crystallinity can change during the course of a stress-relaxation experiment with some polymers. This effect is especially pronounced with natural rubber when stretched at a temperature near $-20°C$[27, 64]. When first stretched, the rubber has little or no crystallinity, but crystallization takes place during the experiment. Stretching the rubber tends to orient the molecules parallel to one another in the direction of the elongation. This alignment predisposes the molecules to crystallization and to more nearly perfect alignment in a crystal lattice oriented in the direction of the elongation. Thus, as crystallization takes place, the specimen

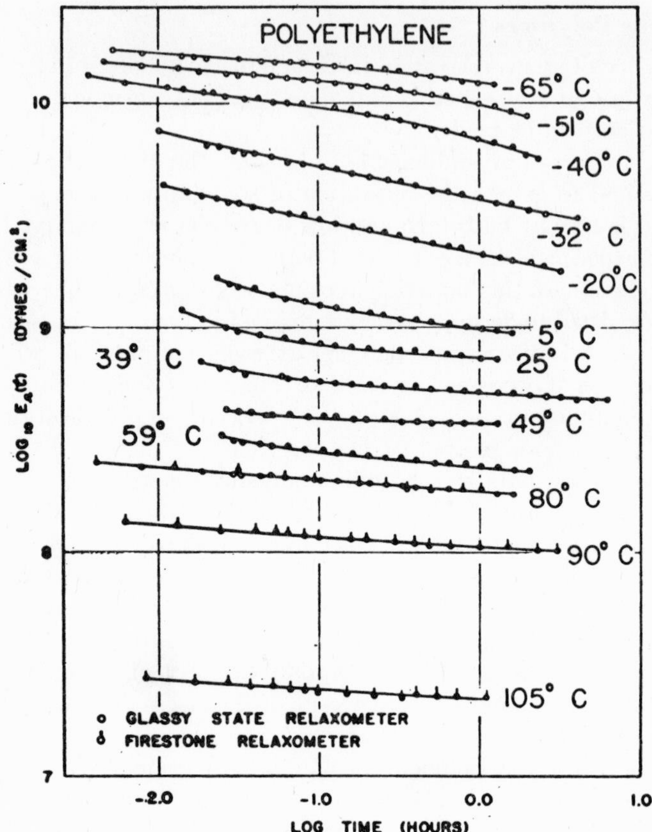

Figure 4.7. Stress relaxation of low-density polyethylene at different temperatures. [*After Catsiff, E., Offenbach, J., and Tobolsky, A. V., J. Colloid Sci.*, **11**, *48* (*1956*)]

tends to elongate more in the direction of the original stretching; if the length is held constant, the stress rapidly decreases. One would expect that the greater the initial elongation the faster the crystallization would take place. This is exactly what is observed. The stress does not decrease rapidly in natural rubber elongated 50 per cent until after about ten hours. However, at 200 per cent elongation, the stress rapidly decays after about one hour.

Effect of Elongation

Stress-relaxation modulus is generally independent of the elongation as long as the elongation is very small. However, in most cases the rate of stress relaxation increases once the elongation is above a critical value[2]. This increased rate is especially true as the stress required to elongate the material approaches the breaking strength of the polymer. As the elongation used in the stress relaxation experiment increases, so does the stress simultaneously. It is not known whether the increased rate of stress decay is really due to the increased elongation or to the increased stress applied to the material.

Some polymers show phenomena known as yielding, drawing, or necking in which the stress on the specimen may reach a maximum or plateau value without breaking and yet permit the elongation to increase. If a stress-relaxation experiment is carried out at an elongation at which the load on the specimen approaches the yield stress, the stress relaxes at a very high rate compared to the rates found at lower elongations[6, 16].

Polyethylene illustrates the point that increasing the elongation does not bring about a corresponding increase in the stress. Increasing the elongation by a factor of 4 from about two per cent to about eight per cent increases the observed stress only by a factor of 2 or 3.[73]

If a polymer is capable of crystallizing, the increased orientation brought about by an increase in elongation will tend to speed up crystallization. As crystallization proceeds, the stress rapidly decreases. This phenomenon was discussed in the previous section.

The Time-Temperature Superposition Principle and Reduced Variables

Leaderman[35] suggested that in viscoelastic materials time and temperature are equivalent to the extent that data at one temperature can be superimposed upon data taken at a different temperature merely by shifting curves. Tobolsky[14, 63] and Ferry[24] have worked out detailed procedures for converting stress-relaxation data at a series of temperatures to a single curve covering many decades of time at some reference temperature. The procedures involve shifting of stress-relaxation curves taken at different temperatures along the log time axis until portions of the curves all superimpose to form one continuous curve.

An example of this time-temperature superposition principle is shown in Figure 4.8[14]. The polymer is polyisobutylene. The curves on the left side of the figure are the reduced stress-relaxation curves obtained at the temperatures shown on the curves. The curve on the right is the master curve for 298°K obtained by shifting the corrected (reduced) experimental curves along the log time axis until they all superimpose on the curve for 298°K (25°C). Before the experimental relaxation curves can be shifted to make the master curve, the modulus values should be corrected for density and temperature. An arbitrary temperature T_0 (°K) is selected as the reference

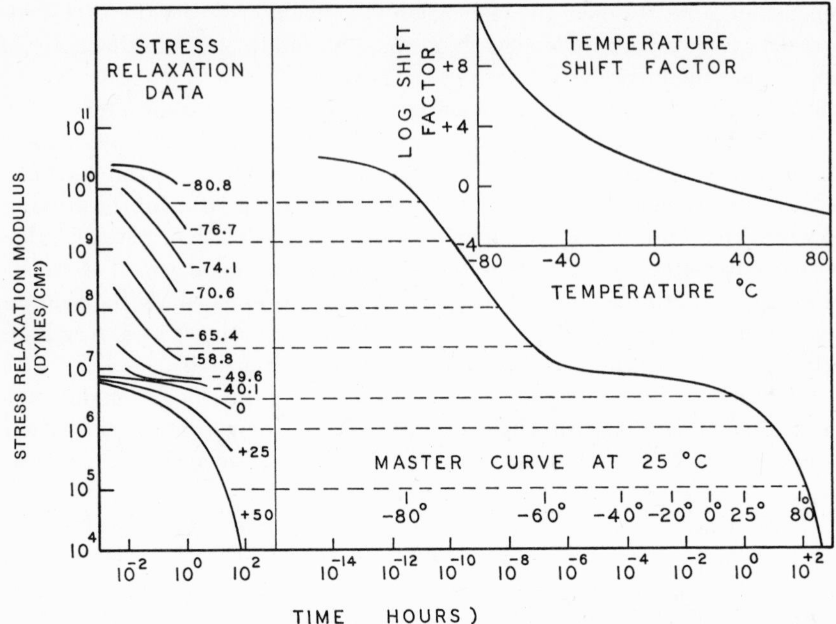

Figure 4.8. Time-temperature superposition principle illustrated with polyisobutylene data. The reference temperature of the master curve is 25°C. The inset graph gives the amount of curve shifting required at the different temperatures. [*After Castiff, E., and Tobolsky, A. V., J. Colloid Sci.*, **10,** *375* (*1955*) *and J. Polymer Sci.*, **19,** *111* (*1956*)]

temperature; the corresponding density of the material is d_0. At some other temperature T (°K) the density is d. In order to reduce the data at temperature T to correspond to the data at T_0, the modulus values at T are multiplied by the factor $(T_0 d_0)/(Td)$. Thus, the reduced modulus values are calculated by

$$E(t)_{\text{reduced}} = \frac{(T_0 d_0)}{Td} E_r(t). \tag{4.24}$$

The density changes are small and can be neglected in most cases. Even the temperature correction (T_0/T) is not large. This correction, which comes from the kinetic theory of rubber elasticity, is expressed in terms of absolute temperature.

After the original experimental curves have been reduced by the above correction, they are replotted as in Figure 4.8 (left). These reduced curves can now be shifted along the log time scale to give a master stress-relaxation curve covering many decades of time. All the curves are shifted, one at a time, with respect to the reference curve at T_0 until portions of the curves superimpose to give a master curve such as shown on the right side of Figure 4.8.

The amount each reduced modulus curve has to be shifted along the log t axis in making the master curve is plotted against the temperature difference from the reference temperature in Figure 4.8 in the upper right corner. A shift is considered to be positive if the curve was shifted to the left (shorter times) in constructing the master curve. The amounts the reduced curves had to be shifted are $(\log t - \log t_0) = \log t/t_0 = \log A_T$.

In Figure 4.8 the reference temperature was taken as 298°K (25°C). For polyisobutylene Williams, Landel, and Ferry chose 243°K as the reference temperature. In this case $\log A_T$ can be represented by[74]

$$\log A_T = \log t/t_0 = \frac{-8.86\,(T - T_0)}{101.6 + T - T_0} \tag{4.25}$$

where $T_0 = 243°K$. If the glass-transition temperature of polyisobutylene (202°K) had been used as the reference temperature instead of 243°K, the W-L-F equation 2.2 could be used to predict the shifts along the log time scale. Equation 2.2 holds for nearly all linear amorphous polymers if T_g is chosen as the reference temperature. Equation 4.25 holds for nearly all such polymers if a reference temperature is chosen which is about 45°C above the glass-transition temperature.

Williams, Landel, and Ferry[74] have defined the reduced variables shift factor A_T as the ratio of the relaxation times at temperature T to the relaxation times at temperature T_0. The relaxation time τ is intimately related to the viscosity η as indicated in the definition at A_T:

$$A_T = \tau/\tau_0 = \frac{\eta}{\eta_0}\frac{T_0\,d_0}{Td} \tag{4.26}$$

In the discussion of the W-L-F equation for viscosity in Chapter 2, the correction factor $(T_0\,d_0)/(Td)$ was neglected. Since the change in both temperature and density is small over the temperature range where the W-L-F equation is applicable, the correction factor makes little difference.

Master stress-relaxation curves may be constructed at temperatures other than either T_g or $(T_g + 45°C)$. These two temperatures have the advantage that the W-L-F equations 2.2 or 4.25 may be used. In addition, if one of these temperatures is chosen as the reference temperature, the results may more easily be compared with much of the data in the literature. Curves of shift factor A_T versus $(T - T_0)$ made at some other temperature may be converted to either T_g or $(T_g + 45°)$ as the reference temperature. This involves both a horizontal and vertical shifting of the A_T versus $(T - T_0)$ curve; the process has been clearly described by Payne and Scott[5] and by Williams, Landel, and Ferry[74].

Master curves of modulus versus log time are important because they enable one to calculate the distribution of relaxation times over a much greater period of time than can be determined experimentally. Once the distribution of relaxation times has been determined over a very long time (10 to 20 decades), many other mechanical properties can be calculated. The theory of viscoelasticity enables one to calculate creep behavior, dynamic mechanical modulus, mechanical damping and stress-strain behavior from the distribution of relaxation times[1, 24, 63]. Some of the interrelations between the various mechanical properties will be discussed in a later chapter.

Chemical Reactions in Polymers

Stress relaxation is a useful tool in studying some chemical reactions which may occur in polymers, especially in rubbers. An example of such a reaction is the oxidative degradation of rubbers at high temperatures. A theory of stress relaxation when such reactions occur has been worked out by Tobolsky[63, 70] for crosslinked rubbers.

In developing the theory it is assumed that the rate of the chemical reaction is independent of the strain on the sample. The evidence is that this assumption is true at least up to high elongations. Stress relaxation occurs when a chain which is carrying a load breaks in a crosslinked rubber. When a stretched chain segment breaks, it returns to a relaxed state. Relaxed chain segments may also break, but they contribute nothing to the stress-relaxation process. Only stretched chains carry the load, and since the elongation is held constant, the load on a broken chain cannot usually be shifted to other chains. Therefore, a second assumption in developing the theory seems reasonable. This second assumption is that the rate at which stretched network chains are broken is proportional to the total number of chains carrying the load; that is:

$$\frac{-dN(t)}{dt} = KN(t), \tag{4.27}$$

where $N(t)$ is the number of network chains carrying the load at any time, and K is a constant which depends upon temperature. From rubber theory it is known that the stress on a stretched rubber sample is given by

$$\sigma(t) = N(t)kT\left[\frac{L}{L_0} - \left(\frac{L_0}{L}\right)^2\right]. \tag{4.28}$$

In this equation the stress at any time $\sigma(t)$ is calculated using the original cross-sectional area of the specimen before it is stretched. It can be shown that if the stress is calculated by using the cross-sectional area of the specimen after it is stretched, the proper equation to use is:

$$\sigma(t) = N(t)kT\left[\left(\frac{L}{L_0}\right)^2 - \frac{L_0}{L}\right] \tag{4.29}$$

Integrating equation 4.27 and combining the result with either equation 4.28 or 4.29, gives

$$\frac{\sigma}{\sigma_0} = \frac{\sigma(t)}{\sigma_0} = e^{-Kt} = e^{-t/\tau} \tag{4.30}$$

where in this case the relaxation time τ is

$$\tau = 1/K. \tag{4.31}$$

The stress-relaxation equation given by equation 4.30 is exactly the same as that given by the simple Maxwell model used earlier in this chapter. Thus, in rubber networks where the stress relaxation is due to such a chemical reaction, the stress decay can be represented by a single relaxation time rather than by a broad distribution of relaxation times as required by most other mechanisms of stress relaxation.

Chemical reactions go much faster as the temperature is raised. The variation in relaxation time with temperature may be expressed by an Arrhenius equation

$$\frac{1}{\tau} = K = K_0 e^{-\Delta H_A/RT} \tag{4.32}$$

where K_0 is a constant, and ΔH_A is the energy of activation for the chemical reaction. Typical values of ΔH_A are 30 kcal/mole for the oxidative degradation of rubbers[70].

Stress-relaxation experiments have been used to show interchange of polysulfide bonds in polysulfide rubbers[58], the effect of water on the interchange of "Si—O" bonds in silicone rubbers[32], and that disubstituted urea and biuret linkages are the weak links in polyurethane rubbers[15, 49].

Since stress relaxation is a very sensitive technique for studying the oxidative degradation of rubbers in which chain scission occurs, such experiments are useful in evaluating antioxidants for these rubbers[20, 40, 54]. Stress relaxation may be used to screen new antioxidants or to study the mechanism of the action of antioxidants.

Stress Relaxation Studies on Polymers

Tobolsky[63] has made the most extensive compilation of the stress-relaxation data on polymers. He also reviews the theory of stress relaxation in detail. The same author has written other reviews[61, 62].

Most of the data to be found in the literature are on rubbers of various kinds. Polyisobutylene has been intensively studied over a wide range of temperatures and molecular weights[2, 3, 7, 14, 65, 67]. Natural rubber studies include those of Gee, Allen, and Read[26], Tobolsky and Brown[64], and Gent[27]. Styrene-butadiene rubbers have been studied by Bischoff, Catsiff and Tobolsky[5], Catsiff and Tobolsky[13], and Landel and Stedry[34]. These last authors show how the Williams-Landel-Ferry treatment[74] may be modified to apply to rubbers at large strains. The stress relaxation of polysulfide rubbers as a function of temperature was studied by Stern and Tobolsky[58]. In addition to the usual continuous stress-relaxation tests, they used an intermittent stress-relaxation technique in which the specimens were subjected to heat treatments in the unstretched state part of the time rather than being subjected to the heat treatment in the stretched state during the complete course of the test. Silicone rubbers have been studied by Warrick[72]. Plasticized polyvinyl chloride and several types of rubbers were studied by Stein and Tobolsky[57].

Crosslinking reactions and effect of antioxidants on the aging of rubbers have been investigated by Pedersen and Nielsen[52], Dunn[20], Mullins and Turner[42], Johnson, McLoughlin, and Tobolsky[32], Robinson and Vodden[54], and Berry and Watson[4]. A study of the weakest chemical bonds in polyurethane rubbers was carried out by Offenbach and Tobolsky[49] and by Colodny and Tobolsky[15].

Stress-relaxation data on polyethylene have been reported by Dunell and Dillon[17], Catsiff, Offenbach, and Tobolsky[12], Nagamatsu, Takemura, Yoshitomi, and Takemoto[43], and Faucher[21]. Data on polypropylene have been given by Dunkel and Westlund[19]. Stress-relaxation work on some crystalline polymers has been reviewed by Hopkins and Baker[31]. Nylon 6-6 filaments have been studied by Hammerle and Montgomery[29], Price, McIntyre, Pattison, and Dunell[53], and Dunell, Joanes, and Rye[18]. Yoshitomi, Nagamatsu, and Kosiyama[75] studied nylon 6. Polytrifluorochloroethylene was studied by Nagamatsu and Yoshitomi[44]; they also studied polytetrafluoroethylene[45]. Cellulose monofilaments were studied by Passaglia and Koppehele[50]. They found the stress-relaxation results to depend upon the initial strain; the modulus decreases with strain.

The stress-relaxation behavior of a number of amorphous or slightly crystalline polymers is known. Polystyrene near the glass temperature and above was studied by Tobolsky and Murakami[68, 69], and Nielsen and Buchdahl[46]. Curran, Andrews, and McGarry[16] found with a rigid polystyrene polyblend that the stress decays much more rapidly than usual once craze cracks develop. McLoughlin and Tobolsky[38, 39] studied polymethyl methacrylate over the temperature range both above and below the glass transition. They found that stress relaxes more rapidly with a rigid polymer quenched from the melt than from a polymer cooled slowly from the melt. This should be a general phenomenon since the quenched polymer has a larger free volume. The effect of molecular weight distribution on the stress relaxation of polyvinyl acetate was studied by Ninomiya[47], and Ninomiya and Sakamoto[48]. The stress relaxation of a blend made up of two fractions of different molecular weight was best described by

$$E_b(t) \doteq W_1E_1(t/\lambda_1) + W_2E_2(t/\lambda_2) \tag{4.33}$$

where $E_b(t)$ is the stress-relaxation modulus of the blend, $E_1(t)$ and $E_2(t)$ are the stress-relaxation modulus of fractions 1 and 2, W_1 and W_2 are the weight fractions of the two fractions making up the blend, λ_1 is the ratio of the number average molecular weight of the blend to the number average molecular weight of component 1, and λ_2 is the ratio of the number average molecular weight of the blend to the number average molecular weight of component 2. The constants λ_1 and λ_2 change the time scale from t to t/λ_1 or t/λ_2. The validity of the above equation for other materials has not been established.

References

1. Alfrey, T., "Mechanical Behavior of High Polymers," New York, Interscience Publishers, Inc., 1948.
2. Andrews, R. D., Hofman-Bang, N., and Tobolsky, A. V., *J. Polymer Sci.*, **3,** 669 (1948).
3. Andrews, R. D., and Tobolsky, A. V., *J. Polymer Sci.*, **7,** 221 (1951).
4. Berry, J. P., and Watson, W. F., *J. Polymer Sci.*, **18,** 201 (1955).
5. Bischoff, J., Catsiff, E., and Tobolsky, A. V., *J. Am. Chem. Soc.*, **74,** 3378 (1952).
6. Bobalek, E. G., and Evans, R. M., *Trans. Soc. Plastics Eng.*, **1,** 93 (1961).
7. Brown, G. M., and Tobolsky, A. V., *J. Polymer Sci.*, **6,** 165 (1951).
8. Bueche, F., *J. Chem. Phys.*, **22,** 603 (1954).
9. Bueche, F., *J. Chem. Phys.*, **22,** 1570 (1954).
10. Bueche, F., *J. Appl. Phys.*, **26,** 738 (1955).
11. Catsiff, E., Alfrey, Jr., T., and O'Shaughnessy, M. T., *Textile Research J.*, **23,** 808 (1953).
12. Catsiff, E., Offenbach, J., and Tobolsky, A. V., *J. Colloid Sci.*, **11,** 48 (1956).
13. Catsiff, E., and Tobolsky, A. V., *J. Appl. Phys.*, **25,** 1092 (1954).
14. Catsiff, E., and Tobolsky, A. V., *J. Colloid Sci.*, **10,** 375 (1955).
15. Colodny, P. C., and Tobolsky, A. V., *J. Am. Chem. Soc.*, **79,** 4320 (1957).

16. Curran, R. J., Andrews, Jr., R. D., and McGarry, F. J., *Modern Plastics*, **38,** No. 3, 142 (1960).
17. Dunell, B. A., and Dillon, J. H., *Textile Research J.*, **21,** 393 (1951).
18. Dunell, B. A., Joannes, A. A., and Rye, R. T. B., *J. Colloid Sci.*, **15,** 193 (1960).
19. Dunkel, W. L., and Westlund, Jr., R. A., *Soc. Plastics Eng. J.*, **16,** 1039 (1960).
20. Dunn, J. R., *J. Appl. Polymer Sci.*, **4,** 151 (1960).
21. Faucher, J. A., *Trans. Soc. Rheology*, **3,** 81 (1959).
22. Ferry, J. D., Landel, R., and Williams, M., *J. Appl. Phys.*, **26,** 359 (1955).
23. Ferry, J. D., "Rheology," Vol. 2, Chap. 11, p. 433. Eirich, F. R., Ed., New York, Academic Press, Inc., 1958.
24. Ferry, J. D., "Viscoelastic Properties of Polymers," New York, John Wiley & Sons, Inc., 1961.
25. Flory, P. J., "Principles of Polymer Chemistry," Chapt. 11, Ithaca, Cornell University Press, 1953.
26. Gee, G., Allen, G., and Read, B., "Rheology of Elastomers," p. 54, Nason, P., and Wookey, N., Ed., New York, Pergamon Press, 1958.
27. Gent, A. N., *Trans. Faraday Soc.*, **50,** 521 (1954).
28. Gurnee, E. F., Patterson, L. T., and Andrews, R. D., *J. Appl. Phys.*, **26,** 1106 (1955).
29. Hammerle, W. G., and Montgomery, D. J., *Textile Research J.*, **23,** 595 (1953).
30. Harris, W. D., Burlew, W. W., and McGarry, F. J., *Soc. Plastics Eng. J.*, **16,** 1231 (1960).
31. Hopkins, I. L., and Baker, W. O., "Rheology," Vol. 3, Chap. 10, p. 365, Eirich, F. R., Ed., New York, Academic Press, Inc., 1960.
32. Johnson, D. H., McLoughlin, J. R., and Tobolsky, A. V., *J. Phys. Chem.*, **58,** 1073 (1954).
33. Kubu, E. T., *Textile Research J.*, **22,** 765 (1952).
34. Landel, R. F., and Stedry, P. J., *J. Appl. Phys.*, **31,** 1885 (1960).
35. Leaderman, H., "Elastic and Creep Properties of Filamentous Materials and Other High Polymers," Washington, D. C., The Textile Foundation, 1943.
36. Leaderman, H., "Rheology," Vol. 2, Chap. 1, Eirich, F. R., Ed., New York, Academic Press, Inc., 1958.
37. McLoughlin, J. R., *Rev. Sci. Instr.*, **23,** 459 (1952).
38. McLoughlin, J. R., and Tobolsky, A. V., *J. Polymer Sci.*, **7,** 658 (1951).
39. McLoughlin, J. R., and Tobolsky, A. V., *J. Colloid Sci.*, **7,** 555 (1952).
40. Mesrobian, R. B., and Tobolsky, A. V., *Ind. Eng. Chem.*, **41,** 1496 (1949).
41. Miyake, A., *J. Polymer Sci.*, **22,** 560 (1956).
42. Mullins, L., and Turner, D. T., *J. Polymer Sci.*, **43,** 35 (1960).
43. Nagamatsu, K., Takemura, T., Yoshitomi, T., and Takemoto, T., *J. Polymer Sci.*, **33,** 515 (1958).
44. Nagamatsu, K., and Yoshitomi, T., *J. Colloid Sci.*, **14,** 377 (1959).
45. Nagamatsu, K., Yoshitomi, T., and Takemoto, T., *J. Colloid Sci.* **13,** 257 (1958).
46. Nielsen, L. E., and Buchdahl, R., *J. Colloid Sci.*, **5,** 282 (1950).
47. Ninomiya, K., *J. Colloid Sci.*, **14,** 49 (1959).
48. Ninomiya, K., and Sakamoto, M., *J. Phys. Chem.*, **64,** 181 (1960).
49. Offenbach, J. A., and Tobolsky, A. V., *J. Colloid Sci.*, **11,** 39 (1956).
50. Passaglia, E., and Koppehele, H. P., *J. Polymer Sci.*, **33,** 281 (1958).
51. Payne, A. R., and Scott, J. R., "Engineering Design with Rubber," Chap. 2, New York, Interscience Publishers, Inc., 1960.

52. Pedersen, H. L., and Nielsen, B., *J. Polymer Sci.*, **7,** 97 (1951).
53. Price, S. J. W., McIntyre, A. D., Pattison, J. P., and Dunell, B. A., *Textile Research J.*, **26,** 276 (1956).
54. Robinson, H. W. H., and Vodden, H. A., *Ind. Eng. Chem.*, **47,** 1477 (1947).
55. Rouse, Jr., P. E., *J. Chem. Phys.*, **21,** 1272 (1953).
56. Staverman, A. J., and Schwarzl, F., "Die Physik der Hochpolymeren," Vol. 4, Chap. 1, Stuart, H. A., Ed., Berlin Springer Verlag, 1956.
57. Stein, R. S., and Tobolsky, A. V., *Textile Research J.*, **18,** 302 (1948).
58. Stern, M. D., and Tobolsky, A. V., *J. Chem. Phys.*, **14,** 93 (1946).
59. Takemura, T., *J. Polymer Sci.*, **38,** 471 (1959).
60. Tobolsky, A. V., *J. Am. Chem. Soc.*, **74,** 3786 (1952).
61. Tobolsky, A. V., *J. Appl. Phys.*, **27,** 673 (1956).
62. Tobolsky, A. V., "Rheology," Vol. 2, Chap. 2, p. 63. Eirich, F. R., Ed., New York, Academic Press, Inc., 1958.
63. Tobolsky, A. V., "Properties and Structure of Polymers," New York, John Wiley & Sons, Inc., 1960.
64. Tobolsky, A. V., and Brown, G. M., *J. Polymer Sci.*, **17,** 547 (1955).
65. Tobolsky, A. V., and Catsiff, E., *J. Polymer Sci.*, **19,** 111 (1956).
66. Tobolsky, A. V., Dunell, B. A., and Andrews, R. D., *Textile Research J.*, **21,** 404 (1951).
67. Tobolsky, A. V., and McLoughlin, J. R., *J. Polymer Sci.*, **8,** 543 (1952).
68. Tobolsky, A. V., and Murakami, K., *J. Polymer Sci.*, **40,** 443 (1959).
69. Tobolsky, A. V., and Murakami, K., *J. Polymer Sci.*, **47,** 55 (1960).
70. Tobolsky, A. V., Prettyman, I. B., and Dillon, J. H., *J. Appl. Phys.*, **15,** 380 (1944).
71. Treloar, L. R. G., "The Physics of Rubber Elasticity," Oxford, Clarendon Press, 1958.
72. Warrick, E. L., *J. Polymer Sci.*, **27,** 19 (1958).
73. Watson, M. T., Kennedy, W. D., and Armstrong, G. M., *J. Appl. Phys.*, **26,** 701 (1955).
74. Williams, M. L., Landel, R. F., and Ferry, J. D., *J. Am. Chem. Soc.*, **77,** 3701 (1955).
75. Yoshitomi, T., Nagamatsu, K., and Kosiyama, K., *J. Polymer Sci.*, **27,** 335 (1958).
76. Zimm, B. H., *J. Chem. Phys.*, **24,** 269 (1956).

Chapter 5

STRESS-STRAIN MEASUREMENTS

Importance and Nature of Tests

Probably the most widely used mechanical test is the stress-strain test; however, it is one of the least understood from the theoretical point of view, and its practical importance is often overrated. The plastics industry inherited the test from other industries, and it has become conventional to report stress-strain measurements in tables of data. Supposedly the data are to be used by engineers designing plastic objects, but often they are so incomplete as to be practically useless. The reasons for the inadequacy of stress-strain data obtained at a single temperature and at a single speed of testing go back to the tremendous variation in the properties of plastics as a function of time, temperature, and thermal history compared to other structural materials such as metals.

However, stress-strain measurements made over a wide range of temperatures and speeds of testing are very important for the practical use of polymeric materials. Such measurements are among the few which tell one something about the strength of a material or the conditions under which it will break.

Stress-strain measurements are generally made in tension by stretching the specimen at a uniform rate and simultaneously measuring the force on the specimen. The test is continued until the specimen breaks. Often, the change in length is determined from measurements of the separation of the jaws or clamps holding the specimen. Although this is the simplest way of determining the elongation, it can lead to serious errors. For instance, there is always some slippage in the specimen grips; this leads to an apparent elongation greater than the true elongation. A second type of error may arise from the restrictions imposed upon the specimen by the clamps. During the stretching process the cross-sectional area will decrease, but near the clamps the test specimen is forced to retain its original width and thickness. Thus, the whole specimen cannot stretch uniformly.

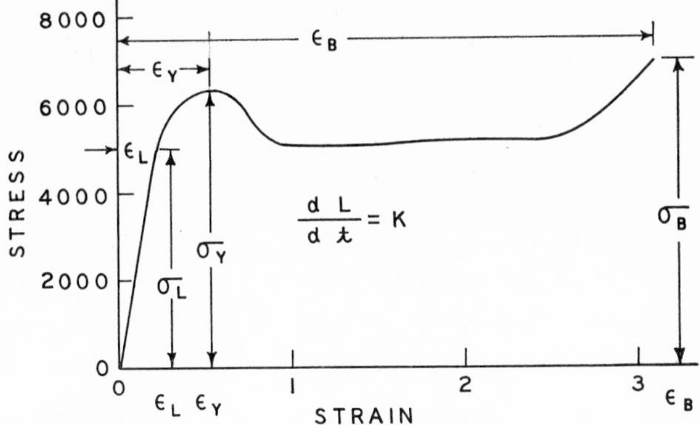

Figure 5.1. A schematic stress-strain curve.

The best way of measuring the elongation is to use a separate device attached to the specimen inside the clamps[18]. The elongation may be determined from measurements of the separation of two fiducial marks on the specimen with a rule or from more elaborate devices using differential tranformers to measure the separation of specimen grips[56, 68] or the separation of auxiliary clamps which carry no load. In many instruments the separation of the specimen grips is indirectly measured by synchronizing the time scale of a recorder with elongation in the specimen; this is possible when the rate of separation of the specimen clamps is constant.

The stretching of the specimen may be carried out by a motor-driven screw[13, 14, 54], by a hydraulic piston[21, 68, 69], or in a number of other ways. Generally the specimen is stretched at a constant rate of jaw separation. However, more accurate measurements are made by carrying out the tests so that a constant rate of elongation occurs within the specimen. This eliminates such errors as those due to slippage in the specimen clamps.

The total load on the specimen is measured by strain gages[21, 54, 55, 68] or by differential transformers[7, 28, 56], these electronic transducers being in turn actuated by small deformations of some member such as a proving ring, tension bar, or a cantilever beam.

Figure 5.1 illustrates a possible stress-strain curve. The experimental curve gives a force F as a function of the time or the change in length $(L - L_0)$ since the time and amount of elongation are equivalent. The experimental curve must be replotted to give a curve of stress σ against strain ϵ. The two curves will be similar in shape since the stress is force per unit of cross-sectional area, and the strain is the change in length per unit of length. Thus, the strain as a function of time is given by

$$\epsilon = \frac{L - L_0}{L_0} = \frac{Kt}{L_0} \tag{5.1}$$

where K is the rate of extension, say in inches per second.

Generally, stress at any time during a test is calculated on the basis of the original cross-sectional area. However, the cross-sectional area of a specimen decreases as it is stretched so that the true stress is greater than the ordinarily calculated stress. The true stress is the force per unit of cross-sectional area at any time (or elongation). If Poisson's ratio is near 0.5, the area A at any time can be calculated from the original area A_0 by

$$A = \frac{A_0 L_0}{L} \tag{5.2}$$

Sometimes the strain defined as $\epsilon = \Delta L/L_0$ is better replaced by the so-called "true strain" defined by

$$\epsilon = \ln (L/L_0) \tag{5.3}$$

Table 1.1 shows that the two definitions of strain are the same for very small elongations, but they are quite different at large elongations. The definition of true strain can be seen to be reasonable from the following equation:

$$\epsilon = \int_{L_0}^{L} \frac{dL}{L} = \ln (L/L_0). \tag{5.4}$$

In discussing stress-strain curves, one must be familiar with the terms tensile or Young's modulus E, yield stress σ_y, elongation at yield ϵ_y, ultimate strength or tensile strength σ_B, and ultimate elongation or elongation at break ϵ_B. Most of these terms are illustrated in Figure 5.1. The yield point occurs where the stress goes through a maximum; sometimes the yield point shows up as an inflection point or a plateau on the curve rather than as a well-defined maximum. The ultimate values are determined by the point where the specimen breaks. Brittle materials generally break at the yield point or before a yield point is reached. In the case of these materials the stress-strain curve is very simple—essentially the straight line shown in the first part of the curve in Figure 5.1. Young's modulus may be calculated from the initial straight line portion of a stress-strain curve; the tensile modulus is the slope of this straight line, that is,

$$E = \frac{d\sigma}{d\epsilon} = \frac{\sigma_L}{\epsilon_L} \tag{5.5}$$

Types of Stress-Strain Curves

Carswell and Nason[15, 16] have divided the types of stress-strain curves obtained with polymers into five classes. These classes are: (1) soft, weak, (2) hard, brittle, (3) soft, tough, (4) hard, strong, (5) hard, tough. The various types of curves are illustrated in Figure 5.2.

Soft, weak materials have a low modulus, a low tensile strength, and only moderate elongations to break. This type of curve is characteristic of soft polymer gels and "cheesy" materials. Hard, brittle polymers have high moduli, and quite high tensile strengths, but they break at small elongations without any yield point. Polystyrene, polymethyl methacrylate, and many phenol-formaldehyde resins at room temperature or lower show hard, brittle behavior. Such materials generally have elongations to break of less than 2 per cent. Hard, strong polymers have high Young's modulus, high tensile strengths, and elongations of roughly 5 per cent before breaking. The curves often look as though the material broke about where a yield point might be expected. Some rigid polyvinyl chloride formulations and polystyrene polyblends give this type of stress-strain curve. Soft, tough materials are characterized by low moduli, yield values or plateaus, very high elongations (20 to 1000 per cent), and moderately high breaking strengths. Rubbers and plasticized polyvinyl chloride give

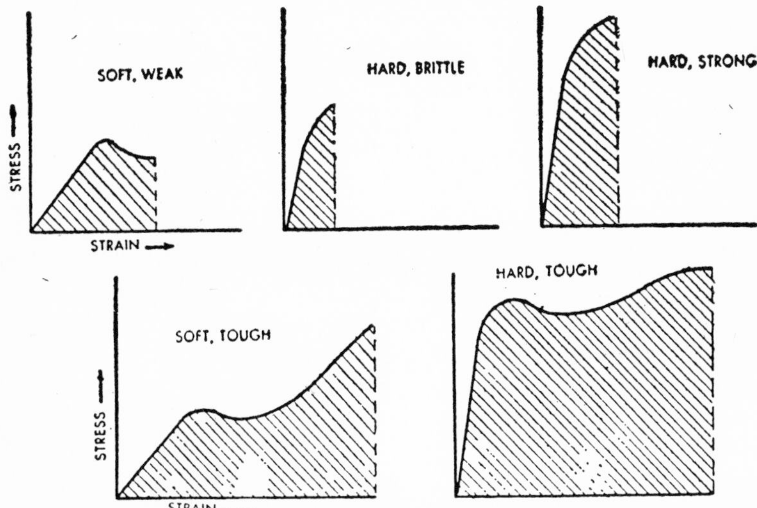

Figure 5.2. Types of stress-strain curves. [*After Carswell, T. S., and Nason, H. K., Modern Plastics,* **21,** *121 (June, 1944)*]

this type of curve. Hard, tough polymers such as cellulose acetate or nitrate and nylons have high moduli, yield points, high tensile strengths, and large elongations. Most polymers of this category show cold-drawing or "necking" during the stretching process[44, 72]. The specimen does not elongate uniformly, but at the yield point a constriction develops in the specimen. The material in the constricted region undergoes very large elongations, and as the stretching process continues, the constricted area "grows" in both directions towards the specimen clamps. The cross-sectional area of the drawn portion remains constant during the stretching, and it is separated from the undrawn region by a well-defined shoulder. Cold-drawing is important in fiber technology as a way of developing strength in fibers.

Although nearly everyone has a feeling for what is meant by the word toughness, a satisfactory scientific method of measuring it is lacking. One definition of toughness is the energy required to break a material. This energy is equal to the area under the stress-strain curve, that is, the energy to break $= \int_0^{\epsilon_B} \sigma \, d\epsilon$. On the basis of this definition, it is obvious which classes of materials in Figure 5.2 are tough. The toughest materials should be those with very great elongations to break accompanied by high tensile strengths; such materials nearly always have yield points.

Stress-strain tests may be made in compression as well as in tension. Young's modulus may be calculated from the initial slope of the compression stress-strain curve. Materials under compression are much less brittle than when they are under tension; therefore, many materials which are brittle when tested under tension become ductile and show yield points when tested under compression. Polystyrene is an example of a polymer which behaves as a ductile material under compression[34]. The ultimate strength in compression is greater than the ultimate strength in tension. Typical values of ultimate strength in compression are roughly twice the tensile strength for a number of polymers. Flexure tests, in which part of the specimen is under tension and part is under compression, generally give values of ultimate strengths which are between the values for tension and compression.

The usual tensile test is primarily a uniaxial test in which the force is applied to a specimen in one direction. Biaxial tests are those in which two stresses at right angles to each other are applied to the specimen simultaneously. Such tests may be made by stretching films or plastic sheets in two directions, by applying pressure to circular diaphragms clamped at the edges[20], or by applying pressure to a fluid in a short closed section of plastic pipe or cylinder[33]. In many practical applications, biaxial stresses are applied to plastic objects. For instance, plastic pipes or tubes and plastic packaging bags are subjected to biaxial stresses when filled with a fluid or powder. Toy rubber balloons undergo very large biaxial deformations when they are blown up.

A biaxial stress-strain curve is not the same as a uniaxial one. In most cases a polymer behaves in a more brittle manner when subjected to biaxial stresses than to uniaxial stresses[5, 33]. The elongation-to-break is less, and the ultimate strength or the yield stress is greater for biaxial tests. An apparent exception to the above generalization is to be found in Miklowitz's work on nylon[47]. In biaxial tests the initial slope of the stress-strain curve is greater than for a uniaxial test. This is to be expected since the test specimen is forced to stretch in two directions and can decrease in only one direction during a biaxial test, while during a uniaxial test, the specimen dimensions can decrease in two directions. In a uniaxial test the initial part of the stress-strain curve is given by $\sigma = E\epsilon$, while for a biaxial test[42]

$$\sigma = \frac{E\epsilon}{1 - \nu} \tag{5.6}$$

where ν is Poisson's ratio. In the extreme case where Poisson's ratio is 0.5, the stress in each of the two directions of stretch is twice the expected value for a uniaxial test at the same elongation.

Models

Models made up of springs and dashpots may be used to illustrate many of the stress-strain properties of polymers. Figure 5.3 shows the stress-strain curves of the four simplest models: A. spring, B. dashpot, C. spring and dashpot in parallel (Voigt, or Kelvin element), D. spring and dashpot in series (Maxwell element).

The curves in Figure 5.3 show the effect of the speed of testing. The curves were calculated for two rates of elongation, $K = d\epsilon/dt$. $K_1 = 1$ and $K_2 = 2$. In the calculations the springs were assumed to have moduli E of 10^8 dynes/cm^2, and the dashpots have viscosities η of 10^8 poises.

For the spring (Case A) the stress and strain are related by $\sigma = E\epsilon$, so the curve is independent of the speed of testing. For the dashpot (Case B) $\sigma = K\eta$, so the stress is proportional to the rate of elongation but independent of the elongation itself.

For the Voigt or Kelvin element (Case C) the stress and strain are related by the equation

$$\sigma = K\eta + E\epsilon. \tag{5.7}$$

Since the spring and dashpot are both forced to move at a constant rate,

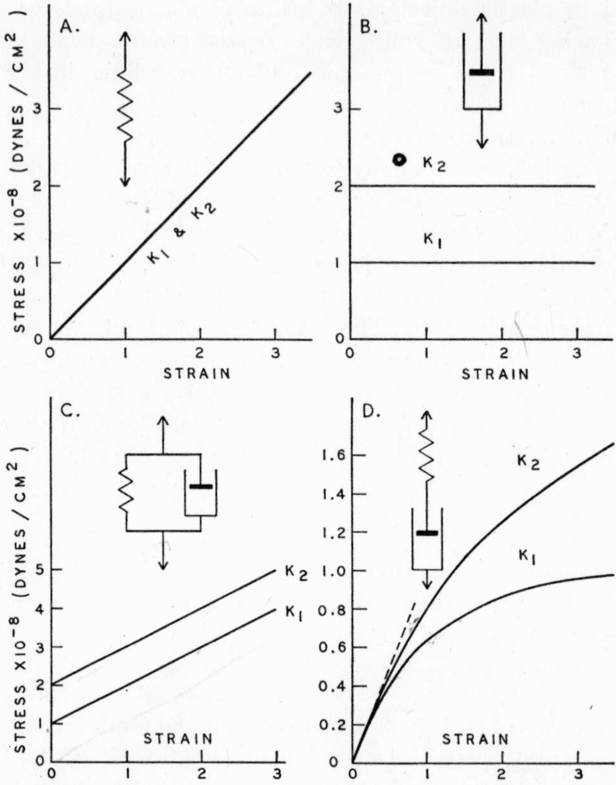

Figure 5.3. The stress-strain behavior of four simple models at two speeds of testing. $d\epsilon/dt = K$. $K_2 = 2K_1$.

the force due to the dashpot immediately jumps to a constant value and remains constant. The force on the spring starts at zero and gradually builds up. Different rates of elongation give curves which are parallel to one another. The slope of the curves is the modulus E.

The Maxwell element (Case D) gives more realistic stress-strain curves. The stress and strain are related by the equation

$$\sigma = K\eta(1 - e^{-E\epsilon/K\eta}) \tag{5.8}$$

This equation is derived in the appendix. The initial slope of the curves is Young's modulus. In this simple model the modulus is independent of the rate of elongation over a large range of rates; with actual plastics this is not quite true. The stress, however, increases with the rate of elongation.

Initially, all the stress goes into stretching the spring, but as the spring elongates, more and more of the stress is carried by the dashpot. Eventually, the spring stretches no more, and all the additional stress goes into flow in the dashpot. At this point the stress-strain curves have zero slope.

The best these simple models can hope to do is to simulate the first part of stress-strain curves. They cannot be expected to predict yield values or the values at break for any real polymer. The theory of the strength of materials is in its infancy. Some of the theories will be discussed in the following chapter.

Cold-Drawing

Most polymers under the proper conditions will cold-draw. The stress-strain curves show three distinct regions as in Figure 5.1. The first part of the curve is fairly linear where all the specimen stretches uniformly. At the yield point the specimen necks down in one region and the stress drops to a nearly constant value as the stretching continues. In this second region there are both undrawn and drawn regions in the specimen. The cold-drawn regions grow at the expense of the undrawn ones until all of the specimen is in the drawn state. The third region of the stress-strain curve involves further straining of cold-drawn polymer. This last region is characterized by a rapid increase in the stress as drawn material has a high modulus and is very strong. The maximum at the yield point only appears in the stress-strain curve if the stress is calculated on the original cross-sectional area. If the stress is calculated on the actual cross section of the drawn material, no maximum is found in the curve[50, 53].

In going from the undrawn to the drawn state all the material becomes elongated a constant amount, usually of the order of several hundred per cent. In other words, the cross-sectional areas of the drawn regions and the undrawn regions have a constant ratio to one another. The natural draw ratio is the ratio of the length of a cold-drawn region to the length of the same material before it was stretched. The natural draw ratio is not strictly a constant for a polymer, but it depends upon the experimental conditions. Marshall and Thompson[44] found that the natural draw ratio of amorphous polyethylene terephthalate increases with the speed of stretching and decreases as the temperature is raised. If the specimens contain some molecular orientation before being cold-drawn, the natural draw ratio decreases as the molecular orientation increases. This might be expected, since in the cold-drawn state the molecules are very highly oriented. Therefore, if the molecules are partly oriented before being cold-drawn, less stretching will be required to orient the molecules to a given degree in the cold-drawn state. Brittle amorphous polymers such as polystyrene tend to break before the yield point[51]. However, this tendency can be minimized by partially orienting the molecules before attempting to cold-draw the material. The orientation is brought about by stretching the polymer in the molten state above its glass temperature and then cooling the polymer before the orientation relaxes out.

The cold-drawing process is strongly temperature dependent. At low temperatures polymers tend to be brittle, and they may break before a yield point is reached. At higher temperatures cold-drawing takes place. At still higher temperatures the definite yield point disappears, and an inflection appears in the stress-strain curve in its place; at this point necking disappears, and the specimen stretches uniformly throughout its length.

Cold-drawing can take place with either amorphous or crystalline polymers. Cold-drawing occurs most easily at temperatures somewhat below the glass temperature for amorphous polymers. At the glass temperature and above, the specimen stretches without necking. With crystalline polymers, cold-drawing may take place from temperatures well below the glass temperature up to near the melting point. Yumoto[77] found with polycaprolactam (nylon 6) that the nature of the stress-strain curves changed drastically at both the glass temperature and at a temperature slightly below the melting point. The elongation at the yield point varies from less than 2 to over 15 per cent. The softer polymers often have the higher elongations at yield.

Some polymers such as polyethylene can be stretched so slowly that they elongate uniformly without necking down. At higher rates of testing, cold-drawing occurs. At very high rates, polymers tend to break before they cold-draw extensively.

During the cold-drawing process very great changes in molecular arrangement take place especially near the yield point and beyond. The molecules tend to become highly oriented parallel to the stretching direction. The crystallites in crystalline polymers also become rearranged so that the molecules line up parallel to the stretching direction. In some cases the crystals may become broken up into smaller units during this orientation process, but in other cases a recrystallization takes place. The crystals melt and then recrystallize in an oriented condition. Cold-drawn material does not easily go back into an unoriented state. Crystalline polymers may have to be heated up to near the melting point before the polymer shrinks back to an undrawn state even though the cold-drawing took place at a much lower temperature. Amorphous polymers have to be heated to near the glass temperature before they shrink.

One theory of cold-drawing assumes that the energy of stretching the polymer largely goes into heating the polymer in the region of the neck[35, 44, 48, 49]. In viscoelastic materials part of the energy is dissipated as heat. This heat generation will tend to be concentrated in a weak section where a neck will develop. In the chapter on dynamic mechanical properties, it will be shown that the maximum amount of heat will be generated near the glass-transition temperature. Thus, when a polymer is stretched, heat will build up in small regions where deformation occurs[6]. As the temperature of this small region builds up, more heat will be generated, and at the same time the modulus will decrease. In this manner, necking will tend to occur in very localized regions. The temperature in the neck where drawing takes place should be stabilized near the glass temperature. Touching the specimen will convince one that the neck gets hot. Higher temperatures than the glass temperature would not be expected since not much heat is generated when a rubber is stretched. If the polymer is crystalline instead of amorphous, the temperature might have to increase to near the melting point at the neck in order for cold-drawing to take place. However, for crystalline polymers such as polyethylene, it may not be essential to evoke the concept of a temperature rise to explain cold-drawing[49].

Vincent[72] objects to the above theory of cold-drawing. He proposes a theory in which the stress on the polymer lowers the softening temperature to about the temperature at which drawing occurs rather than the straining process generating heat which raises the temperature of the material to the softening temperature. Vincent does not offer a molecular mechanism for the lowering of the modulus and softening temperature when a material is strained. However, it is well-known that a large stress on a viscoelastic polymer will greatly reduce its relaxation times and lower its apparent softening or glass temperature[23]. Lazurkin[40] has proposed a similar theory which attempts to explain cold-drawing on the basis of the marked acceleration of stress relaxation by large stresses.

Aspects of both of these theories may be correct, or it is possible that we still do not know the true nature of the cold-drawing process. In general, cold-drawing can be expected to take place with the following types of polymers:

(1) The polymer is crystalline with a degree of crystallinity between about 35 and 75 per cent, and the glass temperature is below the temperature of stretching.

(2) The material is amorphous, and the temperature of stretching is not much below the glass-transition temperature.

(3) The material is amorphous but has a strong secondary glass transition. Drawing is carried out at temperatures between the main glass transition and the secondary one.

(4) The polymer is amorphous and normally very brittle, but the molecules have been partially oriented by stretching the material above the glass temperature. The material should then be quenched from the molten state in order to freeze in a larger than normal free volume and to keep the orientation from relaxing[18, 51].

Two factors are important in the complete cold-drawing process. In addition to a softening of the material as manifested by a yield point, there must be a strain-hardening process. After a neck develops in the specimen, the drawn region has a much higher stress than the undrawn portion because of the reduction in cross-sectional area. If there were no strain-hardening process, the material would break soon after the neck develops since the stress continues to rise as the cross section decreases. The strain hardening comes about as a result of the orientation of the molecules. As the molecules get more and more oriented, the material becomes stronger and stronger. Highly oriented materials can have tensile strengths several times greater than unoriented ones[3, 51]. Not all polymers which have a yield point show cold-drawing. For instance, some low molecular weight polymers break at or just beyond the yield point. The short molecules cannot become highly enough oriented to prevent breaking of the polymer. Also, if the straining rate is too high, the polymer may not cold-draw. At high rates of strain, there is not enough time in many cases for some stress relaxation to occur to prevent brittle fracture and to relieve some of the stress at points of stress concentration.

Effects of Temperature and Plasticizers

As with other mechanical tests, the stress-strain properties of polymers are sensitive to temperature. Figure 5.4[16] illustrates the characteristic effects of temperature. The modulus, yield strength, and tensile strength generally increase as the temperature decreases; the elongation usually decreases as the temperature is lowered for rigid polymers, but for rubbers the elongation may increase as the temperature decreases. The data in Figure 5.4 show that an increase in temperature can change the type of stress-strain curve from hard brittle to hard-tough and finally to soft-tough type.

The modulus of amorphous polymers remains fairly constant until the

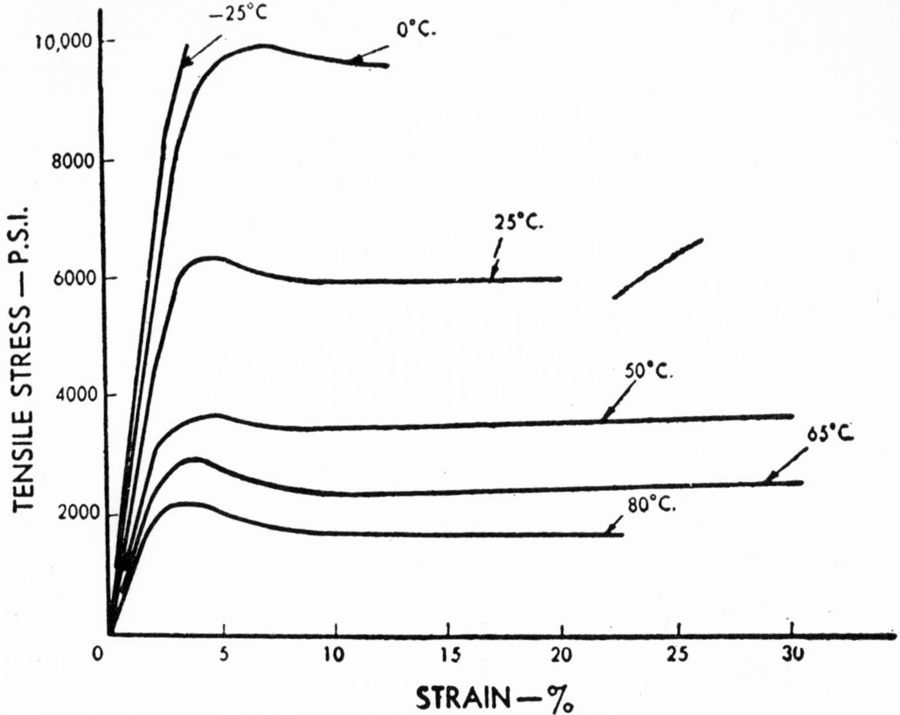

Figure 5.4. Effect of temperature on the stress-strain properties of cellulose acetate. [*After Carswell, T. S., and Nason, H. K., Modern Plastics*, **21**, *121* (*June, 1944*)]

temperature approaches the glass temperature. At this point the modulus or slope of the stress-strain curve may decrease by a factor of a thousand on increasing the temperature only a few degrees. With crystalline polymers of about 50 per cent crystallinity, the modulus decreases by a factor of about ten through the glass-transition region. The modulus then decreases gradually with temperature until the neighborhood of the melting point; at this point the modulus again takes a large drop. The modulus of uncrosslinked rubbers decreases quite rapidly with temperature. However, the modulus of crosslinked rubbers is quite insensitive to temperature and may actually increase slightly with temperature.

The elongation to break generally follows the opposite behavior of the tensile modulus. For instance, with amorphous polymers the elongation is small below the glass temperature, but near the glass temperature the elongation rapidly becomes very large as the temperature is raised. At still higher temperatures the elongation goes through a maximum and then decreases[27, 58, 60, 62]. The elongation may vary from about one per cent for a brittle rigid polymer to 1000 per cent for a rubber or a tough crystalline polymer.

Although the modulus and elongation may change by a factor of a thousand for polymers, the tensile strength seldom changes by a factor of more than ten. For many polymers the tensile strength is between 300 and 10,000 psi. Higher values may be obtained by cold-drawing, by molecular orientation, or by the use of certain fillers; poorly crosslinked rubbers may have values lower than a 1000 psi. Likewise, the yield stress shows small variation compared to the modulus or elongation. If a polymer has a yield point, the stress at yield will generally be between 2000 and 10,000 psi.

In summary, for amorphous materials which have a glass temperature, the elastic modulus (initial slope of the stress-strain curve) and the tensile strength give sigmoidally shaped curves when plotted against temperature. The decrease in modulus with temperature is generally much larger than the decrease in tensile strength. The elongation to break goes through a pronounced maximum as the temperature is varied. The maximum in ultimate elongation occurs at about the same temperature at which the sigmoidal tensile strength curve has its maximum slope, that is, the maximum occurs at a temperature corresponding to the midpoint of the drop in the tensile strength.

The highly crosslinked thermosetting polymers, such as the phenol-formaldehyde materials, are much less sensitive to temperature than are the linear amorphous or crystalline polymers. These highly crosslinked materials are always rigid; their glass temperature, if they have one, is generally higher than their decomposition temperature. Over a temperature range of more than 200°C the modulus or tensile strength may change only a few per cent for such materials. Their elongation is always small—of the order of 1 per cent[17].

The addition of plasticizers to a polymeric material has an effect very similar to an increase in temperature[52]. The properties of a material depend upon the difference between the test temperature T and the glass temperature T_g. Thus, raising the temperature of test or lowering the glass temperature each produces about the same effect on the behavior of a material. However, since most plasticizers not only lower the transition temperature but also increase the width of the transition region, the effect of a plasticizer is not exactly analogous to a change in temperature. These secondary effects of plasticizers are often more pronounced with crystalline materials and with polymers which have several transitions.

Water is a very efficient plasticizer for many polymers. Polar plastics such as cellulosics, nylons, and polyesters readily take up appreciable quantities of water when exposed to either the liquid or the vapor. Carswell and Nason[15, 16] have reviewed the available literature on the effect of relative humidity on the stress-strain properties of plastics and fibers. The results are in agreement with what would be expected in the light of the above discussion. Even the highly crosslinked thermosetting plastics absorb enough moisture to decrease the modulus and tensile strength by approximately 25 per cent. From zero to 100 per cent relative humidity the tensile strength of a polymer such as cellulose acetate may decrease by a factor of two. Nonpolar polymers such as polystyrene or polyethylene are little affected by relative humidity or contact with water as they absorb only very small quantities of it. However, aqueous solutions of some surface active materials bring about stress cracking of polyethylene and thereby decrease the strength of the material.

Effects Due to Speed of Testing

The stress-strain curve of a polymeric material depends upon the speed of testing or the rate at which the specimen is elongated. Typical results are shown in Figure 5.5[19, 38]. As the rate of elongation increases, the tensile strength and the modulus or initial slope of the curve also increase. Common rates of elongation are generally in the range 0.01 to 20 inches per minute, but some work has been done at both lower and higher rates of testing. With rigid polymers such as polymethyl methacrylate and with some rubbers the elongation to break generally decreases as the testing speed increases[2, 19, 21, 27, 38]. However, with rubbers the elongation often increase as the rate of elongation increases[10, 29, 58]. Smith[58] has found that the Williams-Landel-Ferry[74] reduced variables treatment can be applied to rubbers and rigid plastics to give master curves for the tensile strength and elongation as well as for the modulus. Thus, an increase in speed of testing is similar to a decrease in temperature. The master curve for elongation to break goes through a maximum. This indicates there are a number of combinations of temperatures and speeds of testing where the elongation to break is large. For moderate or fairly slow speeds of testing, the maximum elongation will occur at temperatures near but somewhat above the glass-transition temperature. At lower temperatures the material will act as a brittle solid and will have a very low elongation to break, while at higher temperatures the polymer behaves more like a viscous liquid, and its elongation will decrease with temperature. The master curve for tensile strength is high at temperatures below T_g for normal testing speeds or at very high speeds of testing at temperatures above T_g. For normal speeds of testing

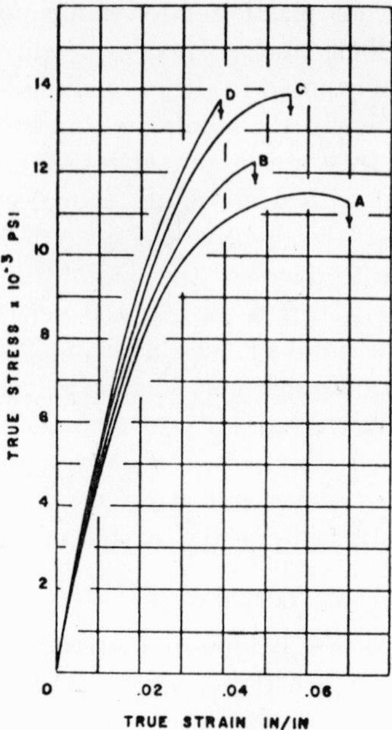

Curve	Crosshead Rate (ipm)
A	0.02
B	0.08
C	0.32
D	1.28

Figure 5.5. Effect of speed of testing on the stress-strain behavior of polymethyl methacrylate. [*After Knowles, J. K., and Dietz, A. G. H., Trans. Am. Soc. Mech. Eng.*, **77**, *177* (*1955*)]

the master curve for tensile strength decreases rapidly at temperatures near the glass transition. The tensile strength levels off again to a lower value at either higher temperatures or very low speeds of testing.

Strella[68] has measured stress-strain curves up to speeds of 5000 inches per minute by observing force-time curves on a cathode ray oscilloscope. In general his results agree with what one would expect from the above discussion. The stress and modulus increase, and the elongation decreases as the speed of testing increases. In the case of polyethylene, the yield point is more pronounced at very high speeds than at low speeds. One surprising result was found, however. One type of polystyrene gave an ultimate elongation of about 2 per cent at a testing speed of 1800 inches per minute while an elongation of slightly over 1 per cent was found at a testing speed of 0.05 inch per minute.

If the first part of a stress-strain curve can be represented by a model made up of Hookean springs and Newtonian dashpots, the stress-strain curve obtained at a rate K_1 can be used to predict the curve to be expected at a rate K_2[1]. To obtain a point on the curve at a rate of testing of K_2, choose a point on the curve obtained at the rate K_1 and multiply both its abscissa and ordinate by the ratio K_2/K_1. The greater the curvature of a stress-strain curve, the greater is the effect of speed of testing. If no relaxation process occurs during the course of the test, a stress-strain curve should be a straight line independent of rate.

Rubbers

The stress-strain properties of rubbers have been intensively studied[11, 12, 26, 71]. This type of test is well justified with vulcanized or crosslinked rubbers as most applications of rubbers require that they be capable of large extensions without breaking.

The stress-strain curves of rubbers are similar to the curve for a soft tough material shown in Figure 5.2. Most rubber formulations do not show a yield point, but there may be a region of the stress-strain curve where a plateau exists followed by a rapid increase in stress. The upturn in the stress-strain curve at large elongations may be due to either crystallization induced by molecular orientation or to non-Gaussian behavior of chain segments stretched to near their maximum length[25, 71].

The kinetic theory of rubber predicts that the stress-strain curve should be given by

$$\sigma = \frac{dRT}{M_c}\left(1 - \frac{2M_c}{\bar{M}_n}\right)\left[\frac{L}{L_0} - \left(\frac{L_0}{L}\right)^2\right] \tag{5.9}$$

where d is the density of the polymer, R is the gas constant, T is the absolute temperature, $\bar{M}_n$ is the number average molecular weight of the original polymer before crosslinking, and M_c is the average molecular weight between crosslinked points. The stress σ is calculated on the basis of the unstretched cross-sectional area. The stretched length is L, and the unstretched length is L_0. The strain defined by the terms in the square brackets is three times the normal strain at small elongations. The term $(1 - 2M_c/\bar{M}_n)$ is a correction term to take care of the flaws in the network structure due to chain ends. If the initial molecular weight is high or if the material is highly crosslinked, this correction term can be neglected.

Young's modulus E is given approximately by

$$E = \frac{3dRT}{M_c} \tag{5.10}$$

The shear modulus G is

$$G = \frac{dRT}{M_c} \tag{5.11}$$

since for a simple shear deformation[71]

$$\sigma_s = G\epsilon_s = \frac{dRT}{M_c}\left(\frac{L}{L_0} - \frac{L_0}{L}\right) = G \tan \theta \tag{5.12}$$

where the shear stress σ_s is based on the strained dimensions in this case. For the case of uniform two-dimensional stretching in which a sheet is simultaneously stretched lengthwise and crosswise, the stress, based on the strained dimensions, is given by

$$\sigma = \frac{E}{3}\left[\left(\frac{L}{L_0}\right)^2 - \left(\frac{L_0}{L}\right)^4\right]. \tag{5.13}$$

This equation shows that it is more difficult to stretch a material in two directions at a time than it is to stretch it in one direction as is done in a normal stress-strain test. Normally a specimen shrinks in all directions perpendicular to the direction of stretch. In two-dimensional (or biaxial) stretching an additional stress must be applied to overcome this tendency for shrinkage; only the thickness remains free to decrease in biaxial stretching.

The kinetic theory of rubber has been quite successful in predicting the modulus of rubbers, the temperature dependence of the modulus, and the shape of the first part of the stress-strain curve. The predicted modulus is usually somewhat lower than the observed modulus. This is partly due to chain entanglements, which act as temporary crosslinks in increasing the modulus.

Rubber theory predicts, and experiments verify, that the modulus of a rubber increases with degree of crosslinking. However, rubber theory cannot predict all of the other stress-strain properties. Numerous experiments[22, 26, 32, 61, 70] have shown though that the elongation to break continuously decreases as the crosslinking increases. The tensile strength of rubbers goes through a maximum as the crosslinking increases. Typical data are shown in Table 5.1[26]. Yanko[76] studied the effect of changing the

TABLE 5.1. EFFECT OF CROSSLINKING ON THE STRESS-STRAIN PROPERTIES OF RUBBER*

Equivalent Concentration of Crosslinking Agent	Average Ultimate Elongation (%)	Average Tensile Strength (psi)
0.1	1000	920
0.2	940	1774
0.3	920	2288
0.4	850	2846
0.5	830	2892
1.0	680	3102
1.5	570	2924
2.0	490	2655
2.5	440	2353
3.0	400	2038
3.2	350	1487
3.5	280	968
4.0	250	848
6.0	130	554
8.0	90	655

* Flory, P. J., Rabjohn, N., and Schaffer, M. C., *J. Polymer Sci.*, **4**, 435 (1949).

molecular weight of rubbers while holding the degree of crosslinking constant. The modulus and tensile strength at first increased with molecular weight and then reached a plateau at high molecular weights. The ultimate elongation went through a broad maximum as the molecular weight increased.

Properties of Various Polymers and Effect of Structure

In addition to speed of testing and the temperature relative to the glass temperature, the stress-strain behavior of polymers depends upon a number of structural factors.

Molecular weight and molecular weight distribution affect the stress-strain properties[46, 63, 64, 76]. Generally, below a certain minimum molecular weight, the value of the properties is low. The properties increase over a molecular weight range and then asymptotically approach a maximum at high molecular weights. Merz and co-workers[46] found that as long as the weight average molecular weight of polystyrene was high enough so that specimens could be prepared, the stress-strain properties depended primarily upon the number average molecular weight. Others[41] have found that although the properties depend primarily upon the number average molecular weight of polystyrene, the weight average also has an influence since the narrower the molecular weight distribution the poorer are the tensile properties at a given number average molecular weight. The tensile strength and elongation to break both approach zero at number average molecular weights someplace between 20,000 and 50,000. The tensile modulus is independent of molecular weight down to very small values.

Sookne and Harris[63, 64] found that the tensile properties of cellulose acetate also depend upon the number average molecular weight $\bar{M}_n$. The tensile strength was zero below degrees of polymerization of 50, and it became independent of molecular weight above a number average degree of polymerization of 400. The elongation to break was zero below a degree of polymerization of 100, but the elongation rapidly approached its maximum value as $\bar{M}_n$ increased. The stress-strain properties such as tensile strength σ_B obey an equation of the form

$$\sigma_B = A - \frac{B}{\bar{M}_n} \tag{5.14}$$

where A and B are constants. Flory[24] has predicted that such an equation should be obeyed on the basis that end groups act as imperfections which adversely affect the tensile properties.

Lawton, Balwit, and Bueche[39] found that the tensile properties of polyethylene increased with $\bar{M}_n$, went through a maximum at about a molecular weight of 20,000, and then gradually decreased as $\bar{M}_n$ continued to increase. However, the degree of crystallinity may have also changed with $\bar{M}_n$, so it is impossible to say that the observed results were due only to molecular weight. Sperati, Franta, and Starkweather[65] found that the stress-strain properties of polyethylene depend primarily upon density or degree of crystallinity rather than upon molecular weight. Both the modulus and yield point increase linearly with density. The tensile strength, however, increases with the weight average molecular weight. The elongation to break increases with molecular weight but decreases as the crystallinity increases. During the stretching of crystalline polymers, both the amorphous and crystalline phases become oriented[8, 36].

An increase in crystallinity generally tends to make a polymer more brittle. Increasing crystallinity raises the modulus, but decreases the elongation to break. This has been observed for a number of polymers such as crystalline polypropylene[73] and crystalline polystyrene. With tough or rubbery polymers the tensile strength increases with crystallinity. However, with the more brittle polymers such as isotactic polystyrene or polyethylene terephthalate, crystallinity decreases the strength if the polymer is unoriented. Apparently the crystallites can act as stress concentrators and thereby weaken the material.

Nylons are examples of tough crystalline polymers. Starkweather and co-workers[67] have studied nylon 6-6 (polyhexamethylene adipamide) and nylon 6-10 (polyhexamethylene sebacamide). With nylon 6-10 the modulus, yield strength, and tensile strength all increase with increasing crystallinity in the range from 7 to 40 per cent. The following equations were found to hold for dry polymer:

$$E \text{ (psi)} = 216{,}100\ W_c + 53{,}100$$

$$\text{Yield stress (psi)} = \sigma_y = 11{,}830\ W_c + 4670$$

Tensile strength (psi) $= \sigma_B = 9760\ W_c + 6290$ where W_c is the degree of crystallinity in the range 0.07 to 0.40. At higher crystallinity the tensile strength would be expected to reach a maximum and then decrease. Nylon polymers normally cold-draw; the elongation to break in the drawn sections was found to be about 300 per cent. At the higher crystallinities the nylon 6-10 specimens tended to break before drawing was complete. At equal crystallinities the Young's modulus and yield stress were nearly the same for both nylon 6-10 and nylon 6-6.

The spherulitic structure of crystalline polymers has an effect on strength properties beyond the effects due to degree of crystallinity[9, 31, 37, 66, 73]. Large spherulites generally decrease the elongation to break and the toughness of a polymer. Large spherulites are promoted by slow cooling and annealing, while quenching from the melt produces small spherulites.

Molecular orientation can have a tremendous effect upon the stress-strain behavior of polymers. The subject of orientation will be discussed in more detail in a later chapter, but with regard to tensile properties the following generalizations may be made: If the applied force is in the direction parallel to the molecular orientation, the modulus, tensile strength, and often the elongation increase over the values found with an unoriented polymer. Orientation may change a polymer from a brittle material to a ductile one which has a yield point. However, if the tensile load is applied in the direction perpendicular to the molecular orientation, the modulus, tensile strength, and elongation are all found to be less than for the brittle unoriented material. If the unoriented material is tough and ductile, the elongation perpendicular to the molecular orientation may in some cases be greater than the elongation to break in the direction parallel to the orientation.

It is often assumed that the nature of stress-strain curves depends upon the strength of the Van der Waal's forces between the polymer molecules. The addition of aliphatic side chains to a polar molecule such as cellulose should lower the strength of the Van der Waal's forces. Hagedorn and

TABLE 5.2. STRESS-STRAIN PROPERTIES OF CELLULOSE DERIVATIVES*

Polymer	Tensile Strength (Kg/mm^2)	Ultimate Elongation (Per cent)
Cellulose acetate	10.5	20
Cellulose proprionate	6.5	12
Cellulose butyrate	5.5	15
Cellulose valerate	4.5	25
Cellulose pelargonate	3.7	30
Cellulose caprate	2.2	65
Cellulose laurate	1.0	115
Cellulose stearate	0.5	145

* From Hagedorn, M., and Moeller, P., *Cellulosechemie*, **12,** 29 (1931); data have been smoothed by reading from a graph of the experimental data.

Moeller[30], Sheppard and Newsome[57], and Malm and co-workers[43], have studied the changes in cellulose derivatives as longer side chains are added to the polymer chain. Some approximate results are shown in Table 5.2. As the nonpolar side chain lengthens, the tensile strength drops and the ultimate elongation increases. Unfortunately, it is not certain that all the observed effects can be attributed to reduction of intermolecular forces. Other factors, such as decreased crystallinity and lowering of the glass temperatures, may also play important roles.

A tremendous volume of data exists on the effect of fillers in rubbers[4, 59], phenol-formaldehyde resins[17], and other polymers[75]. If the filler is rigid with a modulus greater than the modulus of the polymer, the modulus of the mixture increases with filler content. If fillers in the form of fine powders are added to most polymers, especially brittle polymers, the elongation to break and the ultimate strength both generally decrease as the amount of filler in the polymer increases. However, the addition of carbon black to rubber has a beneficial effect. Apparently carbon black imparts some of the properties of crosslinks in increasing the modulus and the strength of a rubber.

Large elongated fillers, especially strong tough ones, can greatly improve the strength properties of even brittle polymers. Such fillers include glass fibers and cotton fibers with a length of about 0.1 inches or longer. In the extreme case, the fillers may be paper sheets or woven fabrics so that the final product is a tough laminate.

Especially tough polymers may be obtained by adding microscopic rubbery fillers to rigid plastics to form polyblends. Polyblends have lower moduli and tensile strengths than the rigid polymers, but they may have yield points and show very large elongations to break[45]. The properties of polyblends will be discussed in more detail in later sections.

References

1. Alfrey, T., Jr., "Mechanical Behavior of High Polymers," New York, Interscience Publishers Inc., 1948.
2. Amborski, L. E., and Mecca, T. D., *J. Appl. Polymer Sci.*, **4,** 332 (1960).
3. Bailey, J., *India Rubber World*, **118,** 225 (1948).
4. Bills, K. W., Jr., Sweeny, K. H., and Salcedo, F. S., *J. Appl. Polymer Sci.*, **4,** 259 (1960).
5. Boonstra, B. B. S. T., *J. Appl. Phys.*, **21,** 1098 (1950).
6. Brauer, P., and Mueller, F. H., *Kolloid Z.*, **135,** 65 (1954).
7. Breazeale, F. B., and Irvin, H. D., *Textile Research J.*, **22,** 549 (1952).
8. Brown, A., *J. Appl. Phys.*, **20,** 552 (1949).
9. Bryant, W. M. D., *J. Polymer Sci.*, **2,** 547 (1947).
10. Bueche, F., *J. Appl. Phys.*, **26,** 1133 (1955).
11. Bueche, F., *J. Polymer Sci.*, **25,** 305 (1957).
12. Bueche, F., *Rubber Chem. and Tech.*, **32,** 1269 (1959).
13. Burr, G. S., *Electronics*, **22,** No. 5, 101 (1949).
14. Burr, G. S., Gailus, W. J., Silvey, J. O., Yurenka, S., and Dietz, A. G. H., *ASTM, Bull. No. 149*, 51 (Dec. 1947).
15. Carswell, T. S. and Nason, H. K., "Symposium on Plastics," Spec. Tech. Publ. No. 59, p. 22, Philadelphia, Pa., Am. Soc. Testing Materials, Feb., 1944.
16. Carswell, T. S., and Nason, H. K., *Modern Plastics*, **21,** 121 (June, 1944).
17. Carswell, T. S., Telfair, D., and Haslanger, R. V., *Modern Plastics*, **19,** 65 (July, 1942).
18. Cheatham, R. G., and Dietz, A. G. H., *Trans. Am. Soc. Mech. Eng.*, **74,** 31 (1952).
19. Dietz, A. G. H., and McGarry, F. J., "Symposium on Speed of Testing," Spec. Tech. Publ. No. 185, p. 30, Philadelphia, Pa. Am. Soc. Testing Materials, 1956.
20. Dietz, A. G. H., and McGarry, F. J., *Modern Plastics*, **36,** 135 (Sept., 1958).
21. Ely, R. E., *Plastics Tech.*, **3,** 900 (1957).
22. Epstein, L. M. and Smith, R. P., *Trans. Soc. Rheology*, **2,** 219 (1958).
23. Ferry, J. D., and Stratton, R. A., *Kolloid Z.*, **171,** 107 (1960).
24. Flory, P. J., *J. Am. Chem. Soc.*, **67,** 2048 (1945).
25. Flory, P. J., "Principles of Polymer Chemistry," Chap. 11, Ithaca, N. Y., Cornell University Press, 1953.
26. Flory, P. J., Rabjohn, N., and Schaffer, M. C., *J. Polymer Sci.*, **4,** 435 (1949).
27. Fromandi, G., Ecker, R., and Heidemann, W., "*Proc. Intern. Rubber Conf.*," p. 177, Washington, D. C., Nov., 1959.
28. Gilman, J. J., *Rev. Sci. Instr.*, **23,** 759 (1952).
29. Greensmith, H. W., *J. Appl. Polymer Sci.*, **3,** 175 (1960).
30. Hagedorn, M., and Moeller, P., *Cellulosechemie*, **12,** 29 (1931).
31. Hammer, C. F., Koch, T. A., and Whitney, J. F., *J. Appl. Polymer Sci.*, **1,** 169 (1959).
32. Hill, F. B., Young, C. A., Nelson, J. A., and Arnold, R. G., *Ind. Eng. Chem.*, **48,** 927 (1956).
33. Hopkins, I. L., Baker, W. O., and Howard, J. B., *J. Appl. Phys.*, **21,** 206 (1950).
34. Hsiao, C. C., and Sauer, J. A., *ASTM, Bull. No. 172*, 29 (Feb., 1951).
35. Jaeckel, K., *Kolloid Z.*, **137,** 130 (1954).
36. Kauffman, J., and George, W., *J. Appl. Phys.*, **21,** 431 (1950).
37. Keith, H. D., and Padden, Jr., F. J., *J. Polymer Sci.*, **41,** 525 (1959).

38. Knowles, J. K., and Dietz, A. G. H., *Trans. Am. Soc. Mech. Eng.*, **77,** 177 (1955).
39. Lawton, E. J., Balwit, J. S., and Bueche, A. M., *Ind. Eng. Chem.*, **46,** 1703 (1946).
40. Lazurkin, J. S., *J. Polymer Sci.*, **30,** 595 (1958).
41. McCormick, H. W., Brower, F. M., and Kin, L., *J. Polymer Sci.*, **39,** 87 (1959).
42. McCrackin, F. L., and Bersch, C. F., *Soc. Plastics Eng. J.*, **15,** 791 (1959).
43. Malm, C. J., Mench, J. W., Kendall, D. L., and Hiatt, G. D., *Ind. Eng. Chem.*, **43,** 688 (1951).
44. Marshall, I., and Thompson, A. B., *Proc. Royal Soc. London*, **221A**, 541 (1954).
45. Merz, E. H., Claver, G. C., and Baer, M., *J. Polymer Sci.*, **22,** 325 (1956).
46. Merz, E. H., Nielsen, L. E., and Buchdahl, R., *Ind. Eng. Chem.*, **43,** 1396 (1951).
47. Miklowitz, J., *J. Colloid Sci.*, **2,** 217 (1947).
48. Mueller, F. H., *Kolloid Z.*, **126,** 65 (1952).
49. Newman, S., *J. Polymer Sci.*, **27,** 563 (1958).
50. Newman, S., *J. Appl. Polymer Sci.*, **2,** 252 (1959).
51. Nielsen, L. E., and Buchdahl, R., *J. Appl. Phys.*, **21,** 488 (1950).
52. Nielsen, L. E., Buchdahl, R., and Levreault, R., *J. Appl. Phys.*, **21,** 607 (1950).
53. Orowan, E., Rep. Phys. Soc., *Progress in Physics*, **12,** 185 (1948, 1949).
54. Oth, J. F. M., and Flory, P. J., *J. Am. Chem. Soc.*, **80,** 1297 (1958).
55. Patterson, G. D., Jr., and Miller, W. H., Jr., *J. Appl. Polymer Sci.*, **4,** 291 (1960).
56. Reichardt, C. H., Schaevitz, H., and Dillon, J. H., *Rev. Sci. Inst.*, **20,** 509 (1949).
57. Sheppard, S. E., and Newsome, P. T., *J. Phys. Chem.*, **39,** 143 (1935).
58. Smith, T. L., *J. Polymer Sci.*, **32,** 99 (1958).
59. Smith, T. L., *Trans. Soc. Rheology*, **3,** 113 (1959).
60. Smith, T. L., *Soc. Plastics Eng. J.*, **16,** 1211 (1960).
61. Smith, T. L., and Magnusson, A. B., *J. Polymer Sci.*, **42,** 391 (1960).
62. Smith, T. L., and Stedry, P. J., *J. Appl. Phys.*, **31,** 1892 (1960).
63. Sookne, A. M., and Harris, M., *J. Research*, **34,** 467 (1945).
64. Sookne, A. M., and Harris, M., *Ind. Eng. Chem.*, **37,** 478 (1945).
65. Sperati, C. A., Franta, W. A., and Starkweather, H. W., Jr., *J. Am. Chem. Soc.*, **75,** 6127 (1953).
66. Starkweather, H. W., Jr., and Brooks, R. E., *J. Appl. Polymer Sci.*, **1,** 236 (1959).
67. Starkweather, H. W., Jr., Moore, G. E., Hansen, J. E., Roder, T. M., and Brooks, R. E., *J. Polymer Sci.*, **21,** 189 (1956).
68. Strella, S., "High Speed Testing," Vol. 1, Dietz, A. G. H., and Eirich, F. R., Ed., New York, Interscience Publishers, Inc., 1960.
69. Strella, S., and Gilman, L., *Modern Plastics*, **34,** 158 (1957).
70. Taylor, G. R., and Darin, S. R., *J. Polymer Sci.*, **17,** 511 (1955).
71. Treloar, L. R. G., "Physics of Rubber Elasticity," 2nd Ed., Oxford, Clarendon Press, 1958.
72. Vincent, P. I., *Polymer*, **1,** 7 (1960).
73. Wijga, P. W. O., "Physical Properties of Polymers," Monograph No. 5, Soc. Chem. Ind., p. 35, New York, Macmillan Co., 1959.
74. Williams, M. L., Landel, R. F., and Ferry, J. D., *J. Am. Chem. Soc.*, **77,** 3701 (1955).
75. Wohnsiedler, H. P., Updegraff, I. H., and Hunt, R. H., Jr., *Ind. Eng. Chem.*, **48,** 82 (1956).
76. Yanko, J. A., *J. Polymer Sci.*, **3,** 576 (1948).
77. Yumoto, H., *Bull. Chem. Soc. Japan*, **29,** 45, 141, 353 (1956).

Appendix

Stress-Strain Behavior of a Maxwell Unit

The differential equation of a Maxwell Unit is

$$\frac{d\epsilon}{dt} = \frac{1}{E}\frac{d\sigma}{dt} + \frac{\sigma}{\eta}. \tag{5.15}$$

If the rate of elongation $d\epsilon/dt$ is a constant K, the above equation can be rearranged to give the following linear ordinary differential equation:

$$\frac{d\sigma}{dt} + \frac{E}{\eta}\sigma = EK. \tag{5.16}$$

The homogeneous solution of this equation, where $EK = O$, is

$$\sigma = Ae^{-(E/\eta)t} \tag{5.17}$$

The particular solution, where the stress is some constant B, is obtained by substitution into the differential equation to give

$$\frac{EB}{\eta} = EK$$

or

$$B = K\eta. \tag{5.18}$$

Therefore, the complete solution (homogeneous solution plus particular solution) is

$$\sigma = Ae^{-(E/\eta)t} + K\eta. \tag{5.19}$$

Since the initial condition is the stress is zero at time zero, the above equation gives

$$0 = A + K\eta$$

or

$$A = -K\eta \tag{5.20}$$

Since $\epsilon = Kt$, the final solution for the stress-strain behavior is

$$\sigma = K\eta(1 - e^{-(Et/\eta)}) = K\eta(1 - e^{-(E\epsilon/K\eta)}) \tag{5.21}$$

The initial slope of the stress-strain curve of a Maxwell unit is E. This initial slope is independent of the speed of testing K, but the slope at larger elongations depends upon K. At very large elongations the stress levels off to a value equal to $K\eta$; that is, the greater the speed of testing, the greater is the limiting value of the stress.

Chapter 6

IMPACT STRENGTH AND THEORIES OF STRENGTH OF POLYMERS

Impact Tests

Nature of Impact Tests. Impact tests are supposed to measure the toughness or the resistance to breakage of materials under high velocity impact conditions. The characteristics measured by most impact tests are complex quantities difficult to define in scientific terms, but they have great practical importance. One prefers to have plastic objects which do not break when dropped on the floor or when struck by another object. Impact tests attempt to rank materials in terms of their resistance to breakage; this ranking is generally done by measuring the energy required to break a standard plastic object of the material under certain specified conditions. The impact strength (or energy to break) of a ductile polymer may be much greater than the impact strength of a brittle polymer.

The field of impact testing is very complex for a number of reasons. First, there are a large number of impact tests. These tests all measure somewhat different quantities, some of which are not clearly defined or understood. Tests are made on specimens of various sizes and shapes. The specimens are broken under different kinds of stress distributions and under different speeds of impact. Finally, variations in the specimens themselves make it difficult to obtain reproducible results. Specimens may have surfaces which differ in behavior from their interiors, or they may have varying degrees of molecular orientation which may be parallel or perpendicular to the stresses encountered during the impact test. As a result, many of the values of impact strengths published in the literature are practically useless. It is not realistic to highly orient a material and then test it in its strongest direction when in nearly all practical situations, the object will break in the direction in which it is weakest[1]. However, tables on the physical properties of polymers are full of such misleading information.

Types of Impact Tests. Only a few of the many impact tests will be discussed here; these will be the most important or the most widely used ones. These tests are: the Izod impact test, the Charpy impact test, the falling weight test, and the high-speed, stress-strain tests.

The Izod and Charpy testers[2, 29] are pendulum instruments which break the specimen with a hammer that has more than enough kinetic energy to fracture the specimen. The Izod test uses a notched cantilever-beam type of specimen which is struck on the free end, while the Charpy test uses a beam supported at two points near the ends which is struck in the middle by the hammer. Telfair and Nason[42] have analyzed the pendulum type of tester. Such tests use a standard specimen which gives results that cannot be compared with specimens of other dimensions, therefore, the data have no absolute physical significance. These tests do not measure the true energy required to fracture the specimen. In addition to the energy to initiate a fracture crack and the energy to propagate the crack through the specimen, these tests also measure the energy to permanently deform the material and the energy to throw the broken ends of the specimen. The energy used in throwing the pieces of the broken specimen contributes nothing to the toughness of the material, but this factor may represent a large fraction of the total energy measured by the test. For instance, a polystyrene had an Izod impact strength of 0.305 ft.-lb. per inch of notch; 0.152 ft.-lb. per inch of notch of this energy was used in throwing the broken pieces[42].

In the falling weight type of tests[1, 11, 13, 18, 24, 27] a ball, a standard weight, or a dart is dropped onto a bar or sheet from a known height. These tests are run under conditions such that the falling weight barely has enough energy to crack or break the test specimen. This type of test generally correlates much better with field tests and practical experience than does the pendulum type. Energy is not wasted in throwing the broken pieces. Likewise, the tests can measure just the energy to form a crack rather than the energy to completely fracture the specimen. In many practical applications, the plastic object can be considered as having failed as soon as the first crack forms. The falling weight tests suffer from the fact that a specimen of a standardized size must be used in order to compare one material with another, and different materials are compared at different velocities of impact.

One advantage of the falling weight tests is that they may be used with oriented or injection-molded sheets. If the test specimen is a bar, it is tested in its strongest direction if it contains oriented molecules, as is nearly always the case with injection-molded bars. With an oriented sheet, however, the falling weight test breaks the specimen in its weakest direction, thus simulating practical conditions[1].

High-speed stress-strain tests may be the best for evaluating the impact strength of a material[18, 29, 39, 40]. Evans, Nara, and Bobalek[18] found that a standard commercial stress-strain tester operated at its fastest rate (20 inches per minute) gave results which correlated well with falling weight impact values. However, better results should be obtained with even higher rates of elongation; such an instrument has been built by Strella and Gilman[39] and others.

The area under a stress-strain curve is proportional to the energy required to break a material, and if the test is made at a high enough rate, the area under this curve should be the same as the impact strength of the material. The impact strength is related to both the tensile strength and the elongation to break. In a high-speed stress strain test each of these factors can be evaluated independently while they cannot be in a standard impact test. As the speed of testing increases, the tensile strength goes up, but the elongation goes down. The impact strength may in some cases increase with the speed of testing if the tensile strength increases at a faster rate than the elongation decreases. For brittle thermosetting materials, the impact properties may be so insensitive to speed of testing that the area under a normal slow speed stress-strain curve gives a good estimate of the impact strength. Tough, ductile polymers are more sensitive to speed of testing. However, even for these materials, the impact strength may change only by a factor of two for an increase in speed of a hundred or thousand fold[43].

Stress-strain tests differ from impact tests in one important respect. Very strong vibrations are introduced in the impact specimen when struck by the hammer or falling weight[31, 46]. The hammer does not strike the specimen just once, but because of vibrations set up in the test piece, the hammer may strike the specimen at least two or three times before the specimen fails. This all takes place within about a thousandth of a second. The vibrations and stress waves in the polymer undoubtedly affect its indicated impact strength, but this problem has not been investigated in detail.

Factors Affecting Impact Strength. A notch in a test specimen may drastically lower the measured impact strength of a material. A notch concentrates the stress in a small region during the impact test; the smaller the radius of curvature at the base of the notch the greater the stress concentration[29]. A notch has an effect similar to increasing the speed of testing by increasing the stressing rate in the neighborhood of the notch. By concentrating the stress in a small volume, a notch tends to decrease the apparent ductility of a material. Thus, a notch often has a greater apparent effect on ductile materials than on brittle ones[43]. However, even with a brittle, thermosetting, asbestos-filled phenolic, a notch decreases the Izod impact strength by a factor of eight. With a tough, cotton-cord-filled phenolic material, a notch drops the Izod impact strength from 2.9 to 1.4[43].

Fillers, especially fibrous ones, increase the impact strength of thermosetting phenolics and other brittle polymers[12, 43]. Fibers distribute the stress over a larger volume at the base of the notch; they can also stop the propagation of a crack by carrying a large portion of the loads in the neighborhood of a crack. Large quantities of nonfibrous fillers such as ground calcium carbonate in brittle polymers such as polystyrene decrease the impact strength. The filler particles act as stress concentrators in these cases.

The impact strength of thermosetting polymers varies little with temperature over a very wide range. Between −80 and 200°C the impact strength may be nearly constant. If the material contains an organic filler such as cotton fibers, the filler degrades at about 200°C, and the impact strength of the filled polymer drops.

The impact strength of thermoplastic materials is generally strongly temperature dependent. Near the glass temperature the impact strength dramatically increases with temperature. However, at temperatures well below the glass transition two rigid polymers can differ greatly in impact strength. For instance, cellulose nitrate and polycarbonates have much higher impact strengths than polystyrene or polymethyl methacrylate. The differences between these polymers is due primarily to secondary transitions. A polymer with a low temperature secondary glass transition is nearly always much tougher than a polymer which has no such transition[5]. One of the chief reasons for making polyblends is to increase the impact strength of a brittle material by adding a rubber to it so that the material will have a low temperature transition in addition to its normal glass transition[7, 8, 28, 38].

Crystalline polymers have high impact strengths if their glass transition is well below the temperature at which the test is carried out. The impact strength decreases as the degree of crystallinity increases or as the size of spherulites increases[33]. Low pressure polyethylene (crystallinity 70 to 80 per cent) has an impact strength (ft-lb/in. notch) of approximately 2, while high pressure polyethylene (crystallinity roughly 50 per cent) has an impact strength of greater than 10. If the glass temperature is above the

TABLE 6.1. IMPACT STRENGTH OF RIGID PLASTICS AT 24°C.*

Plastic	Notched Izod Impact Strength
Polystyrene	0.25–0.60
Polystyrene polyblends	0.6–3.0
Polyvinyl chloride (rigid)	0.4–1.0
Polyvinyl chloride (polyblends)	3.0–15.0
Polymethyl methacrylate	0.4–0.5
Cellulose acetate	1.0–5.6
Cellulose nitrate	5.0–7.0
Ethyl cellulose	3.5–6.0
Nylon 6-6	0.9–>10
Nylon 6	1.0–4.0
Polyoxymethylene	2–3
Polyethylene (low density)	>10
Polyethylene (high density)	0.5–3.5
Polypropylene	0.5–11
Polycarbonate (Bis Phenol-A)	2–16
Polyvinyl formal	1–20
Phenol-formaldehyde (gen. purpose)	0.25–.35
Phenol-formaldehyde (cloth-filled)	1–3
Polytetrafluoroethylene	2.0–4.0

* From various sources including, "Technical Data on Plastics," Washington, D. C., Manuf. Chemists Assoc., Feb., 1957.

test temperature, crystallinity decreases the impact strength as long as the material is not oriented. Crystallites appear in these cases to act as stress concentrators.

The Izod impact strength of a number of common polymers at 24°C is listed in Table 6.1. In using impact data, it must be remembered that the values are not true material constants. The values for a given material can be changed by orientation of the molecules, type of notch, whether it is compression or injection molded, and type of heat treatment.

Theories of Fracture and Strength of Polymers

Stress Concentrators. In spite of its great practical importance, the theory of fracture and the ultimate strength of materials is not well advanced. Theories of strength based on bond strengths and intermolecular forces give estimates of strength greater by about a factor of a hundred than those encountered in practice[14, 22].

Stress concentrators lower the apparent strength of materials; these include cracks, notches, imbedded particles, and voids. When a stress concentrator is present, the stress acting on a small volume of the material may be much greater than the average stress applied to the test specimen. As a result, the material breaks at a stress which is less than the expected value. Stress concentrators may be large enough to be easily seen, or they may be so small that they are invisible.

A simple model of a stress concentrator is a circular hole cut in a thin sheet. The tangential stress components σ_t at the edge of the hole is[4]

$$\sigma_t = \sigma_0 - 2\sigma_0 \cos 2\theta \qquad (6.1)$$

where σ_0 is the average external tensile stress applied to the sheet, and θ is the angle from the direction of the applied tensile stress. This equation shows that in the direction parallel to the stress ($\theta = 0$), the tangential stress at the edge of the hole is compressive and equal to σ_0. In the direction perpendicular to the stress ($\theta = \pi/2$), the tangential stress is tensile and equal to $3\sigma_0$. Thus, the stress has been concentrated by a factor of three by the hole.

If an ellipse is cut in a large sheet or thin plate, the tensile stress at the edge of the ellipse when it is oriented in a direction perpendicular to the applied stress is

$$\sigma_t = \sigma_0 + \frac{2a\sigma_0}{b}. \qquad (6.2)$$

The average tensile stress applied to the sheet is σ_0, a is the half axis length of the ellipse perpendicular to the direction of the stress, and b is the half axis length of the ellipse in a direction parallel to the tensile stress. If the ellipse is very elongated so that it has the appearance of a crack, a will be much greater than b; so a very high concentration of stress can be developed at the tips of the ellipse. If the ellipse (or crack) is oriented parallel to the stress ($b > a$), the concentration of stress is small.

Spheres imbedded in a material act as stress concentrators[20]. The spheres are assumed to have good adhesion to the matrix material. On the equator of a sphere in the direction at right angles to the tensile stress, the stress is concentrated by a factor of about two if the modulus of the matrix material is much greater than the modulus of the material in the spheres. The extreme case would be a foam in which the material in the spheres is a gas. There is no stress concentration if the modulus and Poisson's ratio of the matrix and spheres are the same as long as there is perfect adhesion. If the modulus of the material in the spheres is much greater than that of the continuous phase, there is a reduction of the tensile stress on the equator of the sphere, and in the extreme case, a small compressive stress may even develop.

Embedded elliptical particles oriented with their long axes perpendicular to the direction of stress are more efficient stress concentrators than spheres[16, 17, 37]. However, even with ellipses the stress is generally not concentrated by more than a factor of three.

Griffith's Theory. Griffith[21, 34] developed a theory of the strength of brittle solids based on the assumption that cracks are responsible for materials not attaining their theoretical strengths. The surface energy created by the growth of a crack is assumed to be equal to the product of the surface energy (surface tension) and the new area created by the growth of the cracks. Elastic energy is also stored in a material when an external stress is applied. In order for a crack to increase in length, the rate of decrease of elastic energy within a volume of the material must at least equal the rate at which surface energy is created by the growth of the crack. When this condition is satisfied, Griffith showed that the breaking strength σ_B of a sheet or plate is approximately

$$\sigma_B = (2\gamma E/\pi a)^{\frac{1}{2}}. \tag{6.3}$$

In this equation γ is the surface energy per unit of area, E is Young's modulus, and a is the depth of the crack or half the length of the major axis of the ellipse cut in the sheet. The long axis of the ellipse (crack) is assumed to be perpendicular to the direction of the applied stress. At the tip of the crack, the stress is concentrated by the factor

$$\sigma_m/\sigma = 2\sqrt{a/r} \tag{6.4}$$

where σ_m is the maximum stress at the tip of the crack, σ is the applied stress, a is the length of the crack, and r is the radius of curvature of the tip of the crack.

The cracks or faults, which determine the strength of a material, may not be visible as their lengths may be only of the order of one micron (10^{-3} mm), and their widths may be so small as to approach molecular dimensions.

The strength of a brittle material depends upon its surface energy. For most solids, γ is between 100 and 1000 ergs/cm^2. The value of the surface energy may be decreased by absorbed molecules[34] in the same way that the surface tension of water is decreased by soap molecules absorbed at the air-water interface. Thus, the strength of rigid polymers might be expected to change with the atmosphere in which they are immersed. Absorption may be important in the stress crazing of polystyrene by such materials as hexane[32, 47] or in the stress cracking of polyethylene by aqueous solutions of surface active agents[23].

Another consequence of the flaw theory of strength of materials is that tensile strength should depend upon the length of the test specimen. There is a greater probability of finding a large flaw in a long specimen than in a short one. Thus, the tensile strength should increase as the length of the specimen is decreased. Likewise, the strength of fibers should increase as the diameter decreases. Experimental data generally tend to confirm these predictions. The strength is generally related to the specimen length L_0 or its diameter by an equation of the form

$$\sigma_B = A + B/L_0 \tag{6.5}$$

where A and B are constants.

Orowan[35, 36] and Irwin[25] have extended Griffith's theory to materials which are somewhat tougher than materials originally considered by Griffith. The theory cannot be applied to ductile polymers, but it can be extended to cases where plastic flow takes place in a thin layer on the surface of the growing crack. The fracture still appears to be brittle in nature. In the modified theory the surface energy γ is replaced by p, the plastic work done in the layer around the surface of the crack as it grows. The tensile strength of a material is then given by an equation of the form

$$\sigma_B \doteq (Ep/a)^{\frac{1}{2}}. \tag{6.6}$$

The plastic work or fracture energy p may be many times greater than the surface energy γ. For instance, Benbow and Roesler[3] found that $p = 4.9 \times 10^5$ dynes/cm for polymethyl methacrylate and 2.5×10^6 dynes/cm for polystyrene.

Other Theories. The resistance to fracture of polymers is explained by some theories without applying the concepts of flaws or cracks to weaken a material by stress concentration. Fuerth[19] developed a thermodynamic theory of tensile strength that assumed the material melts in the region where fracture takes place. By his theory the tensile strength σ_B is given by

$$\sigma_B = \Delta H d \left(\frac{1 - 2\nu}{3 - 5\nu}\right) \tag{6.7}$$

where ΔH is the heat of fusion, d is the density, and ν is Poisson's ratio. This theory gives tensile strengths of the correct magnitude for some materials, but it should not apply to amorphous polymers since they have no heat of fusion.

Buchdahl[6, 15] has proposed that the tensile strength of rigid amorphous polymers should be related to their tensile modulus E by

$$\sigma_B \doteq \frac{E}{30}. \tag{6.8}$$

This theory assumes that fracture does not involve the simultaneous rupture of a large number of bonds, but instead the bonds are broken consecutively. When a critical stress is applied, a point of instability develops which then propagates itself through the material until fracture occurs. Since the bonds are broken one at a time, the tensile strength is much less than the elastic modulus, and the concept of flaws is not required to explain the low tensile strength by this theory. Experimentally it is observed that many polymers do have tensile strengths which are roughly 3 per cent of their elastic moduli as predicted. However, this theory is not universally accepted[45].

Theories of the tensile strength of rubbers have been developed by Taylor and Darin[41] and Bueche[9, 10]. These theories assume that the tensile strength is proportional to the number of polymer chains capable of carrying stress that are oriented parallel to the direction of the applied stress. The number of chains per unit of volume is proportional to the reciprocal of the number average molecular weight $\bar{M}_n$ for uncrosslinked polymers and to the reciprocal of the molecular weight between crosslinks M_c for highly crosslinked rubbers.

Taylor and Darin assumed the tensile strength is also proportional to the number of orientable chains and an orientation factor. That is

$$\sigma_B = K(\text{total no. of chains/vol})(\text{fraction orientable chains})(\text{orientation factor}) \qquad (6.9)$$

Chain ends not included in the network structure cannot be oriented on stretching. These flaws in the network structure may be corrected for in the same manner that such flaws are taken into account in the kinetic theory of rubber. The fraction of orientable chains is given by $[1 - 2M_c/(\bar{M}_n + M_c)]$. The orientation factor takes into account that not all chains reach their maximum or breaking elongation at the same time. Most of the total load is carried by a few highly oriented chains. It is these highly extended chains that break first and bring about the fracture of the material since every time a chain breaks, its load is distributed to other chains so that they also eventually break. The tensile strength σ_B predicted by the Taylor-Darin theory is

$$\sigma_B = \frac{K}{\bar{M}_n}\left(\frac{\bar{M}_n}{M_c} - 1\right)[1 - (1 + \delta^2\alpha_B^3)^{-\frac{1}{2}}] \qquad (6.10)$$

where α_B is the extension ratio L/L_0, and K and δ are constants. If experimental values of the elongation to break are substituted into this equation, the tensile strength goes through a maximum, in agreement with experiment, as the degree of crosslinking is varied.

Strength and Moduli of Two-Phase Systems

Polyblends. The types of two-phase systems to be discussed in this section include: (1) polyblends or mixtures of two polymers, (2) polymers containing incompatible plasticizers or insoluble liquids, (3) polymers with rigid inert fillers, (4) polymer foams. In these systems the dispersed phase acts to concentrate the stresses and thereby tends to reduce the apparent tensile strength of the material. The dispersed phase, however, may also bring about improvements in other properties so that the detrimental tensile effects of the dispersed phase or filler are more than compensated for.

Polyblends generally consist of a rubbery polymer dispersed in a rigid polymer. They are important commercially because they can be made to have very great impact strength and ductility compared to the pure rigid polymers. The impact strength of a brittle rigid polymer can easily be increased by a factor of five or ten times by polyblending with the proper rubber. At least three conditions must be fulfilled to produce a high impact polyblend[7, 8, 28, 38]: (1) the glass temperature of the rubber must be well below the test temperature (The glass temperature should be below 0°C for a polyblend to have good impact strength at room temperature.); (2) the rubber must form a second phase and not be soluble in the rigid polymer; (3) the two polymers should be similar enough in solubility behavior that good adhesion between the phases does occur. Although the polymers must not be completely soluble in one another, they should be slightly soluble in one another or have some molecular attraction for each other.

Many of the properties of polyblends can be explained by the simple theory of Merz, Claver, and Baer[28]. The rubber is assumed to be dispersed in the form of small aggregates or balls. When a fracture crack comes to a rubber particle, the rubber becomes stretched as shown successively in Figure 6.1 (A, B, C). Energy is absorbed in stretching the rubber. The energy absorption properties (area under the stress-strain curve) of a good rubber may be much greater than the energy absorption properties of the rigid polymer. Thus, the rubber absorbs much of the energy required to break the polyblend, and the two-phase system can have a high impact strength compared to the rigid polymer alone.

The simple theory given above cannot be entirely correct as relatively ductile materials may be produced in some cases by replacing the rubber phase with an insoluble liquid or with air bubbles as in a foam. Recent work[30, 31, 38] has shown the importance of an entirely different mechanism

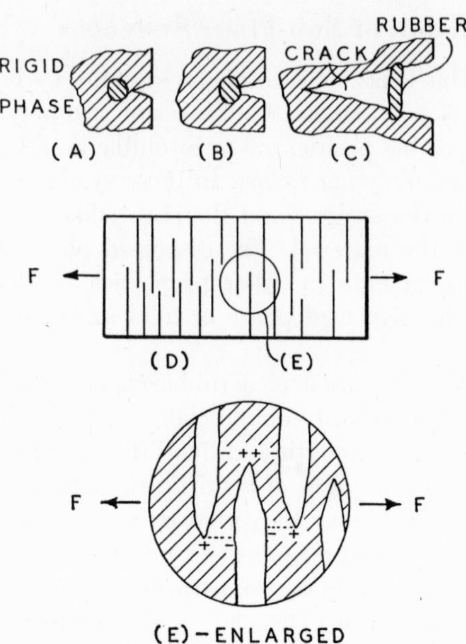

Figure 6.1. Fracture of polyblends. A, B, and C; progressive growth of a crack around a rubber particle. D, crack pattern developed during the breaking of a polyblend. E, enlarged view of three crack tips. As crack tips pass near one another, the stress field changes. Tension develops at points marked +, and compression stresses are developed at points marked −.

for energy absorption in two-phase systems. The particles of the dispersed phase act as stress concentrators and tend to reduce the average tensile strength of the rigid matrix. These stress concentrators introduce many weak points in the material rather than only a few as found with a single-phase polymer. As a result, a great many small cracks develop in the two-phase material when it breaks as shown in Figure 5.1 (D) rather than just a few. In polyblends the cracks are often crooked rather than straight. A single crack can rapidly propagate through a single-phase polymer, bringing about fracture with only a small amount of energy. However, when there are many cracks, their stress fields interfere with one another's reducing the stress at the tips of the cracks. This interaction between cracks may stop the growth of the cracks. As shown in Figure 6.1 (D), most of the cracks do not extend all the way across the specimen, but the tips of two cracks end roughly opposite one another. According to Griffith's theory[21, 34] the energy of fracture should be proportional to the amount of new surface developed by the fracture. Thus, if many cracks are formed during the fracture process, more energy should be absorbed in breaking the material, and this energy is dissipated throughout a larger volume of the material.

If many cracks are formed during the fracture of a material, it is easily seen how the elongation to completely break the material might be much greater than the normal elongation to break. Figure 6.1 (E) is a greatly magnified schematic diagram of three closely spaced cracks. The cracks grow perpendicular to the direction of tensile stress until shortly after their tips pass each other. At this point the stress tending to propagate the crack decreases to the extent that crack growth stops. At the same time the stress pattern changes so that at the tips, a tensile stress develops which is perpendicular to the applied stress. The material between the overlapping ends of the cracks behaves as a beam which becomes bent in flexure. The material does not completely break until the bent beams fracture by developing cracks perpendicular to the cracks first formed. Since long, thin beams can bend a lot before the side under tension is stretched enough to reach the ultimate elongation of the material, the total elongation may be quite large. However, in this type of two-phase systems, the first set of cracks will develop in the neighborhood of the yield point of the material; this yield point will correspond approximately to the ultimate elongation of the pure brittle matrix material.

Still another factor may be important in making some polyblends tough and ductile. The polyblend may have higher mechanical damping than the brittle matrix material, so more heat is generated by any deformation of the polyblend. This heat generation warms up the polymer to near its glass temperature, at which point the brittle polymer becomes very ductile. The dispersed particles of the rubber phase give rise to small regions of high-stress concentration. It is at these stressed points where most of the heat is generated by mechanical damping so that the temperature at these points tends to rise quickly to the softening temperature. The stressed parts of the polyblend, therefore, may deform with a high elongation as a rubbery material rather than as a brittle solid[31].

At the same time that damping is raising the temperature towards the glass transition, the stress is lowering the glass temperature because of the increase in volume as long as Poisson's ratio is less than 0.5. This stress dependence of the glass temperature is another factor which may be of some importance in determining the ductility of some polyblends. The relative importance of these various factors which may affect the toughness and ductility of polyblends has never been determined.

Kerner's Equation. In two-phase systems, if the modulus of the dispersed phase is greater than the modulus of the continuous phase, the modulus of the mixture will be greater than that of the continuous phase or the matrix material. This is the expected behavior when rigid fillers such as inorganic fillers, glass, or metals are added to a polymer. If the modulus of the dispersed filler is lower than that of the matrix, the mixture should have a modulus lower than that of the unfilled material. Examples are polyblends of rubbers in rigid polymers, polymer foams, and insoluble liquids dispersed in a polymer.

Kerner[26] has derived an equation relating the modulus of a filled material to the elastic constants of the matrix and filler, assuming that the dispersed phase is in the shape of spherical particles and that there is perfect adhesion between the two phases. Kerner's equation for the shear modulus is:

$$G_0 = G_1 \left[\frac{\dfrac{v_2 G_2}{(7 - 5\nu_1)G_1 + (8 - 10\nu_1)G_2} + \dfrac{v_1}{15(1 - \nu_1)}}{\dfrac{v_2 G_1}{(7 - 5\nu_1)G_1 + (8 - 10\nu_1)G_2} + \dfrac{v_1}{15(1 - \nu_1)}} \right] \tag{6.11}$$

G_0 is the shear modulus of the two-phase system while G_1 and G_2 are the shear moduli of the continuous phase and the dispersed phase, respectively. The volume fraction of the continuous phase is v_1, while that of the filler if v_2. Poisson's ratio of the material in the continuous phase is ν_1.

TABLE 6.2. SHEAR MODULUS OF A RIGID FOAM.

Volume Fraction of Air, v_2	Modulus, G_0 (Dynes/cm^2)
0	1.00×10^{10}
.10	8.33×10^{9}
.20	6.90×10^{9}
.30	5.65×10^{9}
.40	4.55×10^{9}
.50	3.57×10^{9}
.60	2.71×10^{9}
.70	1.93×10^{9}
.80	1.22×10^{9}
.90	5.82×10^{8}
.95	2.84×10^{8}
1.00	0

Table 6.3. Shear Modulus of Filled Polymers.*

Concentration of Filler (Volume Fraction)	$\frac{\text{G mixture}}{\text{G matrix}}$ when $\frac{\text{G filler}}{\text{G matrix}} = 2$	$\frac{\text{G mixture}}{\text{G matrix}}$ when $\frac{\text{G filler}}{\text{G matrix}} = 10$	$\frac{\text{G mixture}}{\text{G matrix}}$ when $\frac{\text{G filler}}{\text{G matrix}} = 100$
0.00	1.000	1.00	1.00
0.10	1.074	1.22	1.3
0.20	1.152	1.50	1.7
0.30	1.238	1.90	2.4
0.40	1.330	2.44	3.7
0.50	1.426	3.15	6.5
0.60	1.530	4.01	12.3
0.65	1.586	4.48	16.9
0.70	1.636	5.00	21.9
0.75	1.692	5.53	27.6
0.80	1.750	6.12	33.4

* Van der Poel, C., *Rheol. Acta*, **1,** 198 (1958).

In many cases, this complex equation can be greatly simplified. For foams and polyblends of rubbers in a rigid polymer, the modulus of the dispersed phase can be assumed to be zero compared to the modulus of the matrix. Kerner's equation then simplifies to:

$$\frac{1}{G_0} = \frac{1}{G_1}\left[1 + \frac{v_2}{v_1}\left\{\frac{15(1 - \nu_1)}{(7 - 5\nu_1)}\right\}\right]. \tag{6.12}$$

The quantity $15(1 - \nu_1)/(7 - 5\nu_1)$ varies from 2.00 to 1.67 as Poisson's ratio changes from 0.2 to 0.5. Table 6.2 gives the expected modulus of a foam as a function of the volume fraction v_2 of air bubbles for a polymer which has a modulus of 10^{10} dynes/cm^2 in the unfoamed state and a Poisson's ratio of 0.4. This should approximate ideal polystyrene foams.

For rigid fillers which have moduli much greater than that of the polymer, Kerner's equation may be simplified at low volume fractions of filler to

$$G_0 = G_1\left[1 + \frac{v_2}{v_1}\left\{\frac{15(1 - \nu_1)}{8 - 10\nu_1}\right\}\right]. \tag{6.13}$$

The quantity $15(1 - \nu_1)/(8 - 10\nu_1)$ varies between 2.00 and 2.50 as Poisson's ratio changes from 0.2 to 0.5. Van der Poel[44] has developed a different theory of the modulus of filled materials. Table 6.3 gives the relative modulus as a function of the concentration of spherically shaped particles of filler for the case where the matrix material has a Poisson's ratio of 0.5, and the filler has a Poisson's ratio of 0.25. The values in Table 6.3 are in fair agreement with those calculated from Kerner's equation.

References

1. Adams, C. H., Jackson, G. B., and McCarthy, R. A., *Soc. Plastics Eng. J.*, **12**, 13 (March, 1956).
2. ASTM D256-56, "ASTM Standards, 1958," Part 9, p. 284, Philadelphia, Am. Soc. Testing Materials, 1958.
3. Benbow, J. J., and Roesler, F. C., *Proc. Phys. Soc. London*, **70B**, 201 (1957).
4. Bikerman, J. J., "Rheology," Vol. 3, Chap. 13, Eirich, F. R., Ed., New York, Academic Press, Inc., 1960.
5. Bobalek, E. G., and Evans, R. M., *Trans. Soc. Plastics Eng.*, **1**, 93 (1961).
6. Buchdahl, R., *J. Polymer Sci.*, **28**, 239 (1958).
7. Buchdahl, R., and Nielsen, L. E., *J. Appl. Phys.*, **21**, 482 (1950).
8. Buchdahl, R., and Nielsen, L. E., *J. Polymer Sci.*, **15**, 1 (1955).
9. Bueche, F., *J. Polymer Sci.*, **24**, 189 (1957).
10. Bueche, F., *Rubber Chem. and Technol.*, **32**, 1269 (1959).
11. Callendar, L. H., *Brit. Plast.*, **13**, 445, 506 (1942).
12. Carswell, T. S., Telfair, D., and Haslanger, R. U., *Modern Plastics*, **19**, No. 11, 65 (July, 1942).
13. Church, H. F., and Daynes, H. A., *Trans. Inst. Rubber Ind.*, **13**, 96 (1937).
14. Condon, E. U., *Am. J. Phys.*, **22**, 224 (1954).
15. Cottrell, A. H., "Dislocations and Plastic Flow in Crystals," Oxford University Press, 1956.
16. Edwards, R. H., *J. Appl. Mech.*, **18**, A19 (1951).
17. Eshelby, J. D., *Proc. Roy. Soc. London*, **241A**, 376 (1957).
18. Evans, R. M., Nara, H. R., and Bobalek, E. G., *Soc. Plastics Eng. J.*, **16**, 76 (1960).
19. Fuerth, R., *Proc. Roy. Soc. London*, **177A**, 217 (1941).
20. Goodier, J. N., *J. Appl. Mech. Trans., ASME*, **55**, A39 (1933).
21. Griffith, A. A., *Philos. Trans. Roy. Soc. London*, **221A**, 163 (1920).
22. Haward, R. N., "Strength of Plastics and Glass," Chap. 2, London, Cleaver-Hume Press, 1949.
23. Howard, J. B., *Soc. Plastics Eng. J.*, **15**, 397 (1959).
24. Hulse, G., "Physical Properties of Polymers," No. 5, p. 157, Soc. Chem. Ind., London, New York, Macmillan Co., 1959.
25. Irwin, G. R., "Encyclopedia of Physics," Vol. 6, p. 551, Elasticity and Plasticity, Fluegge, S., Ed., Berlin, Springer Verlag, 1958.
26. Kerner, E. H., *Proc. Phys. Soc. London*, **69B**, 808 (1956).
27. Lubin, G., and Winans, R. R., *ASTM Bull.*, No. 128, 13 (May, 1944).
28. Merz, E. H., Claver, G. C., and Baer, M., *J. Polymer Sci.*, **22**, 325 (1956).
29. Morey, D. R., *Ind. Eng. Chem.*, **37**, 255 (1945).
30. Mullins, L., *Rubber Chem. and Tech.*, **33**, 315 (1960).
31. Nielsen, L. E., unpublished data of Monsanto Chemical Co., Springfield, Mass.
32. Nielsen, L. E., *J. Appl. Polymer Sci.*, **1**, 24, (1959).
33. Ohlberg, S. M., Roth, J., and Raff, R. A. V., *J. Appl. Polymer Sci.*, **1**, 114 (1959).
34. Orowan, E., *Rept. Phys. Soc. Progress in Physics*, **12**, 185 (1958).
35. Orowan, E., "Fatigue and Fracture of Metals," (MIT Symposium, June, 1950), New York, John Wiley & Sons, Inc., 1950.
36. Orowan, E., *Welding J.*, N. Y., **34**, No. 3, 157S (March, 1955).

37. Sadowsky, M. A., and Sternberg, E., *J. Appl. Mech.*, **14,** A191 (1947).
38. Schmitt, J. A., and Keskkula, H., *J. Appl. Polymer Sci.*, **3,** 132 (1960).
39. Strella, S., and Gilman, L., *Modern Plastics*, **34,** No. 8, 158 (1957).
40. Strella, S., "High-Speed Testing," Vol. 1, Dietz, A. G. H. and Eirich, F. R., Ed., New York, Interscience Publishers, Inc., 1960.
41. Taylor, G. R., and Darin, S. R., *J. Polymer Sci.*, **17,** 511 (1955).
42. Telfair, D., and Nason, H. K., *Modern Plastics*, **20,** 85 (July, 1943).
43. Telfair, D., and Nason, H. K., *Modern Plastics*, **22,** 145 (Apr., 1945).
44. Van der Poel, C., *Rheol. Acta.*, **1,** 198 (1958).
45. Vincent, P. I., *Polymer*, **1,** 425 (1960).
46. Welch, L. E., and Quackenbos, H. M., Jr., *Trans. Am. Soc. Mech. Eng.*, **68,** 547 (1946).
47. Ziegler, E. E., *Soc. Plastics Eng. J.*, **10,** 12 (Apr., 1954).

Chapter 7

DYNAMIC MECHANICAL TESTING

Significance and Definitions

Dynamic mechanical tests measure the response or deformation of a material to periodic or varying forces. Generally the applied force and the resulting deformation both vary sinusoidally with time. From such tests it is possible to obtain simultaneously an elastic modulus and a mechanical damping. The modulus may be a shear, a Young's, or a bulk modulus depending upon the experimental equipment. The mechanical damping gives the amount of energy dissipated as heat during the deformation of the material.

Perfectly elastic materials have no mechanical damping. Nearly perfectly elastic materials, such as a steel spring or a rubber band, store energy as potential energy when they are stretched. This energy is converted to kinetic energy when the applied load is removed and the material snaps back to its original dimensions. Viscous liquids are examples of the other extreme where all the energy used in deforming them is dissipated into heat. Since liquids can not store potential energy as in a spring, they have high damping. High polymers are examples of viscoelastic materials, which have some of the characteristics of both viscous liquids and elastic springs. Thus, when such materials are deformed, part of the energy is stored as potential energy, and part is dissipated as heat. The energy dissipated as heat manifests itself as mechanical damping.

The field of dynamic mechanical testing is fairly new, but already it has become one of the most important techniques from both the practical and scientific standpoints. Dynamic data are especially important for structural applications of plastics as the variation of properties is easily determined as a function of temperature and frequency (or time). The modulus or stiffness of a material under use conditions is obviously important in any structural application. However, the importance of mechanical damping in the application of plastics is not so well-known or understood. High damping is essential in decreasing the effect of undesirable vibrations, in reducing the amplitude of resonance vibrations to safe limits, and in the damping of acoustic vibrations and noises in all kinds of structures from airplanes to buildings. The effect of damping in reducing noise and vibrations can be dramatically demonstrated by dropping on a hard floor a bar or other plastic object made from two different polymers—one bar made from a low damping polymer (such as polystyrene) and the other made from a high damping polymer (such as cellulose nitrate). The low damping polymer will give out a sharp ringing sound when dropped; the bar made from the high damping polymer will only produce a dull thud when dropped. High damping is also desirable in order to increase the toughness of plastics and to increase the friction of tires against the road surface.

High damping has some undesirable effects, however. For instance, high damping is generally accompanied by a decrease in dimensional stability; in many applications it is important that the polymer retain its size and shape when stresses are applied for long periods of time. High damping in a tire gives rise to an increase in the operating temperature of the tire; this can cause rapid degradation of the rubber and premature failure of the tire.

Dynamic tests have another advantage over most other mechanical tests. Tests may be made over a wide temperature range in a short time, and from the results the over-all performance of the material can be predicted, and many of the other mechanical properties can be estimated.

Dynamic mechanical tests have proved to be extremely useful in studying the structure of high polymers. These mechanical properties are very sensitive to glass transitions, crystallinity, crosslinking, phase separation, and molecular aggregation, and many other features of the molecular structure of polymer chains and the morphology of the bulk materials. Dynamic tests are also useful in analyzing the chemical composition of copolymers and polyblends.

In order to exploit the full potentialities of dynamic mechanical tests, measurements should be made over a wide range of both temperatures and frequencies. However, much useful information may be obtained in a short time by measuring the modulus and damping over a wide temperature range while keeping the frequency constant. If only a single frequency is to be used rather than a range of frequencies, it is generally better to choose a low frequency such as one cycle per second rather than a high frequency such as a million cycles per second. Secondary transitions and other structural features may be more easily detected at the low frequencies, and low-frequency data are more readily related to transitions measured by other techniques.

Instrumentation

Many types of instruments have been used to measure dynamic properties[19, 29, 30, 41, 43, 71, 72, 109, 113, 131]. Until very recently such instruments were not available commercially, so each worker designed and built his own apparatus to fit his own special needs. Some are designed to cover a temperature range at a relatively constant frequency. Many instruments

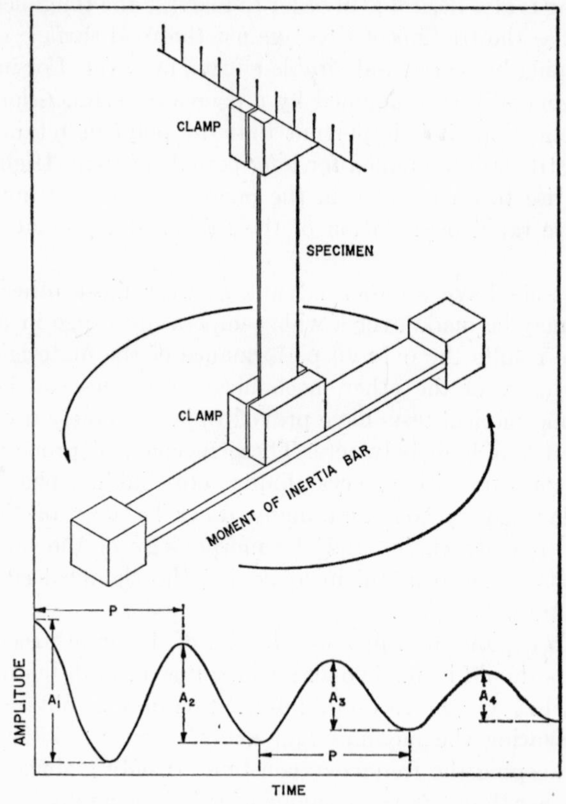

Figure 7.1. Schematic diagram of a torsion pendulum for measuring dynamic shear modulus and damping. A typical damped oscillation curve is illustrated at the bottom of the figure. [*Nielsen, L. E., Soc. Plastics Eng. J.*, **16**, *525* (*1960*)]

cover a range of low frequencies, others cover a high-frequency range. Some instruments measure Young's modulus while others measure shear modulus or even the bulk modulus. Many instruments are useful only with rubbers, others only with rigid polymers, while a few can be used with either rubbery or rigid plastics. Most instruments apply only small forces to the specimen, but a few types of equipment may be used with large forces and elongations[77, 78, 92, 93].

A torsion pendulum such as shown in Figure 7.1 is a simple instrument for measuring the shear modulus and mechanical damping of a polymer[48, 59, 60, 61, 71, 74, 103, 104, 121, 129, 134, 140]. One end of the specimen is rigidly clamped. The other end of the specimen is attached to a moment of inertia member, which is free to oscillate. The oscillations twist and untwist the specimen. The time required for one complete oscillation is the period P. Because of the damping which gradually converts the mechanical energy of the system into heat, the amplitude of the oscillations will decrease with time as shown at the bottom of Figure 7.1. The shear modulus may be calculated from the period—the shorter the period the greater the modulus. The damping, expressed as the logarithmic decrement Δ, is calculated from the rate at which the amplitude of the oscillations decreases; if the damping is high, the oscillations die out rapidly.

For damped torsional harmonic vibrations of rectangular beams, the shear modulus, up to quite high damping ($\Delta \leqq 1$), the shear modulus is given by:

$$G = \frac{5.588 \times 10^{-4} LI}{CD^3\mu P^2} \quad \text{(psi)} \qquad (7.1)$$

or

$$G = \frac{38.54\ LI}{CD^3\mu P^2} \quad \text{(Dynes/cm}^2\text{)} \qquad (7.2)$$

G = shear modulus in pounds per square inch in the first equation and in dynes per square centimeter in the second equation.

In both of the equations

L = length of specimen between the clamps in inches.
C = width of specimen in inches.
D = thickness of specimen in inches.
I = polar moment of inertia of the oscillating system in g cm^2.
P = period of oscillations in seconds.
μ = a shape factor depending upon the ratio of the width to thickness of the specimen. Values are given in Table 1.3.

The shear modulus for specimens with a circular cross section is given by:

$$G = \frac{2.22 \times 10^{-5} LI}{r^4 P^2} \quad \text{(psi)} \qquad (7.3)$$

where r is the radius of the specimen in inches.

At very high damping ($\Delta > 1$) the equation used to calculate the modulus depends upon the mechanism of the damping and the frequency dependence of the dynamic properties. At high damping, an equation of the form

$$G = \frac{I}{KP^2}(4\pi^2 + \Delta^2) \qquad (7.4)$$

is generally used to calculate the shear modulus. In this equation, K is a constant dependent upon the geometry of the test specimen. For specimens of rectangular cross section $K = CD^3\mu/16L$, while for specimens with a circular cross section $K = \pi r^4/2L$. However, this equation is not only more complex than the equations given for lower damping, but it is also of doubtful validity. For these reasons it appears best to use the simpler equations even at very high damping although it must be realized that some error results in the value of the modulus.

The logarithmic decrement Δ is calculated from the logarithm (to the base e) of the ratio of the amplitudes of two successive oscillations:

$$\Delta = \ln\frac{A_1}{A_2} = \ln\frac{A_2}{A_3} = \cdots \qquad (7.5)$$

where A_1 is the amplitude of the first oscillation and A_2 is the amplitude of the second oscillation as shown at the bottom of Figure 7.1.

The above equations for damping and shear modulus are accurate only if there is no tension on the specimen. The correct period to use for calculating the modulus may be found by making measurements with several tensile loads. A plot of $1/P^2$ against the tensile load extrapolated to zero load gives the correct period. The correct period may also be calculated for specimens with a rectangular cross section using only a single load by the use of the following equation when C/D is greater than three[85]:

$$G' = \frac{64\pi^2 IL}{CD^3\mu P^2} - \frac{WgC}{4D^3[1 - 0.63D/C]} \qquad (7.6)$$

where W is the tensile load on the specimen, and g is the acceleration of gravity. The damping also decreases as the tensile load increases. There is no well-accepted method of correcting the damping values, so it is desir-

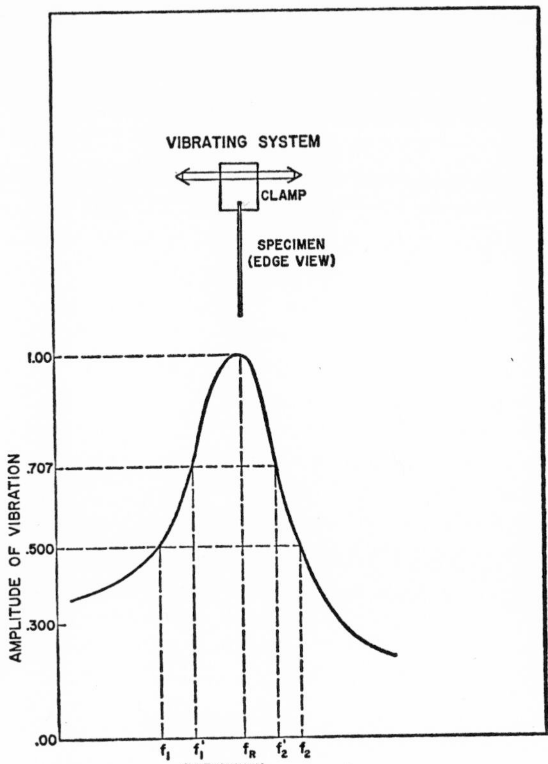

Figure 7.2. Typical amplitude-frequency curve obtained with a vibrating reed apparatus. [*Nielsen, L. E., Soc. Plastics Eng. J.*, **16,** *525* (*1960*)]

able to keep the load on the specimen so near zero that no corrections need to be applied. Kuhn and Kuenzle[74] and Nielsen[103] have described counter-balanced systems which do this.

The vibrating reed[3, 22, 56, 100, 103, 113, 125, 136] is a widely used instrument for measuring Young's modulus and damping. This apparatus is shown schematically in Figure 7.2. The specimen in the form of a plastic strip or reed is clamped at one end and forced to vibrate transversely. The vibrator to which the clamp is attached may be a phonograph cutting head or an electromagnetic vibrator similar to a loudspeaker. The vibrator is driven by a variable frequency oscillator. As the frequency of the vibrations is changed, the natural resonance of the reed will be reached, and the amplitude of the free end of the reed will go through a maximum. The change of amplitude of the free end of the reed with frequency of exciting vibration is shown in Figure 7.2. The amplitude of the vibrations may be measured with a micrometer eyepiece in a microscope, by a capacitance pickup[100], or by a variable reluctance pickup[136].

Young's modulus is calculated from

$$E = \frac{38.24\, dL^4}{D^2} f_r^2 \tag{7.7}$$

E = Young's modulus in dynes/cm^2. (To convert to psi, multiply answer by 1.45×10^{-5}.)
d = density of plastic specimen in g/cc.
L = free length of reed in centimeters.
D = thickness of specimen in centimeters.
f_r = resonance frequency in cycles per second.

A damping term may be calculated from the sharpness of the resonance peak in either of two ways by the equations

$$\text{Half width} = \frac{f_2 - f_1}{f_r} \tag{7.8}$$

$$\text{Half power width} = \frac{f_2' - f_1'}{f_r} \tag{7.9}$$

where as shown in Figure 7.2, f_1 and f_2 are the frequencies at which the amplitude is one-half the maximum amplitude at resonance, and f_1' and f_2' are the frequencies at which the amplitude is $(1/\sqrt{2})$ or 0.707 of the maximum amplitude. In a later section it will be shown how these damping terms are related to the logarithmic decrement and to other ways of specifying damping. The damping may be calculated in still another way for a vibrating reed by measuring the ratio of the amplitudes of the clamped and

TABLE 7.1. DAMPING E''/E' FROM THE RATIO M OF THE AMPLITUDES OF THE FREE AND FIX ENDS OF A VIBRATING REED.

Amplitude Ratio M	Damping E''/E'
5	0.251
10	0.140
20	0.074
50	0.031
100	0.0155

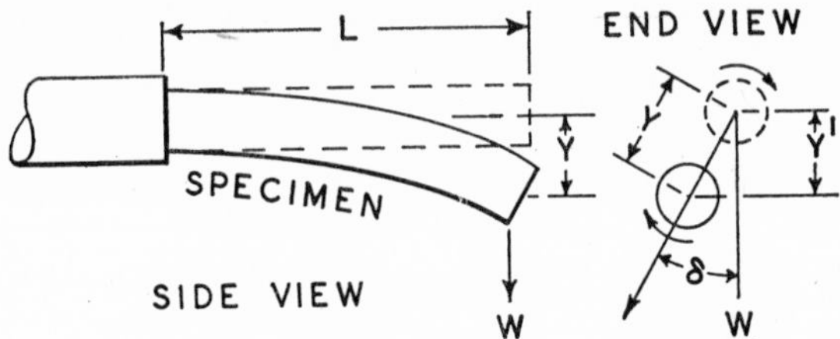

Figure 7.3. Rotating beam dynamic testing apparatus.

free ends of the reed at the resonance frequency. The damping is given by [136]:

$$\text{Damping} = \frac{E''}{E'} \doteq \frac{F}{A_0^3}\left[\frac{16A_0^2 - F^2}{16}\right] \tag{7.10}$$

where

$$F = \frac{-5.478 + 2\sqrt{7.502 + 6.15M^2}}{1.689M^2} \tag{7.11}$$

M is the ratio the amplitudes of the free end of the reed to the fixed or clamped end of the reed, and $A_0 = 1.875$. The significance of the damping term E''/E' will be discussed later in this section and in the next section. Values of E''/E' for various values of the amplitude ratio M are given in Table 7.1. Unless this latter method is used, one must be sure that the amplitude of the vibrator remains nearly constant over the frequency range between f_1 and f_2.

Other forced vibration instruments similar in principle to the vibrating reed use freely supported bars instead of a cantilever beam[69].

A third type of instrument may be illustrated by the rotating beam apparatus[13, 68, 92, 93] of Figure 7.3. This is a nonresonance, forced vibration apparatus in which the specimen in the form of a rod with a circular cross section is clamped at one end and rotated as in the chuck of a lathe. A transverse force is applied to the free end of the rod to bend it away from the center of rotation. However, the combination of the rotation of the rod and the transverse force causes the free end of the rod to deflect in a direction different from the direction of the applied force. The mechanical damping is determined by the tangent of the angle between the applied force and the actual direction of deflection from the position with no load. Young's modulus is determined from the amount of deflection produced by the applied load.

$$E = \frac{416.3L^3W}{r^4Y} \tag{7.12}$$

$$\text{Damping} = \tan \delta \tag{7.13}$$

where

E = Young's modulus in dynes/cm^2;
L = length of rod in cm;
r = radius of rod in cm;
W = load applied to free end of rod in grams;
Y = deflection in cm of free end of rod when a weight W grams is applied;
δ = angle between the direction of applied transverse force and the observed direction of the deflection as seen from the end of the specimen looking along the axis of rotation.

There are many other types of forced vibration, nonresonance instruments besides the rotating beam apparatus. Such instruments measure the amplitude of both the oscillating stress and strain and the phase angle between the stress and strain. Some of these instruments are primarily mechanical[27, 36, 42, 51, 66, 115, 120, 146] while transducer instruments make use

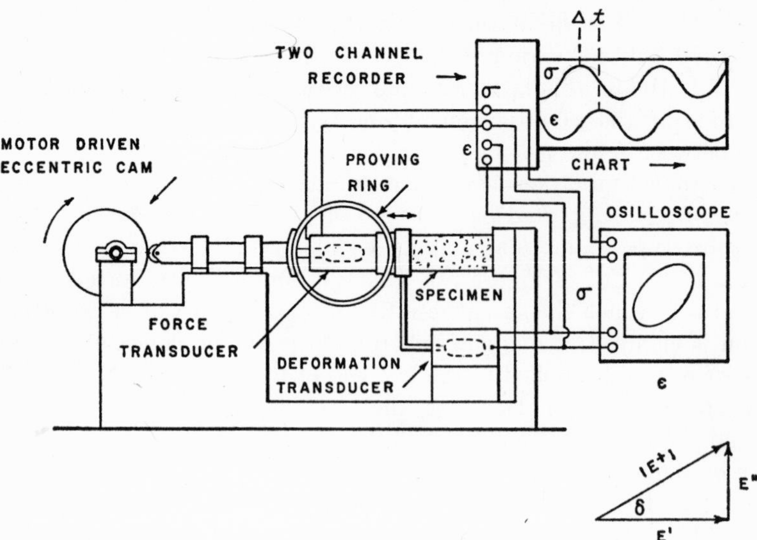

Figure 7.4. Schematic diagram of a nonresonance, forced vibration apparatus for low-frequency measurements.

of electrical analog measurements from which the complex dynamic properties can be calculated[33, 75, 86, 89, 133].

Figure 7.4 illustrates schematically one of the simplest low-frequency nonresonance, forced vibration instruments. A motor-driven eccentric cam converts the rotation of the motor's shaft into an oscillatory motion for deforming the specimen in a sinusoidal manner. The amplitude of the deformation is measured by a transducer such as a differential transformer or by an optical system with mirrors. The magnitude of the load on the specimen is measured by another transducer system such as a proving ring and a differential transformer or by means of strain gages on a beam whose deformation is kept very small compared to the deformation of the specimen. The electrical outputs of the deformation and load transducers can be recorded independently on a two-channel recorder, or the electrical outputs can be fed to the inputs of an X-Y recorder or oscilloscope to give a hysteresis loop whose area is proportional to the damping or energy dissipated in the specimen. The modulus can be calculated from the slope of the hysteresis ellipse after the apparatus has been calibrated. If the electrical outputs of the transducers are recorded on the chart of a two-channel recorder, the modulus can be calculated from the ratio of the magnitudes of the maximum load and deformation while the damping can be calculated from the phase shift between the load and deformation curves. Once the load transducer has been calibrated to measure stress, and the deformation transducer calibrated to measure deformation, the complex modulus E^* is given by the ratio of the maximum stress to the maximum strain. For the case of tensile deformations:

$$| E^* | = \sqrt{E'^2 + E''^2} = \frac{\sigma_{max}}{\epsilon_{max}} \tag{7.14}$$

$$E' = | E^* | \cos \delta \tag{7.15}$$

$$E'' = | E^* | \sin \delta \tag{7.16}$$

$$\frac{E''}{E'} = \tan \delta \tag{7.17}$$

E' is the real part of the modulus; for low or medium damping it is the same as the usual Young's modulus. E'' is the imaginary part of the modulus; E'' is a damping term known as the loss modulus. The angle δ is the phase angle between the stress and the strain. This phase angle δ is equal to angular frequency ω times the shift in time, Δt, of the peak values of the stress and strain curves as measured on the recorder chart, that is $\delta = \omega\Delta t$.

In the frequency range from 25 to 5000 cycles per second, nonresonance instruments generally use electromagnetic vibrators, similar to loudspeakers, to deform the specimens. The stress and strain are not measured directly, but they are calculated indirectly from measurements of the complex electrical currents flowing in the driving coils. The Fitzgerald apparatus[33] is one such versatile apparatus, which is commercially available.

At low and medium frequencies, say below about 10,000 cycles per second, the wavelength of the oscillations is much greater than the specimen dimensions, and inertial effects within the specimen can be neglected. At higher frequencies the dynamic mechanical properties can be measured by wave propagation methods where the wavelength is much less than the size of the specimen[2, 23, 30, 113, 150]. The dynamic moduli are calculated from the velocity of the sound wave in the polymer, and the damping is measured from the attenuation of the vibrations as the sound wave travels along the length of the specimen. If a sound wave is transmitted longitudinally along a long thin strip or along a fiber, the dynamic properties are given by

$$E' = \frac{d\omega^2 v^2(\omega^2 - \alpha^2 v^2)}{(\omega^2 + \alpha^2 v^2)^2} \tag{7.18}$$

$$\frac{E''}{E'} = \frac{4\pi\alpha\lambda}{4\pi^2 - \alpha^2\lambda^2}. \tag{7.19}$$

The density of the polymer is d. The velocity of the wave along the strip is v, λ is the wavelength of the sound wave in the strip, and ω is the angular frequency of the wave. The attenuation α, in nepers per centimeter, is defined by

$$Y = Y_0 e^{-\alpha x} e^{i(\omega t - 2\pi x/\lambda)} \tag{7.20}$$

where Y is the deformation at any point x along the strip. This equation shows that the intensity of the wave decreases as it travels along the plastic strip or fiber. Equations 7.18 and 7.19 can be rewritten in various forms by making use of the equation

$$v = f\lambda = \frac{\omega\lambda}{2\pi} \tag{7.21}$$

where f is the frequency in cycles per second.

Many other types of dynamic test instruments have been described in the literature. Some designed specifically for rubbers may be found in the following references[20, 36, 43, 44, 98, 115, 126, 146]. A few instruments for fibers and filaments include[23, 27, 41, 82, 122]. An instrument which covers an unusually great frequency range has been described by Philippoff[42, 120]. Some of the more interesting forced vibration instruments not previously discussed include[51, 80, 86, 97, 115, 133].

Each type of dynamic test instrument has its advantages and disadvantages. The torsion pendulum may be used over the entire modulus range normally encountered with polymers—from 10^5 to 10^{11} dynes per square centimeter. It is also useful over the entire range of damping from logarithmic decrements less than 0.01 to over 5. If the dynamic mechanical properties are studied as a function of temperature, it is difficult to keep the frequency approximately constant as the temperature is changed. The torsion pendulum is also restricted to a relatively narrow frequency range—normally between 0.01 and 10 cycles per second.

The vibrating reed apparatus covers the range from roughly 10 to 1000 cycles per second. Since it is a resonance type of instrument, it is difficult to measure dynamic properties over a temperature range keeping the frequency constant. Likewise, with a single specimen, it is difficult to study the effect of frequency, keeping the temperature constant. The vibrating reed apparatus is well suited for rigid polymers, can be used with rubbers, but generally can not be used in the transition regions where the damping is high. This type of instrument may be used to study the effects of molecular orientation; the tensile forces may be applied either parallel or perpendicular to the direction of orientation.

The rotating beam apparatus is admirably suited to study the dynamic mechanical behavior of polymers as a function of frequency over the range from about 10^{-4} to 100 cycles per second. Rigid polymers are most easily studied; measurements become very difficult in the softening range of polymers. This method also has the disadvantage, as normally used, of requiring relatively large amounts of polymer for a test specimen, and the specimens must be carefully prepared. The sensitivity to changes in damping is poor in materials of very low damping.

Forced vibration, nonresonance instruments are best for tests made over a frequency range at constant temperature or for tests over a temperature range at constant frequency. However, these instruments are generally complex and comparatively difficult to operate, and the calculation required to obtain the dynamic properties are relatively complicated and time-consuming. In addition, most such instruments will measure only rubbers or rigid polymers but not both unless the specimen size or shape is changed. This class of instruments is capable of covering a very wide frequency range—from roughly 10^{-5} to 10^4 cycles per second although no single piece of apparatus can cover this complete range.

Relations Between Damping Terms

We have seen how each type of dynamic mechanical test gives rise to a damping term which is defined differently for each type of test. In order to compare data obtained by different methods, it is necessary to convert all data to a common basis. The dynamic mechanical properties may all be interrelated through the use of complex moduli[30]. In the case of shear, the dynamic moduli are defined by

$$G^* = G' + iG'' \tag{7.22}$$

while the complex Young's moduli are defined by

$$E^* = E' + iE'' \tag{7.23}$$

G^* and E^* are the complex moduli. G' and E' are the real parts of the shear and Young's moduli, respectively. The quantity i is equal to $\sqrt{-1}$, so G'' and E'' are the imaginary parts of the moduli. If the damping is very small, $G' = G$ and $E' = E$, so the real parts of the moduli are the same as what we have been used to calling elastic moduli. In general,

$$G = |G^*| = \sqrt{(G')^2 + (G'')^2} \tag{7.24}$$

and

$$E = |E^*| = \sqrt{(E')^2 + (E'')^2} \tag{7.25}$$

The imaginary parts of the moduli are damping terms which determine the dissipation of energy into heat when a material is deformed. G'' and E'' are often called the loss moduli. A very useful damping term, called the dissipation factor or loss tangent, is defined as G''/G' or E''/E'. The dissipation factor is proportional to the ratio of energy dissipated per cycle to the maximum potential energy stored during a cycle.

Most other damping terms may be expressed in terms of the dissipation factor. For instance, the logarithmic decrement Δ is given approximately by

$$\Delta \doteq \pi \frac{G''}{G'}. \tag{7.26}$$

If it is assumed that the dynamic properties are nearly independent of frequency, then the equation relating logarithmic decrement and dissipation factor is

$$\frac{G''}{G'} = \frac{4\pi\Delta}{4\pi^2 - \Delta^2}. \tag{7.27}$$

If it is assumed that the damping is viscous in nature and that the viscosity is a constant independent of frequency, then the proper equation is

$$\frac{G''}{G'} = \frac{4\pi\Delta}{4\pi^2 + \Delta^2} \tag{7.28}$$

Since in general the assumptions used in deriving both of these last two equations are not valid, it appears that the simple approximate equation might as well be used in nearly all cases. The equation $\Delta = \pi G''/G'$ agrees with the more complex equations to better than 3 per cent if the logarithmic decrement is less than unity, which it usually is, except in major transition regions.

The half width of a resonance peak is related to the dissipation factor by

$$\frac{f_2 - f_1}{f_r} \doteq \sqrt{3}\,\frac{E''}{E'} \tag{7.29}$$

and

$$\frac{f_2' - f_1'}{f_r} \doteq \frac{E''}{E'} \tag{7.30}$$

Horio and Onogi[55] give a more exact relationship between the dissipation factor and the half power width of the resonance peak:

$$\frac{E''}{E'} = \frac{f_2' - f_1'}{f_r}\left[1 - \frac{11}{32}\left(\frac{f_2' - f_1'}{f_r}\right)\right] \tag{7.31}$$

For the rotating beam apparatus and some other forced vibration, non-resonance instruments

$$\tan\delta = \frac{E''}{E'} = Q^{-1} \tag{7.32}$$

Other damping terms which may be found in the literature include the specific damping capacity ψ, which is defined as ratio of the energy dissipated per cycle to the maximum elastic strain energy stored during the cycle:

$$\psi = \frac{2\pi E''}{E'} \tag{7.33}$$

or

$$\psi = \frac{2\pi G''}{G'} \doteq 2\Delta \tag{7.34}$$

Resilience is a term that has often been used as an inverse measure of damping. Unfortunately, there are several different definitions of this quantity in the literature. One of the definitions of resilience, R_1, is that it is the ratio of the square of two successive amplitudes in a damped free vibration experiment. It can be shown that

$$R_1 = e^{-2\Delta} \doteq 1 - 2\Delta + \cdots \tag{7.35}$$

Another definition of resilience, R_2, is

$$R_2 = 1 - \psi \doteq 1 - 2\Delta \tag{7.36}$$

For small damping, the two definitions of resilience are equivalent.

In some types of dynamic mechanical tests, a hysteresis loop is obtained in which the horizontal direction corresponds to strain while the vertical direction corresponds to stress. The area of the hysteresis loop is equal to the energy dissipated into heat per cycle. This heat energy H per unit of volume is

$$H = \pi E'' \epsilon_0^2 \tag{7.37}$$

where ϵ_0 is the maximum amplitude of strain during the course of a cycle, assuming Hooke's law is valid.

High-frequency dynamic measurements involving traveling waves often express the damping in terms of decibels or in terms of nepers. Decibels of damping DB are given by:

$$DB = 20 \log_{10} \left(\frac{A_1}{A_2} \right) = \frac{20\Delta}{2.303} \tag{7.38}$$

where A_1 and A_2 are the amplitudes of successive peaks along the traveling wave. There are 8.686 decibels to a neper.

Dynamic mechanical properties may be expressed in terms of complex viscosities rather than by complex moduli. Complex viscosities are defined by:

$$\eta^* = \eta' - i\eta'' \tag{7.39}$$

The complex viscosities are related to complex moduli by such equations as:

$$G' = \omega\eta'' \tag{7.40}$$

$$G'' = \omega\eta' \tag{7.41}$$

where ω is the frequency of oscillation in radians per second, that is, $\omega = 2\pi f$. As expected, the real part of the viscosity η' is related to the imaginary or loss modulus G''.

Dynamic properties are often expressed in terms of complex compliances, $J^* = J' - iJ''$, rather than as moduli. The moduli and compliances are related by the equations:

$$J' = \frac{G'}{G^2} \qquad G' = \frac{J'}{J^2} \tag{7.42}$$

$$\frac{G''}{G'} = \frac{J''}{J'} \tag{7.43}$$

where

$$G^2 = G'^2 + G''^2 \qquad \text{and} \qquad J^2 = J'^2 + J''^2 \tag{7.44}$$

If the dynamic properties are measured by a tensile stress, the damping is expressed as E''/E', while if the properties are measured by an instrument which produces a shearing stress, the damping is given as G''/G'. For a given polymer is there any relation between E''/E' and G''/G'? Fortunately, there is a very simple relation:

$$\frac{E''}{E'} \doteq \frac{G''}{G'} \tag{7.45}$$

A more exact relation is[16, 135]:

$$\frac{E''}{E'} \doteq \frac{G''}{G'}\left[\frac{1}{1 + \frac{G'}{3B}[1 + (G''/G')^2]}\right] \tag{7.46}$$

where B is the bulk modulus of the material. Since G'/B and G''/G' are both generally much less than 1.0, the approximate equation (7.42) holds very well in general.

Models and Viscoelastic Theory

A Maxwell unit, consisting of a spring and a dashpot in series, may be used to illustrate some aspects of the dynamic behavior of viscoelastic materials. As shown in the chapter on stress relaxation, the equation of motion of a Maxwell unit is

$$\frac{d\epsilon}{dt} = \frac{1}{E}\frac{d\sigma}{dt} + \frac{\sigma}{\tau E} \tag{7.47}$$

where

$$\tau = \eta/E. \tag{7.48}$$

This equation can be solved (see Appendix B at end of chapter) to give:

$$E' = \frac{\omega^2\tau^2 E}{1 + \omega^2\tau^2} \tag{7.49}$$

$$E'' = \frac{\omega\tau E}{1 + \omega^2\tau^2} \tag{7.50}$$

where ω is the frequency in radians per second.

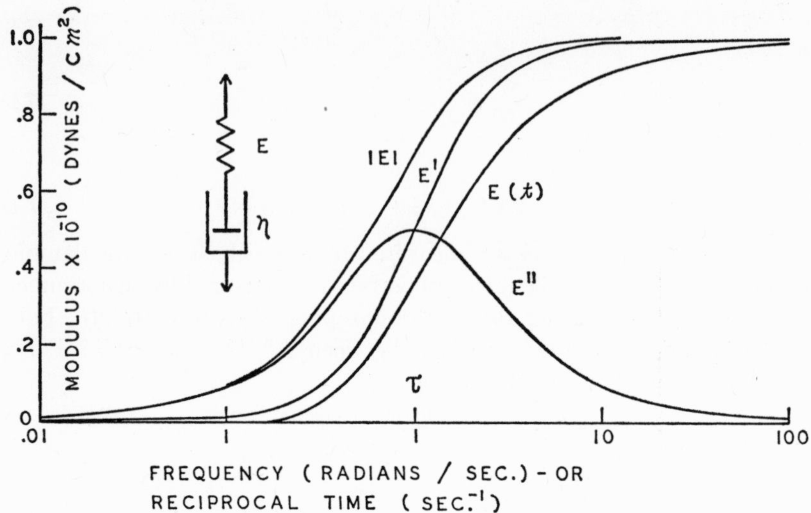

Figure 7.5. Dynamic behavior of a Maxwell unit as a function of frequency. Their relaxation time is one second. The stress-relaxation modulus $E(t)$ of the same model is given for comparison.

The dynamic modulus and damping of a Maxwell unit as a function of frequency are shown in Figure 7.5. In this example, the modulus E of the spring and the viscosity η of the dashpot are both 10^{10}; so the relaxation time τ is one second. At low frequencies where most of the deformation comes from the dashpot, the dynamic modulus E' is very low. At very high frequencies there is not enough time for any appreciable flow to occur in the dashpot during the time of a cycle of oscillation. The motion at high frequencies is due to the stretching of the spring, so the dynamic modulus is equal to the modulus of the spring. At intermediate frequencies where the time for an oscillation is roughly equal to the relaxation time, motion of both the spring and dashpot take place under the action of an applied force. In this frequency range, the dynamic modulus increases rapidly with frequency.

The loss modulus E'' approaches zero at both high and low frequencies. Energy dissipation comes from motion of the dashpot. At high frequencies, a cycle of oscillation takes so little time that no motion of the dashpot can occur. At low frequencies, there is a lot of motion of the dashpot, but the motion is so slow that the rate of shear in the dashpot is small. Equations 7.37 and 7.41 of the previous section show that viscous damping leads to the dissipation of large amounts of energy only when the amount of motion (total shear) and the rate of shear (frequency) are both large. At intermediate frequencies, both the rate of shear and the motion of the dashpot are large, so the dissipation of energy is large. The loss modulus goes through a maximum when $\omega = 1/\tau$.

The absolute value of the modulus $|E|$ is defined as

$$|E| = \sqrt{(E')^2 + (E'')^2} \tag{7.51}$$

$|E|$ is also plotted in Figure 7.5. At low frequencies the absolute value of the modulus is equal to E'' while at high frequencies it equals E'.

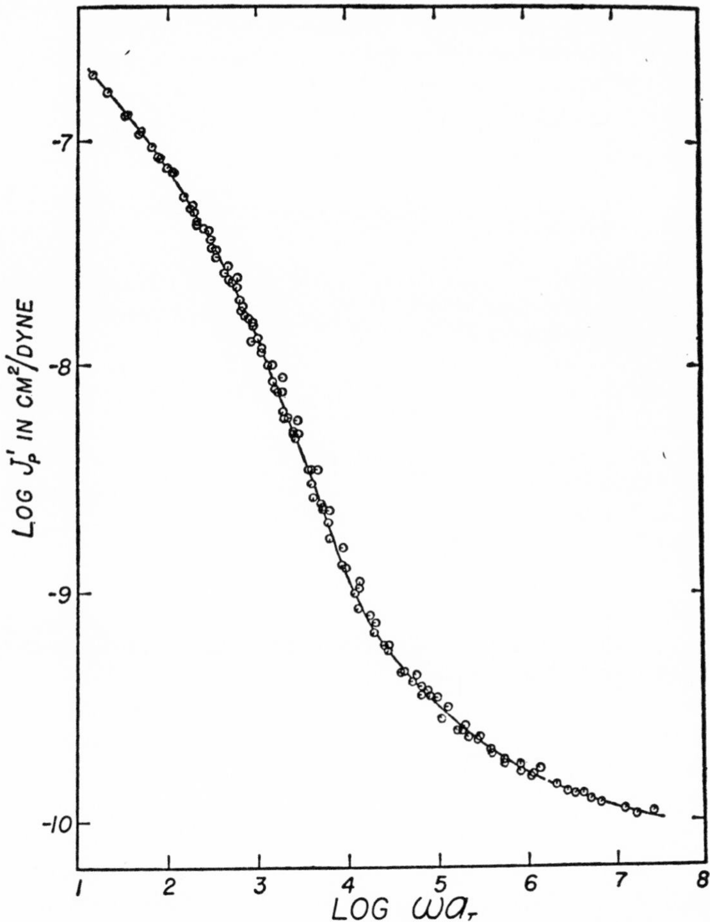

Figure 7.6. Master curve for the real part of the complex compliance of polyvinyl acetate plotted logarithmically against reduced frequency. Reference temperature is 75°C. [*Williams, M. L., and Ferry, J. D., J. Colloid Sci.*, **9**, *479 (1954)*]

The dissipation factor E''/E' of a Maxwell unit is equal to $1/\omega\tau$, so that E''/E' increases continuously as the frequency decreases. Such behavior is characteristic of uncrosslinked rubbers. More complex models predict a maximum in the dissipation factor as well as in the loss modulus; polymers show a similar behavior near their glass temperatures if the frequency is low or at higher temperatures if the frequency is in the range of hundreds or thousands of cycles per second.

The stress relaxation modulus $E(t)$ of a Maxwell unit is also plotted in Figure 7.5. The stress relaxation modulus is lower than the dynamic mod-

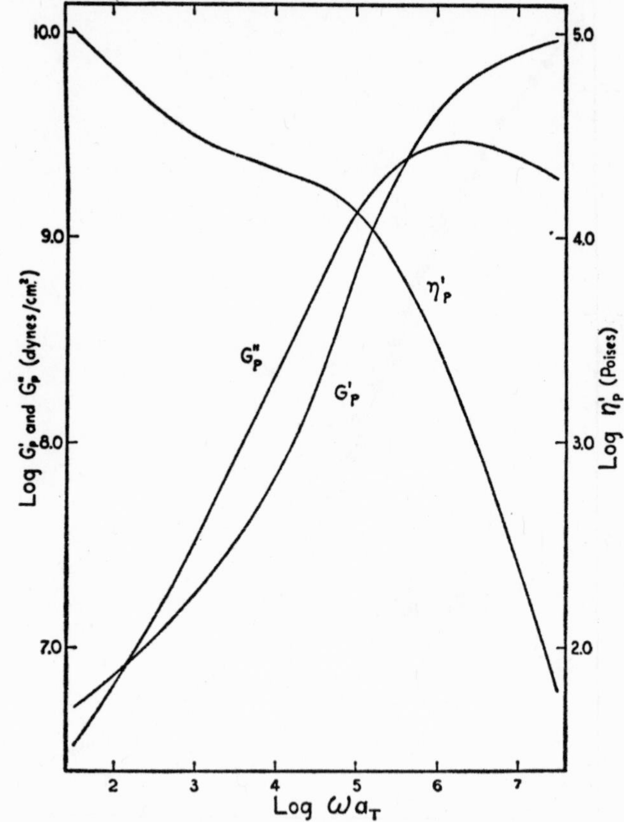

Figure 7.7. Master curves for the real and imaginary parts of the complex shear modulus and the real part of the viscosity of polyvinyl acetate, reduced to 75°C., plotted logarithmically against reduced frequency. [*Williams, M. L., and Ferry, J. D., J. Colloid Sci.*., **99,** *479 (1954)*]

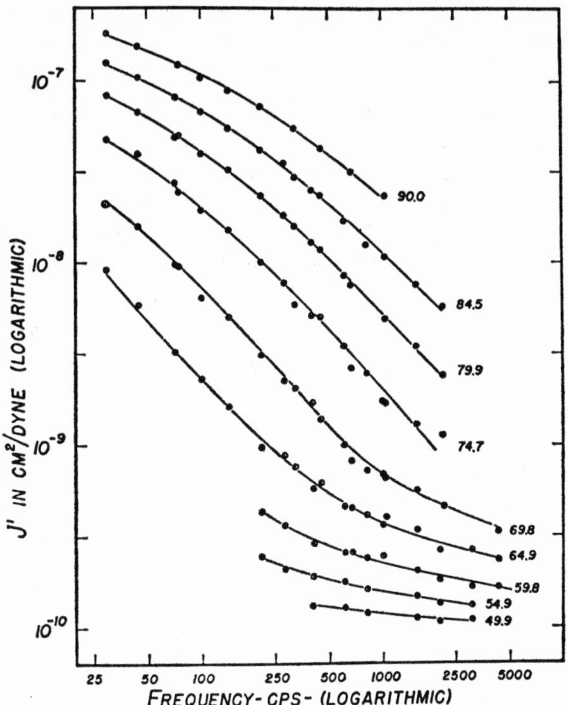

Figure 7.8. Variation of the real part of the dynamic shear compliance J' with frequency for polyvinyl acetate at the nine temperatures indicated on the curves. [*Williams, M. L., and Ferry, J. D., J. Colloid Sci.*, **9**, *479* (*1954*)]

ulus when the two are compared on a frequency scale in which time is considered as a reciprocal frequency, that is, $\omega = 1/t$. As indicated in Chapter 4, the stress-relaxation modulus is given by

$$E(t) = Ee^{-t}/\tau = Ee^{\frac{-1}{\omega\tau}}. \tag{7.52}$$

The dynamic mechanical properties of an actual polymer as a function of frequency are illustrated in Figures 7.6 and 7.7[148]. The frequency range covered is too great to be studied by experiments at a constant temperature. Curves such as those shown in Figures 7.6 and 7.7 are master curves obtained by the shifting of experimental curves, like those shown in Figures 7.8 and 7.9, obtained at different temperatures. The technique uses the same type of time-temperature superposition principle discussed previously for making master curves from stress-relaxation data[30, 119, 139]. However, in the case of dynamic mechanical studies, both the modulus G' and loss modulus G'' curves (or the elastic compliance J' and loss compliance J'' curves) are shifted so that two master curves are made. The Williams-Landel-Ferry[149] treatment works for the reduction of dynamic data just as well as it does for stress-relaxation data. In Figures 7.6 and 7.7 the abscissa scale, log ωA_T, is the frequency scale at the reference temperature (75°C) where A_T is one. At other temperatures the frequency scale is shifted by the reduced frequency factor A_T given in Table 7.2.

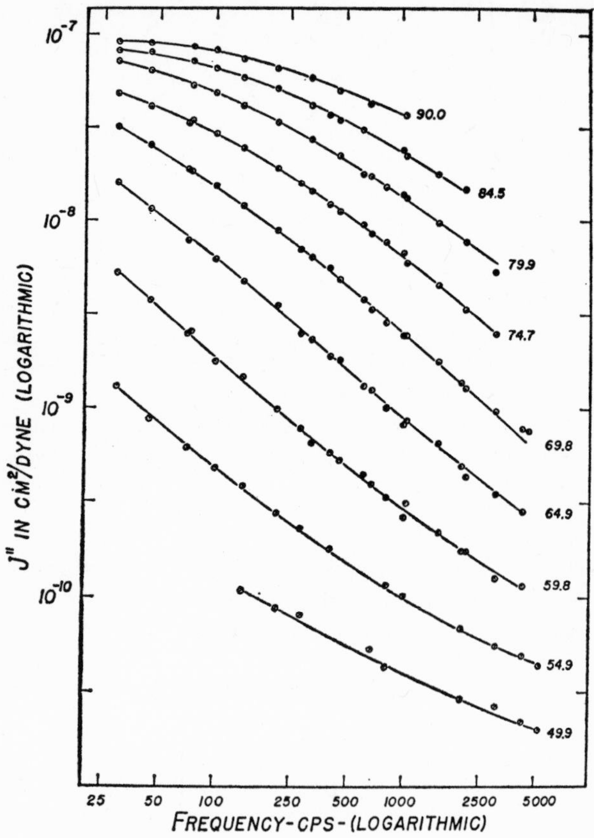

Figure 7.9. Variation of the dynamic loss compliance J'' with frequency for polyvinyl acetate at nine temperatures as indicated. [*Williams, M. L., and Ferry, J. D., J. Colloiid Sci.*, **9**, *479 (1954)*]

TABLE 7.2. TEMPERATURE-FREQUENCY SHIFT FACTOR A_T FOR POLYVINYL ACETATE REDUCED TO A STANDARD TEMPERATURE OF 75°C.*

Temperature (°C)	Shift Factor A_T
49.9	3.12
54.9	2.34
59.8	1.64
64.9	1.02
69.8	0.50
74.7	0.02
79.9	−0.39
84.5	−0.75
90.0	−1.12

* From Williams, M. L. and Ferry, J. D., *J. Colloid Sci.*, **9**, 479 (1954).

Figures 7.6 and 7.7 illustrate the general behavior of nearly all polymers. At very low frequencies the modulus is low, but it gradually increases to a plateau as the frequency increases by many decades. In the region where the modulus changes most rapidly, the loss modulus and the dissipation factor both go through a maximum. Viscous flow becomes important in uncrosslinked polymers at low frequencies; under these conditions, the dissipation factor increases as the frequency decreases. The dynamic viscosity η' is also shown in Figure 7.7. It is characteristic of the dynamic viscosity to decrease as the frequency increases. In high polymers the viscosity is not Newtonian in behavior except at very low frequencies.

Polymers have a broad distribution of relaxation or retardation times. These distributions may be calculated from dynamic mechanical data in a manner very similar to the way they are calculated from creep or stress-relaxation data. The distribution of relaxation times, denoted by $H(\ln\,\omega)$ may be calculated from either the G' or G'' (or E' or E'') master curves[30, 81, 135]. If the data are very accurate, the same distributions should be obtained from either of the two master curves.

The loss factor $G''(\ln\,\omega)$ master curve gives the first approximation to the distribution of relaxation times, $H(\ln\,\omega)$:

$$H(\ln \omega) \doteq \frac{2}{\pi} G''(\ln \omega) \tag{7.53}$$

The distribution of relaxation times may also be approximated from the slope of the dynamic modulus curve, plotted on a logarithmic scale, by:

$$H(\ln \omega) \doteq \frac{dG'(\ln \omega)}{d \ln \omega} \tag{7.54}$$

A better approximation to the distribution may be obtained by using the following equation:

$$H(\ln \omega) \doteq \frac{2}{\pi} G''(\ln \omega) - \frac{d^2G''(\ln \omega)}{d(\ln \omega)^2} \tag{7.55}$$

A number of other ways of calculating distributions of relaxation times have been suggested[30, 135], but they are generally more complex and difficult to use. However, where the effort has been made to obtain very accurate data over a wide frequency range, the more exact methods of calculating the distribution of relaxation times is justified.

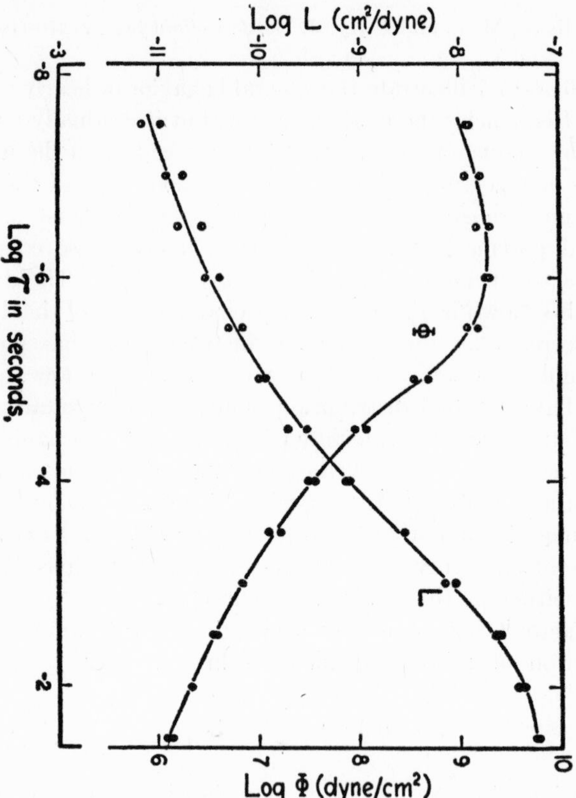

Figure 7.10. Distribution of relaxation times ϕ and distribution of retardation times L as a function of reduced frequency for polyvinyl acetate. Reference temperature is 75°C. [*Williams, M. L., and Ferry, J. D., J. Colloid Sci.*, **9**, *479* (*1954*)]

If the dynamic data are expressed as compliance $J(\ln \omega)$ as a function of frequency, the logarithmic distribution of retardation times $L(\ln \omega)$ may be calculated instead of the distribution of relaxation times. Approximate distributions may be obtained by using the following equations:

$$L(\ln \omega) \doteq \frac{2}{\pi}\left[J''(\ln \omega) - \frac{1}{\omega\eta} \doteq \frac{2}{\pi}\right] J''(\ln \omega) \tag{7.56}$$

$$L(\ln \omega) \doteq -\frac{dJ'(\ln \omega)}{d \ln \omega} \tag{7.57}$$

Figure 7.10 shows the distribution of relaxation times and the distribution of retardation times for the polyvinyl acetate discussed in Figures 7.6, 7.7, 7.8, and 7.9.

The dissipation factor goes through a maximum at a frequency, which shifts with temperature; the higher the temperature, the higher the frequency at which the maximum occurs. This behavior may be illustrated by a model with a single relaxation time where the dissipation factor G''/G' is given by[84, 155]:

$$\frac{G''}{G'} = 2\left(\frac{G''}{G'}\right)_{\max}\left(\frac{\omega\tau}{1+\omega^2\tau^2}\right) \tag{7.58}$$

$(G''/G')_{\max}$ is the maximum value of the dissipation factor, which occurs at $\omega\tau = 1$. Over a small temperature interval, it may be assumed that the relation between the relaxation time and temperature is

$$\tau = \tau_0 e^{\Delta H/RT} \tag{7.59}$$

Combining this with the relation $\omega = 1/\tau$, the frequencies at which the damping is a maximum at temperatures T_1 and T_2°K are:

$$\frac{\tau_1}{\tau_2} = \frac{\omega_2}{\omega_1} = \exp\frac{\Delta H}{R}\left(\frac{1}{T_1} - \frac{1}{T_2}\right) \tag{7.60}$$

where ΔH is the energy of activation. For a decade change in frequency

$$\frac{\omega_2}{\omega_1} = 10 = e^{2.30} = \exp\frac{\Delta H}{R}\left(\frac{1}{T_1} - \frac{1}{T_2}\right) \tag{7.61}$$

or

$$\frac{\Delta H}{R}\left(\frac{1}{T_1} - \frac{1}{T_2}\right) = 2.303 \tag{7.62}$$

This equation gives the shift in temperature of maximum damping for a decade change in frequency as a function of the energy of activation. Table 7.3 lists the expected shifts in temperature of maximum damping brought

TABLE 7.3. TEMPERATURE SHIFT FACTOR OF DAMPING PEAK FOR A DECADE CHANGE IN FREQUENCY.

Temperature of Maxmimum Damping T_1 (°K)	Energy of Activation ΔH (cal/mole)	Shift in Damping Peak per Decade Change in Frequency
200	1×10^4	20
200	5×10^4	4
200	1×10^5	2
300	1×10^4	49
300	5×10^4	8.5
300	1×10^5	4
400	1×10^4	90
400	5×10^4	15
400	1×10^5	7.5

about by changing the frequency by a decade for various values of ΔH and T_1. The higher the energy of activation or the lower the reference temperature, the smaller is the temperature shift of the maximum in the damping peak. Many common polymers have a shift of about 7°C for a decade change in frequency. This indicates they have an apparent energy of activation between 50 and 100 kilocalories per mole. Some polymers show secondary damping peaks in addition to the main peak. These secondary peaks generally have smaller energies of activation and correspondingly larger shifts in the temperature of maximum damping with a change in frequency.

Relation of Dynamic Properties to Molecular Structure

Temperature and Importance of Glass Transitions. Typical dynamic mechanical properties of an amorphous, uncrosslinked polymer as a function of temperature are shown in Figure 7.11. The data in this figure were obtained with a torsion pendulum, so the values are reported as shear moduli, G' and G'', and as the logarithmic decrement. Curves of similar shape would have been obtained if the tensile dynamic properties had been measured with some other type of instrument. The frequency was roughly one cycle per second but decreased somewhat as the temperature increased.

The shear modulus G' of nearly all rigid polymers is roughly 10^{10} dynes/cm^2, and the modulus decreases very slowly as the temperature increases. In the neighborhood of the glass transition, the modulus decreases by a factor of about a thousand in a short temperature interval. In this transition region a polymer is semirigid and has a leathery feel. At temperatures above the transition region, the polymer is a rubber with a shear modulus of about 10^7 dynes/cm^2, and the shear modulus again becomes relatively independent of temperature. The modulus takes another drop at still higher temperatures due to the increasing role of viscous flow.

The damping (dissipation factor G''/G' or logarithmic decrement Δ) goes through a maximum and then a minimum as the temperature is raised for a material such as the polymer shown in Figure 7.11. At low temperatures, molecular motion of the chain segments is frozen in. Deformation results primarily from the bending of valence angles of the atoms in the polymer chain, so the modulus is high, and the material has nearly perfect elasticity. A perfectly elastic spring stores energy only as potential energy and does not dissipate any of it as heat. Thus, an elastic material or a stiff spring has low damping. At temperatures above the glass-transition re-

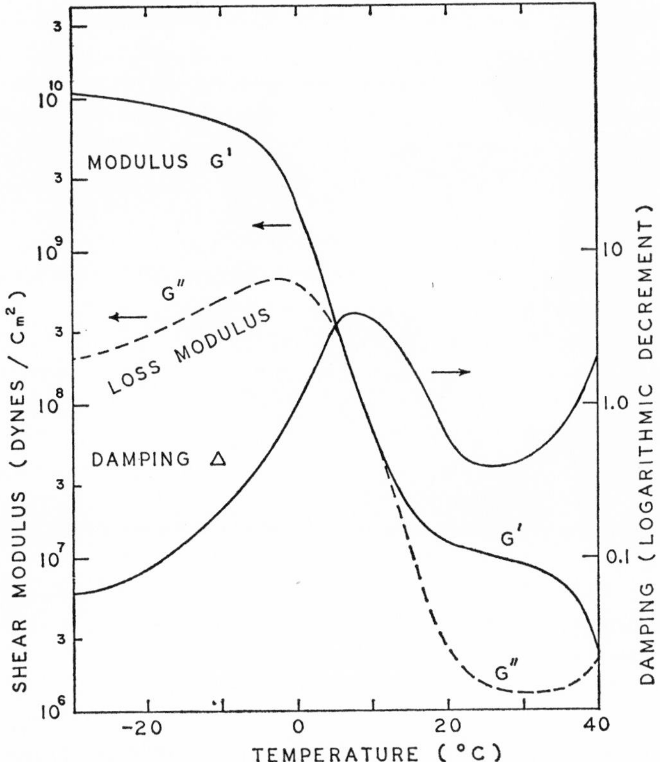

Figure 7.11. Typical dynamic mechanical behavior of uncross-linked amorphous polymers. The material is a copolymer of styrene and butadiene.

gion, the damping is low again. A good rubber, like a weak spring, also stores energy without dissipating it into heat. In the rubbery region, molecular segments are not frozen in but are very free to move, so the modulus is low. Thus, if chain segments are completely frozen in or are completely free to move, damping is low.

In the transition region the damping is high because some of the molecular chain segments are free to move while others are not. A stiff spring (frozen-in segment) can store much more energy for a given deformation than can a weak spring (rubbery segment free to move). Thus, every time a stressed, frozen-in segment becomes free to move, its excess energy is dissipated into heat. It is characteristic of the transition region that part of the molecular segments are free to move, and the longer the time a segment is under stress the greater is the probability that it will have a chance to move so as to relieve part of this stress. This delayed response to a stress gives rise to high damping and makes the deformation lag behind the stress. The damping peak occurs in the temperature interval where many of the frozen-in segments may become mobile in a time comparable to the time required for one oscillation.

The loss modulus G'' goes through a peak at a slightly lower temperature than does the dissipation factor G''/G'. The maximum heat dissipation for a unit deformation occurs at the temperature where G'' is maximum; the temperature of this maximum at one cycle per second is very close to the value of the glass-transition temperature as determined by volume-temperature measurements. The temperature of maximum damping G''/G' generally is 5 to 15°C higher than the conventional glass transition temperature if the dynamic measurements are made at about 0.10 to 1.0 cycle per second. In much of the following discussion, the temperature at which the damping (G''/G' or Δ) is a maximum will for convenience be sometimes referred to as the glass temperature.

The temperature at which the damping is a maximum depends upon the frequency of measurement. For most polymers, an increase of a factor of ten in frequency will raise the temperature of maximum damping approximately 7°C. Table 7.3 shows how this temperature shift is a function of the absolute temperature of the glass transition and the energy of activation. Similar results may be obtained from the Williams-Landel-Ferry treatment discussed in Chapter 2. The close correspondence of the glass-transition temperature and the temperature of maximum damping at low frequencies is one of the important reasons why many dynamic measurements are made at low rather than at high frequencies.

Review articles discussing the effect of temperature and other factors on dynamic properties of polymers include those by Ferry[30], Gehman[43], Schmieder and Wolf[129, 130, 152], Woodward and Sauer[154, 155] and Nielsen[109].

Effect of Molecular Weight and Crosslinking. Molecular weight in general does not affect the dynamic mechanical properties of polymers at temperatures below the glass transition region. If a rigid polymer has a high enough molecular weight to be of practical interest, then its properties are independent of molecular weight and molecular weight distribution except possibly at frequencies much less than one cycle per second[95].

The dynamic properties of molten polymers and uncrosslinked rubbers

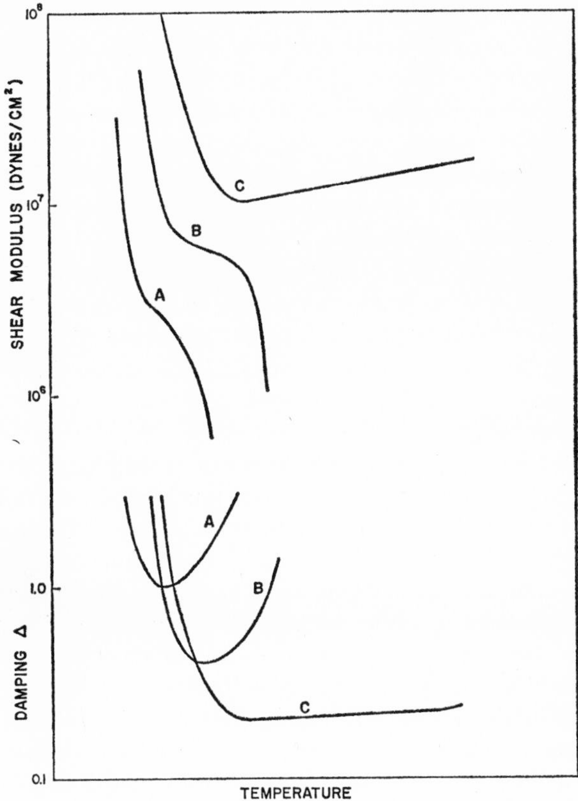

Figure 7.12. Schematic representation of the dynamic mechanical properties of amorphous polymers above the temperature of maximum damping. A. Low molecular weight polymer. B. High molecular weight polymer. C. Crosslinked polymer.

are very sensitive to molecular weight. The general behavior of such materials is shown in curves A and B of Figure 7.12. The last traces of the glass transition region are shown on the left side of the figure where the modulus and damping both increase as the temperature is lowered. The inflection or plateau region of the modulus curves is due to chain entanglements. Since high molecular weight polymers have more entanglements than low molecular weight ones, the plateau region is more prominent and covers a wider temperature range with the higher molecular weight materials. Chain entanglements delay the onset of viscous flow, so the minimum in damping decreases as the molecular weight increases. Cox, Isaksen, and Merz[15] have used the value of the minimum damping to determine the molecular weight of polystyrene polymers. They have also used the width of the damping curve in the neighborhood of the minimum to estimate the distribution in molecular weights. As the ratio of weight average to number average molecular weight increases, the damping minimum broadens. Similar results have been found by Hoegberg, Lovell, and Ferry[52], and by Yin, Lovell, and Ferry[158], and they have predicted a minimum in the damping curve which is dependent upon the molecular weight by using a theory developed by Marvin[88]. The theory predicts the damping at its minimum value is related to the molecular weight M of the polymer and the molecular weight M_c between points of chain entanglement by

$$\left(\frac{G''}{G'}\right)_{\min} = 1.02\left(\frac{2M_c}{M}\right)^{0.80} \tag{7.63}$$

Curve C of Figure 7.12 shows the effect of crosslinking on the dynamic properties of rubbers. Crosslinks prevent much of the viscous flow from taking place, so the second drop in the modulus does not occur. With a very lightly crosslinked rubber, the modulus continues to decrease as the temperature is raised, but with a normally crosslinked rubber the modulus may actually increase slightly with temperature as predicted by rubber theory if the frequency is low. Crosslinking makes the damping small. With very lightly crosslinked materials, however, there may be enough imperfections in the network structure that the viscous flow component is still important, and the damping may go through a minimum similar to uncrosslinked materials[102]. With more highly crosslinked rubbers the damping, as well as the modulus, is relatively insensitive to temperature.

In thermosetting materials, such as phenol-formaldehyde resins, the degree of crosslinking is much greater than in vulcanized rubbers. The general behavior of such materials as a function of extent of crosslinking is illustrated in Figure 7.13[21]. Crosslinking raises the glass temperature

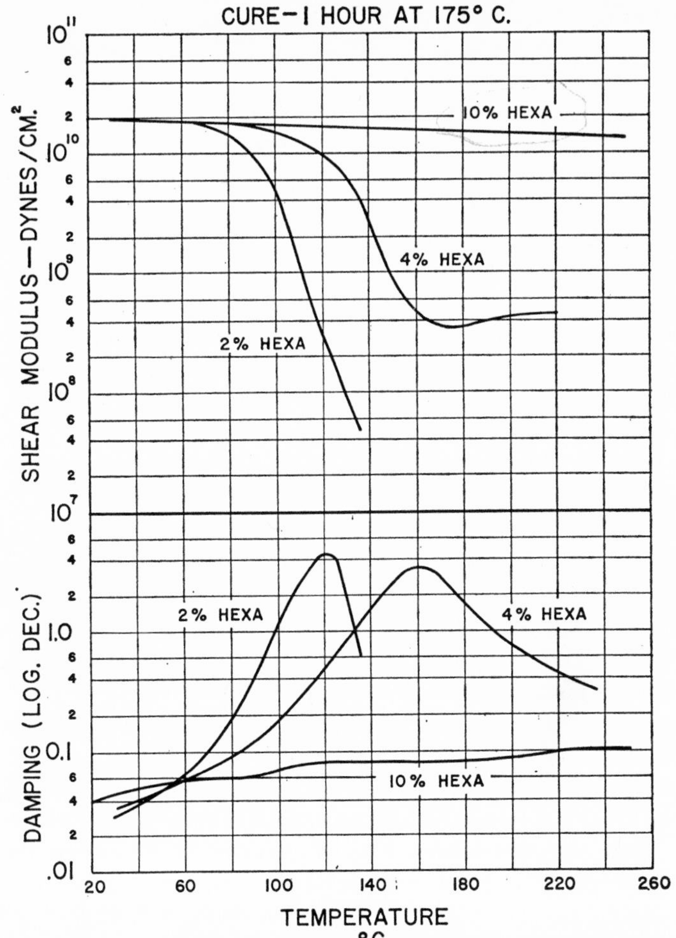

Figure 7.13. Dynamic mechanical properties of a phenol-formaldehyde resin crosslinked with hexamethylene tetramine at concentrations of 2%, 4%, and 10%. Resin was cured for one hour at 175°C. [*Drumm, M. F., Dodge, C. W. H., and Nielsen, L. E., Ind. Eng. Chem.*, **48**, *76 (1956). Reproduced with permission of the copyright owner, the American Chemical Society*]

(or damping peak) and broadens the transition region. In very highly crosslinked materials there is no indication of a glass transition below the decomposition temperature of the polymer. Several workers have studied the shift in glass temperature with crosslinking[40, 87, 143]. The shift in glass temperature may be crudely estimated from the equation:

$$T_g - T_g^\circ \doteq \frac{3.9 \times 10^4}{M_c} \tag{7.64}$$

where T_g is the glass temperature or temperature of maximum damping for the crosslinked polymer. T_g° is the glass temperature of the uncrosslinked material, and M_c is the molecular weight of chain segments between crosslinks. At low temperatures the modulus is independent of the crosslinking. Above the glass temperature the modulus increases as the degree of crosslinking increases. Although there is no theory which enables one to predict the modulus as a function of crosslinking on an absolute basis, this is one of the few methods available for empirically studying high degrees of crosslinking. One could use the equation from rubber theory[38, 141]

$$G = \frac{dRT}{M_c} \tag{7.65}$$

but the equation is not valid for such high degrees of crosslinking, and in some cases, the equation gives values of M_c which are much too small. Both the modulus and damping of highly cured thermosetting polymers are nearly independent of temperature from near absolute zero up to their decomposition temperature of several hundred degrees centigrade.

Effects of Plasticization and Copolymerization. Plasticizers lower the temperature of maximum damping in the same way they lower the glass transition temperature[151]. In order that a liquid lower the glass transition, it must be soluble in the polymer. The amount of lowering of the transition temperature to a large extent depends upon the glass temperature of the pure plasticizer. Plasticizers efficient in lowering the damping peak generally have low viscosities and low temperature coefficients of viscosity.

In addition to lowering the transition temperature, plasticizers usually broaden the transition region. This is illustrated in Figures 7.14 and 7.15 for various plasticized polyvinyl chloride materials. The broadening of the transition depends upon the nature of the plasticizer. The width of the damping peak appears to be determined primarily by the nature of the interaction between the polymer and plasticizer; if the plasticizer has a limited solubility in the polymer, or if the plasticizer tends to associate in the presence of the polymer, a broad damping peak is found. Diethyl phthalate is a relatively good solvent for polyvinyl chloride; dibutyl phthalate is a poorer solvent, while dioctyl phthalate is a very poor one. The transition region broadens as the solubility decreases[110]. As the damp-

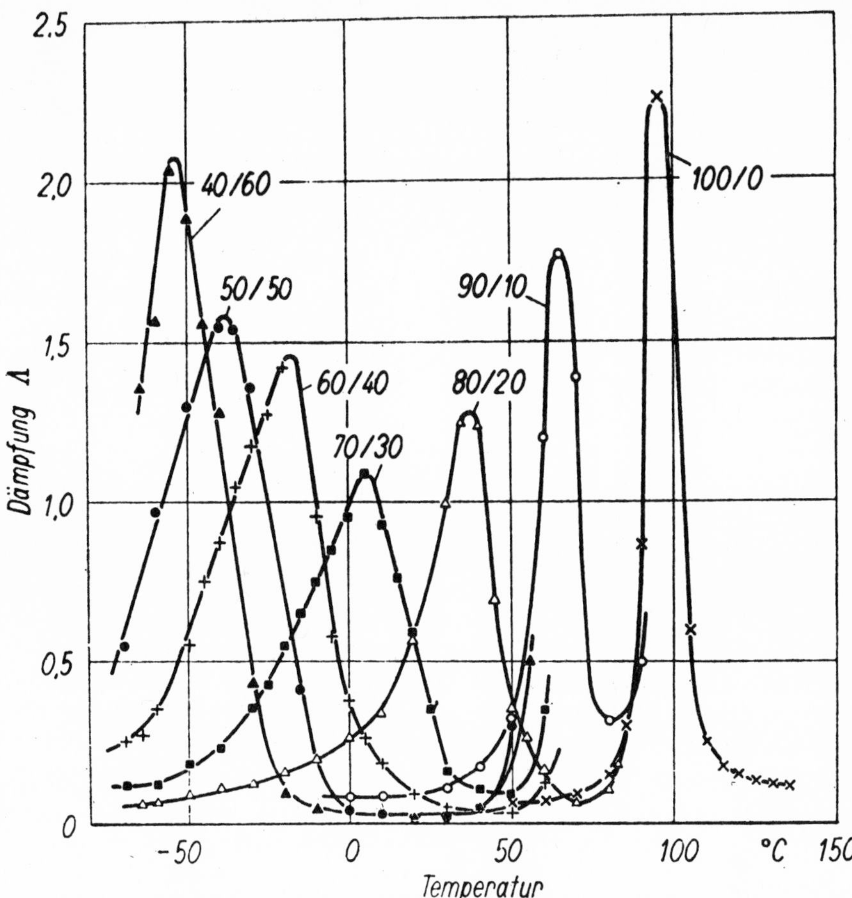

Figure 7.14. Damping (logarithmic decrement) of polyvinyl chloride plasticized with various amounts of di(ethyl-hexyl)phthalate. [*Wolf, K., Kunststoffe*, **41**, *89* (*1951*)]

ing peak broadens, its maximum value tends to be smaller. Also, the slope of the log modulus-temperature curve becomes less as the transition broadens; this is expected, since as a rough approximation, the damping is proportional to the slope of the log modulus curve.

The width of the transition, defined as the temperature interval between the points where the damping is half the maximum value, depends upon the concentration of the plasticizer as well as upon the type of plasticizer

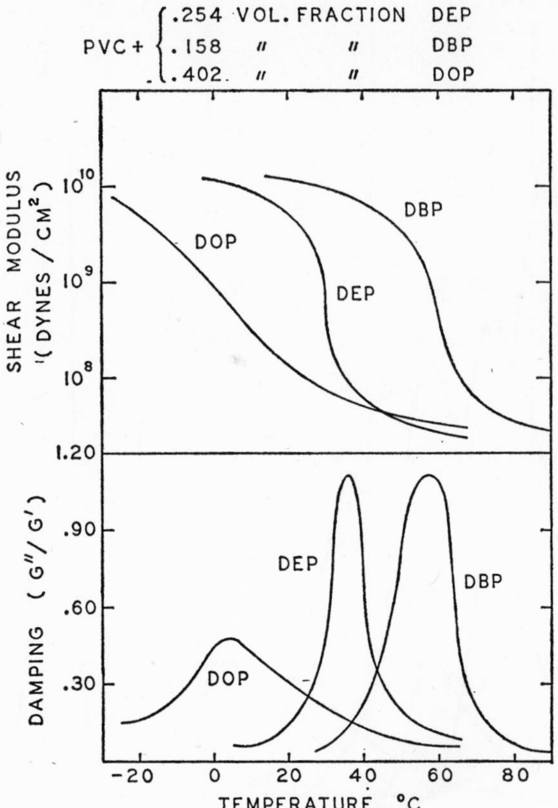

Figure 7.15. Dynamic mechanical properties of plasticized polyvinyl chloride. Diethyl phthalate (DEP, 0.254 volume fraction), dibutyl phthalate (DBP, 0.158 volume fraction), *n*-dioctyl phthalate (DOP, 0.402 volume fraction). [*Nielsen, L. E., Buchdahl, R., and Levreault, R., J. Appl. Phys.*, **21**, *607* (*1950*)]

as shown in Figure 7.14. The maximum width often is found when the plasticizer is in a concentration of about 40 volume per cent[110, 151]. Electrical measurements[157] have shown a second damping peak at low temperatures when the concentration of plasticizer is greater than the concentration required for maximum width of the transition; this probably indicates an association or aggregation of plasticizer molecules although the process has not proceeded to the extent that a separate phase made up mostly of plasticizer separates out.

Copolymers are generally made with the objective being: (1) to lower the glass transition or to lower the softening temperature; (2) to raise the glass temperature; or, (3) to improve the ease of processing the molten polymer. In Chapter 2 it was shown how the glass temperature of a copolymer may be estimated from the glass temperatures of the homopolymers. In the same way it is possible to estimate the temperature of

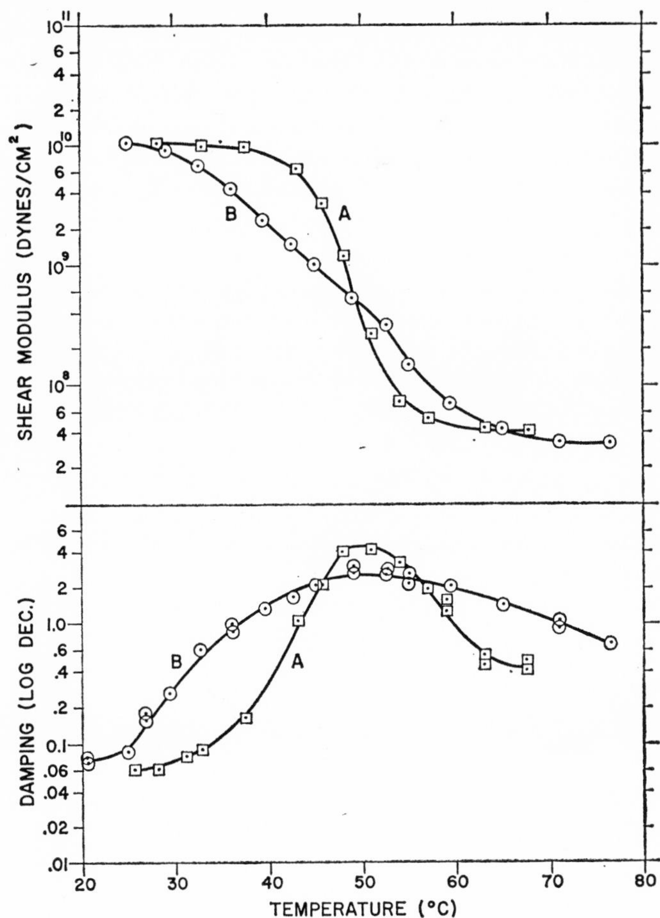

Figure 7.16. Dynamic mechanical properties of vinyl chloride-methyl acrylate copolymers. A. Homogeneous; B. Heterogeneous. [*Nielsen, L. E., J. Am. Chem. Soc.*, **75**, *1435 (1953). Reproduced with permission of the copyright owner, the American Chemical Society*)]

maximum damping of a copolymer from the damping peaks of the homopolymers and the composition of the copolymer.

In a homogeneous copolymer all the molecules have the same chemical composition, and hence would have a single sharp glass transition. As pointed out in Chapter 2, there will be a distribution of sequence lengths within each molecule. Most copolymers are actually more or less heterogeneous, that is, different molecules have different chemical compositions. This heterogeneity of chemical composition comes about because one monomer tends to be more reactive than the other. Thus, at the beginning of the copolymerization reaction the molecules will be rich in the more reactive monomer, while the molecules formed near the end of the reaction will be rich in the less reactive monomer. Dynamic mechanical measurements may be used to study this heterogeneity[105]. Figure 7.16 illustrates the broadening of the transition region by increasing the heterogeneity. The broadening is related to the mutual solubility of the two homopolymers. If the homopolymers tend to be insoluble in one another, then heterogeneous copolymers have broad transitions. If the molecular interaction between the two types of polymers is high, the effect of interchain chemical heterogeneity is small, so there will not be much broadening of the transition region. If two monomers naturally tend to produce heterogeneous copolymers, homogeneous copolymers may be produced by: (1) carrying the copolymerization reaction only to very small degrees of conversion; or, (2) adding small amounts of the more reactive monomer during the course of the polymerization reaction so as to maintain the same ratio of the two monomers at all times.

If the main reason for making a copolymer is to make a material more easily processed or to destroy crystallinity, then one generally wants a homogeneous copolymer. However, if the reason for making a copolymer is to broaden the transition region and to cut down the temperature sensitivity of the mechanical properties, one wants to have a heterogeneous copolymer.

Polyblends and Graft Polymers. It is a common practice to modify the properties of a polymer by mixing it with another polymer (polyblending) or by chemically attaching long side chains of another polymer to it. A graft polymer is one with a backbone of one type of material with a number of long side chains of another type attached to the main backbone chain. A block polymer is similar to a graft polymer except the second polymer is inserted as long blocks in the main chain rather than as side chains. The properties of block and graft polymers are quite similar. Polyblends and graft polymers are commercially used to increase the ductility and toughness of brittle polymers such as polystyrene or to increase the stiffness of rubbers.

The dynamic mechanical properties of polyblends and graft polymers are determined primarily by the mutual solubility of the two homopolymers. If two polymers are completely soluble in one another, the properties of the mixture are nearly the same as those of a copolymer of the same composition. Figure 7.17[111] compares the dynamic properties of an equal

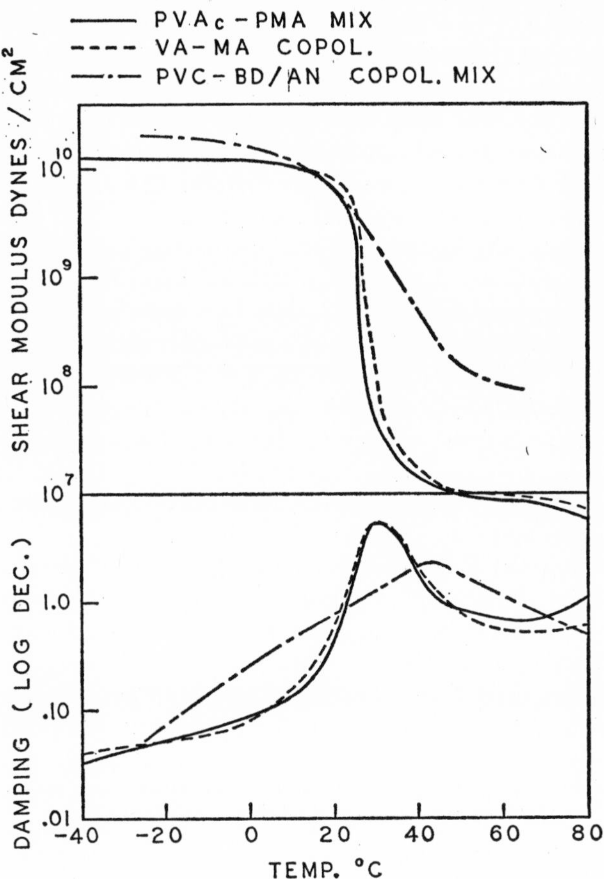

Figure 7.17. Dynamic mechanical properties of miscible polyblends and copolymers. A. 50/50 molar mixture of polyvinyl acetate and polymethyl acrylate. B. Vinyl acetate-methyl acrylate copolymer. C. Mixture of polyvinyl chloride and a copolymer of butadiene and acrylonitrile.

molar mixture of polyvinyl acetate and polymethyl acrylate with a copolymer of vinyl acetate and methyl acrylate of the same over-all composition. The two materials have nearly identical properties. One would expect, and the evidence supports the conclusion, that the two polymers are completely soluble in one another since their chemical composition and structure are so similar. The damping peak of the mixture and copolymer occur at 30°C while the peaks for polymethyl acrylate and polyvinyl acetate occur at about 15°C and 45°C, respectively, at a test frequency of one cycle per second.

Curve *C* of Figure 7.17 is an example in which two polymers are soluble in each other, but the intermolecular attraction is so weak that perfect solubility does not take place. The damping peak is very broad. This is probably an indication that considerable aggregation or association of like segments is taking place in the soluble mixture. This type of mixture has properties similar to a heterogeneous copolymer.

If two polymers are insoluble in one another so that two phases exist, the polyblend will have two glass transitions instead of the usual single one. The two transitions occur at nearly the same temperatures as the individual transitions of the pure polymers making up the mixture[1, 10, 11, 25, 62, 64]. Figure 7.18 gives the dynamic properties of an incompatible (immiscible) polyblend. This polyblend is a mixture of polystyrene and a styrene-butadiene copolymer. The two damping peaks occur at temperatures very close to those found with pure polystyrene (100°C) and pure styrene-butadiene rubber. The modulus-temperature curve shows two steps corresponding to the two transition regions.

The concentration of the components in a polyblend may be estimated from the heights of the damping peaks. The greater the concentration of a polymer, the larger is its damping peak. Table 7.4 lists the maximum damping of a rubber as a function of its concentration in a polystyrene polyblend. However, there is not a perfect correspondence between the maximum damping and the concentration of a component in a polyblend. The

TABLE 7.4. MAXIMUM DAMPING OF THE RUBBER PHASE IN POLYSTYRENE-BUTADIENE/STYRENE MIXTURES.*

Per Cent Rubber in Polyblend	Maximum Damping Δ
0	.04
10	.12
26	.28
40	.58

* After Buchdahl, R. and Nielsen, L. E., *J. Polymer Sci.*, **15**, 1 (1955).

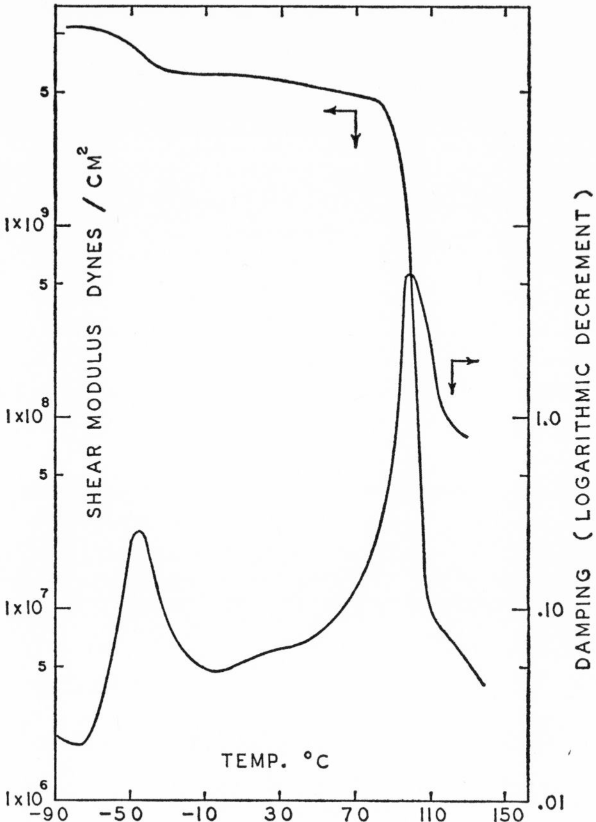

Figure 7.18. Dynamic mechanical properties of an immiscible polyblend. Material is a mixture of polystyrene and a styrene-butadiene copolymer.

extent of solubility and the size of the particles of the dispersed material appear to influence the damping to some extent.

In most graft polymers the backbone chain and the side chains differ enough in chemical composition that the side chains are not soluble in the backbone polymer but prefer to associate with other side chains. This leads to two phase systems even though the components of the different phases are chemically tied to each other. This unusual behavior results from an association phenomenon in which side chains sort themselves out into microscopic aggregates while adjacent pieces of the backbone get together to form another aggregate or a separate phase.

Graft polymers are similar to polyblends in their dynamic behavior[1, 6, 25, 64, 132]. Two damping peaks are found unless the backbone chains and the side chains are soluble in one another. In most two-phase systems one of the components forms the dispersed phase while the other component forms a more or less continuous phase or matrix. In Figure 7.18 the continuous phase has the higher glass temperature. With some systems, especially graft or block polymers, it is possible to reverse the phases and to make the dispersed phase become the continuous phase. The phase reversal can be brought about during the removal of the polymer from

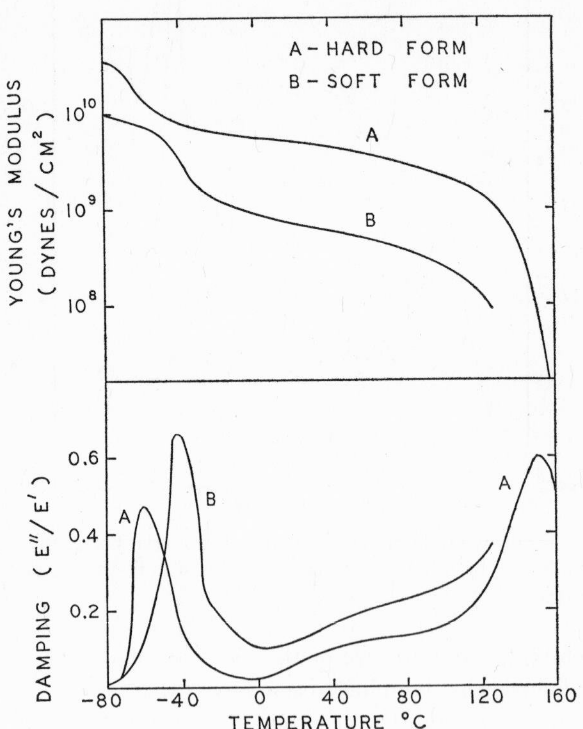

Figure 7.19. Dynamic mechanical behavior of a graft polymer consisting of polymethyl methacrylate side chains on a natural rubber backbone. A. Hard form with polymethyl methacrylate as the continuous phase. B. Soft form with rubber as the continuous phase. (*Atkinson, E. B., and Eagling, R. F., "Physical Properties of Polymers,"* Soc. Chem. Ind. *Monograph No. 5, p. 197, New York, Macmillan Co., 1959, and unpublished data of Monsanto Chemical Co.*)

solution. If the polymer is cast from a solution in which the liquid is a good solvent for the backbone chain but a poor solvent for the side chains, the side chains will coil up into tight balls while the backbones are extended. In this case the backbone chains will form the continuous phase while the side chains are the dispersed phase. However, if the liquid is a better solvent for the side chains than for the backbone chains, the continuous phase will be made up of the side chains while the backbone parts of the molecule tend to be the dispersed phase.

The effect of phase reversal is illustrated in Figure 7.19[1, 102]. This graft polymer is a 50/50 methyl methacrylate/natural rubber graft polymer in which the side chains are polymethyl methacrylate[94]. When the polymethyl methacrylate is the continuous phase, the polymer is rigid, and the dynamic curves are similar to the polyblend curve in Figure 7.18 with a small drop in modulus near the glass temperature of the rubber at −60°. There is another drop in modulus above the glass temperature of polymethyl methacrylate at 125°C. When the rubber backbone forms the continuous phase, the dynamic curves are quite different. There is a large drop in the modulus in the transition region of the rubber; above this transition there is no rigid continuous phase to maintain a high modulus. The rigid phase is now a dispersed phase which acts like an inert filler and has only a small effect in stiffening the polymer. At the transition temperature of the polymethyl methacrylate, the drop in the modulus is so small that it is hard to detect. When the continuous phase has the lower transition temperature, the dynamic properties could be mistaken for those of a single-phase system.

Secondary Glass Transitions. In addition to the main glass transition due to motion of large segments of the polymer chain, many polymers show smaller secondary transitions at lower temperatures. The nature of some of these transitions is not clearly understood, but in some cases these secondary transitions can be traced to motion of side groups or to small segments of the main polymer chain. Although such secondary transitions are generally difficult to detect by most experimental techniques, they are easily measured by mechanical damping tests.

Polymethyl methacrylate was one of the first polymers shown to have a secondary transition[18, 48, 73, 129]. Its dynamic properties, measured at a frequency of about one cycle per second, are shown in Figure 7.20[109]. The damping peak due to the main glass transition occurs at about 125°C. The broad secondary transition is around 40°C. There is no distinct drop in the modulus at this temperature, but its variation with temperature from 0°C to 100°C is greater than expected for a rigid polymer. The energy of activation for the secondary transition is much less than for the primary transition. Therefore, the secondary transition shifts more than the normal 7°C for a decade change in frequency. If a plasticizer or methyl methacrylate monomer is added to polymethyl methacrylate, the main transition is lowered at a much faster rate than the secondary transition; as a result, the secondary damping peak blends in with the main peak and soon becomes lost. The secondary damping peak has been shown to be due to some motion of the $-\overset{\displaystyle O}{\overset{\|}{C}}-O-CH_3$ side group[18, 48], which becomes mobile at a lower temperature than the main chain.

Polyethylene terephthalate has a transition at −40°C in addition to the

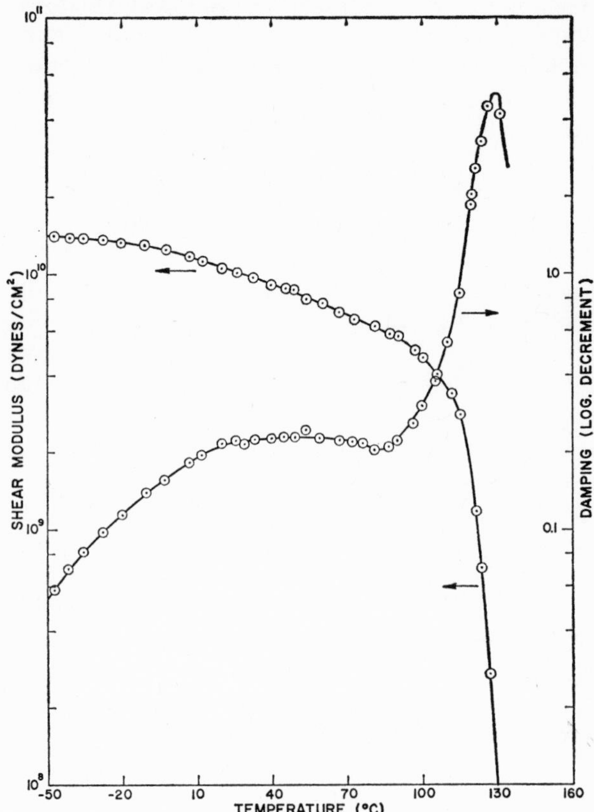

Figure 7.20. Dynamic mechanical properties of polymethyl methacrylate. [*Nielsen, L. E., Soc. Plastics Eng. J.*, **16,** *525 (1960)*]

glass transition at 80°C when measured at one cycle per second[28, 137]. Although this transition has been studied intensively, its exact nature is still in doubt. However, the secondary transition seems to be related to some type of motion of the —O—CH_2—CH_2—O— group such as trans-gauche configurational changes.

All polymers with at least three or four methylene (CH_2) groups in a row have a transition near −120°C[18, 46, 53, 147]. Polymers showing transitions in this temperature region include polyethylene, most of the nylons[153, 156], and poly alkyl acrylates and other polymers with hydrocarbon side chains with lengths equal to or longer than a normal propyl group.

Weak transitions, due to the motion of small groups, can occur at very low temperatures. For instance, it has been reported that the methyl groups in polypropylene produce a damping peak at −260°C[99].

The cyclohexyl group gives rise to a characteristic damping peak in many polymers[46, 47]. The cyclohexyl transition temperature shifts rapidly with frequency, but this temperature is nearly independent of the nature of the remainder of the molecule to which it is attached. The transition occurs at −180°C at 1 cycle/second; at −38°C at 200 cycles/second, and at −23°C at 1000 cycles/second. Heijboer[47] has concluded that the transition is due to the puckered cyclohexyl group changing from one chair configuration to an alternate chair configuration.

Even polystyrene, which is generally considered as an example of a material with only one transition, shows one or more weak transitions at low temperatures if it is crosslinked or plasticized[58]. These transitions may be due to: (1) some motion of the phenyl side group; (2) end groups; (3) defects or imperfections in the glassy state due to such factors as changes from isotactic to syndiotactic configurations in the polymer molecules or changes from head-to-tail to head-to-head polymerization; and, (4) branching.

Some polyvinyl chlorides show a broad secondary transition at −20°C or lower, while in other polyvinyl chloride polymers no transition has been found. This transition is due to, or at least can be modified by, bulky end groups on the polymer molecules[11]. Some polymers containing hydroxyl groups or adsorbed water have secondary transitions at low temperatures[57, 65, 102]. It is not known if the transition is due to motion of the free hydroxyl groups, hydrogen-bonded groups, or water adsorbed by the polymer.

Nearly all crystalline polymers show one or more secondary damping peaks[70, 101, 152, 153, 155]. These transitions may be due to the amorphous phase in some cases and to the crystalline phase in others. These transitions will be discussed in more detail in the following section on crystallinity.

Secondary transitions may be important in determining the toughness of a polymer[7]. Brittle polymers generally have no low temperature transitions or only very weak ones. The toughest amorphous polymers always have large secondary damping peaks well below room temperature. Polyblending is a technique for producing materials with high impact strengths by artifically introducing low temperature transitions. The factors determining the magnitude of secondary transitions are not clearly defined. However, it appears that the larger the group which gives rise to the transition the more probable it is that the polymer will be tough as long as the transition remains below about 0°C. Motion of a small group, such as the methyl group, contributes only a small amount to the toughness of a polymer. Motion of side groups appears to be somewhat less effective than motion of segments of the backbone chain in enhancing toughness.

Crystallinity and Crystalline Polymers. Crystalline polymers show much more complex dynamic mechanical behavior than do amorphous polymers[70, 101, 152, 153, 155]. Crystalline polymers always have a glass transition and generally at least one or two secondary transitions. There may also be transitions within the crystalline phase. In addition, the mechanical properties are strongly dependent upon the degree of crystallinity, the size of the crystallites, and the melting of the crystallites.

Polyethylene is a typical semicrystalline material. The mechanical damping, $Q^{-1} = E''/E'$, of three polyethylenes of different degrees of chain branching is shown in Figure 7.21[70]. The degree of crystallinity decreases as the branching increases[106]; a branch point acts like a comonomer unit in destroying crystallinity[39]. Polyethylenes have damping peaks at about 70°C, −25°C, and −120°C, known as the alpha, beta, and gamma transitions, respectively[70, 114, 130]. The gamma transition at −120°C is due to long CH_2 sequences in the amorphous phase and could be considered as the glass transition of a pure linear hydrocarbon. However, there is some evidence that the gamma transition may also be found in the crystalline phase of hydrocarbons[14]. The magnitude of the beta transition at −25°C increases as the degree of crystallinity decreases. Its position is nearly independent of the composition (degree of branching, or type of comonomer) as long as the polymer is crystalline[108, 130]. The beta transition is related to the amorphous phase containing the branch points or comonomer units. The crystalline phase imposes restrictions on the amorphous phase, and it also tends to keep the composition of the amorphous phase constant. As more impurities in the form of branch points or comonomer are added

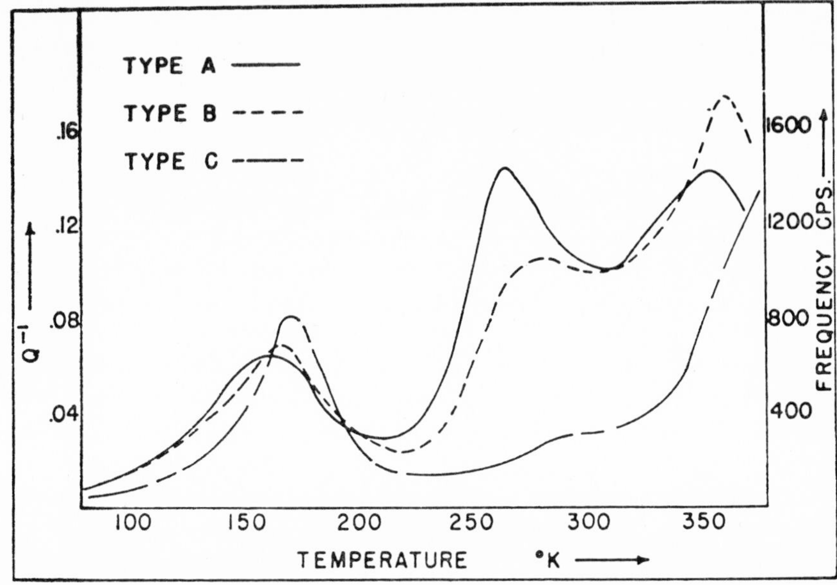

Figure 7.21. Damping of polyethylene as a function of branching. Type A: 3.2 CH_3's/100 CH_2; Type B: 1.6 CH_3's/100 CH_2; Type C: <0.1 CH_3's/100 CH_2. [*Kline, D. E., Sauer, J. A., and Woodward, A. E., J. Polymer Sci.*, **22**, *445* (*1956*)]

to the polymer, part of the crystalline phase melts and adds more linear CH_2 sequences to the amorphous phase. It may be a combination of these factors which keeps the beta transition temperature nearly independent of the composition over such a wide range. The alpha transition is due to the crystalline phase, and in some cases it appears to be really two transitions[130]. In unbranched, slowly cooled, and annealed polyethylene, the alpha transition temperature may be over 100°C. If the polymer is branched, or if it is a copolymer, or if the material is cooled rapidly from the melt, the alpha transition is lowered[106, 108, 109]. The alpha transition may, in such cases, be lowered to at least 0°C; at the same time the degree of crystallinity is decreased, the magnitude of the transition is also decreased. The alpha transition temperature may be correlated with the size of a crystallite or the length of the polyethylene sequences in a crystallite[108]. This transition temperature may be related to the length of the chain folds in the polyethylene crystals. (See section on Morphology of Crystalline Polymers in Chapter 2.) This transition occurs at a temperature where the folded chains can recrystallize in a time comparable to the time

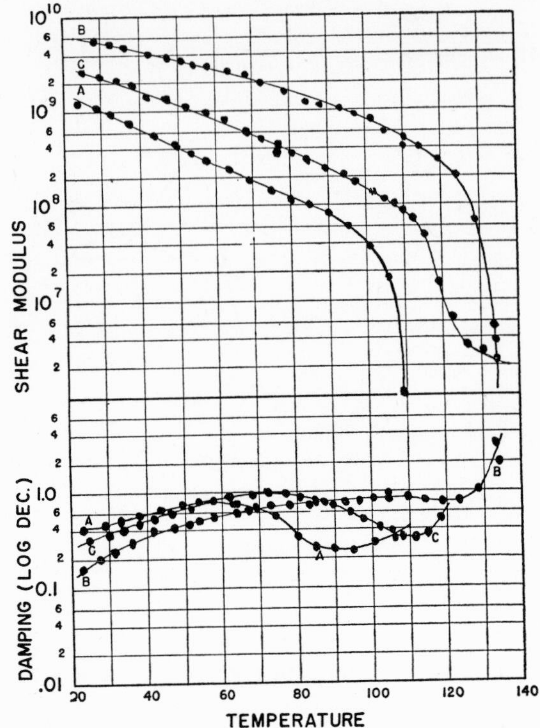

Figure 7.22. Effect of crystallinity (density) on the dynamic mechanical behavior of polyethylenes. A. Density = .91; B. Density = .96; C. Density = .935. Densities of the polyethylenes are the values at 25°C. [*Nielsen, L. E., J. Appl. Phys.*, **25**, *1209* (*1954*)]

required to make a dynamic test. Nuclear magnetic resonance studies also indicate that the alpha transition is related to motion in the crystalline phase[123].

The dynamic shear moduli of polyethylenes of different degrees of branching are shown in Figure 7.22[106]. The greater the crystallinity the higher is the modulus. Nielsen[106] found an amazingly good correlation between the modulus of a series of polyethylenes and the specific volume of the polymers at the same temperature over the temperature range between 20°C and the melting point. The relation is:

$$\log_{10} G = 26.671 - 16.21\bar{v} \tag{7.66}$$

where $\bar{v}$ is the specific volume of the polyethylene in ml/g, and G is the shear modulus in dynes/cm^2.

The degree of crystallinity of nearly all semicrystalline polymers above their glass temperature may be roughly approximated from the dynamic shear modulus by the use of Figure 7.23[107]. This curve was constructed from a series of ethylene copolymers, but it has been checked with a number of other polymers including polytetrafluoroethylene, polypropylene, polybutene-1, and polyvinyl chloride. The dynamic measurements were made at a frequency between 0.1 and 1.0 cycle per second. The correlation

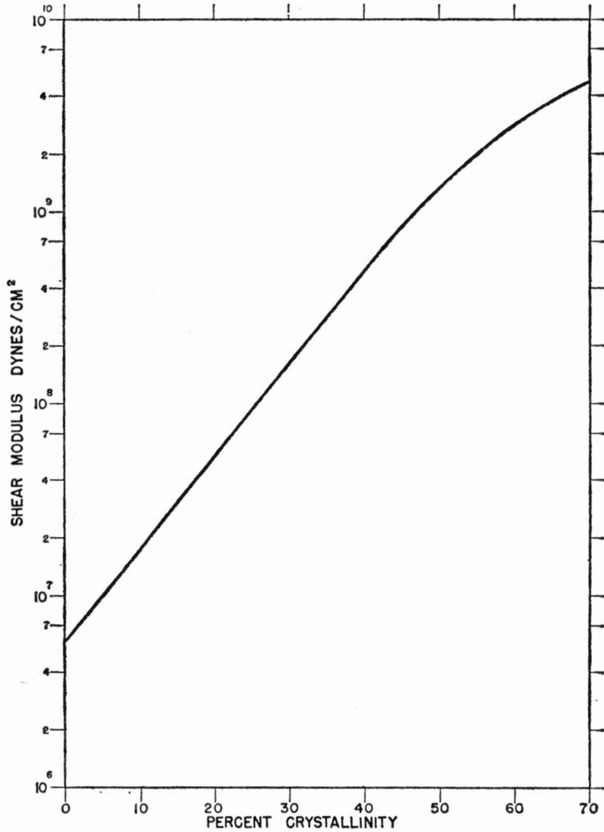

Figure 7.23. Dynamic shear modulus at one cycle per second of semicrystalline polymers as a function of the degree of crystallinity. [*Nielsen, L. E., J. Appl. Polymer Sci.*, **2**, *351* (*1959*)]

of modulus and crystallinity shown in Figure 7.23 is not as good as the correlation between modulus and specific volume given in equation 7.66. The less branched, more highly crystalline polyethylenes tend to fall below the curve in Figure 7.23. The usefulness of the relation between modulus and crystallinity is that the correlation may be used to obtain quickly an estimate of the crystallinity of most crystalline polymers even when there is not enough information to make use of other, more accurate, methods such as x-ray or density measurements.

If Figure 7.23 is replotted as modulus G (rather than as log G) against degree of crystallinity, several interesting features may be noticed. Between zero and about 15 per cent crystallinity the modulus increases nearly linearly with crystallinity. Rubber theory should hold in this region where crystallites behave very much like crosslinks. In the region between 15 and 35 per cent crystallinity, the modulus increases at a rate faster than expected from rubber theory. In this range the amorphous material is under restraints and the amorphous segments may be so short and stretched out that they can no longer be considered as Gaussian coils—an assumption made in the ordinary kinetic theory of rubber elasticity. Above 35 per cent crystallinity the modulus increases very rapidly with crystallinity. This is in the region where Lauritzen[54] has predicted that impingements between crystals will become important. In this region the crystalline phase will form a continuous structure throughout all of the material, and the crystalline phase can carry much of the stress previously carried by the amorphous phase. Since the modulus of a pure polymer crystal is predicted to be about 10^{12} dynes/cm^2 [83, 142], it is easily seen why the modulus should rapidly increase as soon as the crystalline phase becomes the continuous phase rather than the dispersed phase. The relations between mechanical properties and crystallinity are crude approximations today, but with the intensive research being carried out in this field, much better relations are confidently predicted for the future. Bueche[12] has made a theoretical attempt at predicting the modulus of a polymer from its crystallinity and crystallite size and shape. At best, the theory can be expected to give only approximate results.

The modulus of a crystalline polymer should be nearly independent of temperature above the glass temperature as long as the degree of crystallinity does not change with temperature. The modulus decreases as the crystallinity decreases. Crystallites containing short sequence lengths of polymer melt before crystallites which contain long chain sequences. Thus, small and imperfect crystallites melt at a lower temperature than large and more perfect crystallites. For this reason, the temperature dependence of the modulus above the glass temperature gives an estimate of the distribution of crystallite sizes. The size of crystallites depends upon the distribution of crystallizable sequence lengths, which in turn depend upon the factors which break up the uniformity of the backbone chain—branching, comonomer units, and the degree of stereoregularity or tacticity. These factors decrease both the degree of crystallinity and the size or perfection of the crystallites. It is a difficult experimental task to differentiate between the size of a crystallite and its perfection. The difference between a highly crystalline isotactic polypropylene and a slightly crystalline, nearly atactic one is illustrated in Figure 7.24[96, 102]. The high crystallinity of the isotactic polymer is reflected in its high modulus. The small size or imperfections of the crystallites in the nearly atactic material is

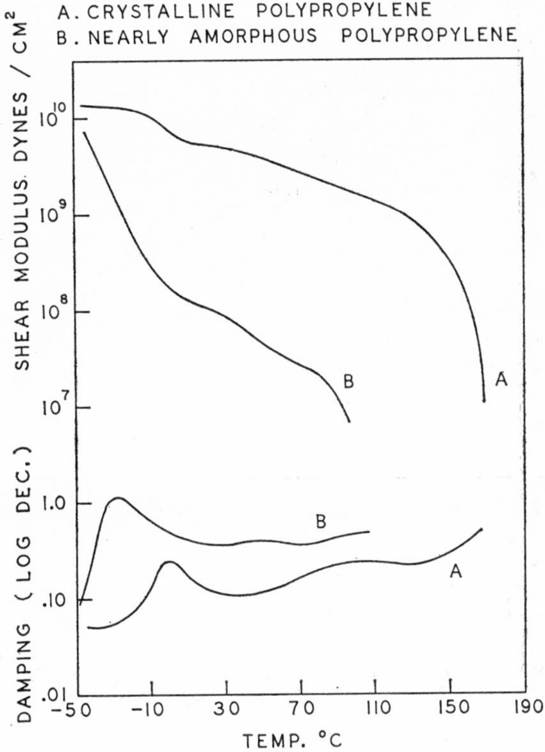

Figure 7.24. Dynamic mechanical properties of polypropylenes. (*Nielsen, L. E., unpublished data of Monsanto Chemical Co.*)

partly responsible for its low melting point. Crystallization shifts the main damping peak to a higher temperature.

The melting point of crystalline polymers can be measured by dynamic mechanical measurements[106, 108]. As long as there are enough crystallites to bind the molecules together, the modulus will be well above 10^6 dynes/cm^2. Near the final melting point the modulus drops rapidly, and the damping rapidly increases. A very high molecular weight has the effect of raising the apparent melting point, but the method can generally be relied upon to give the correct melting point within five degrees.

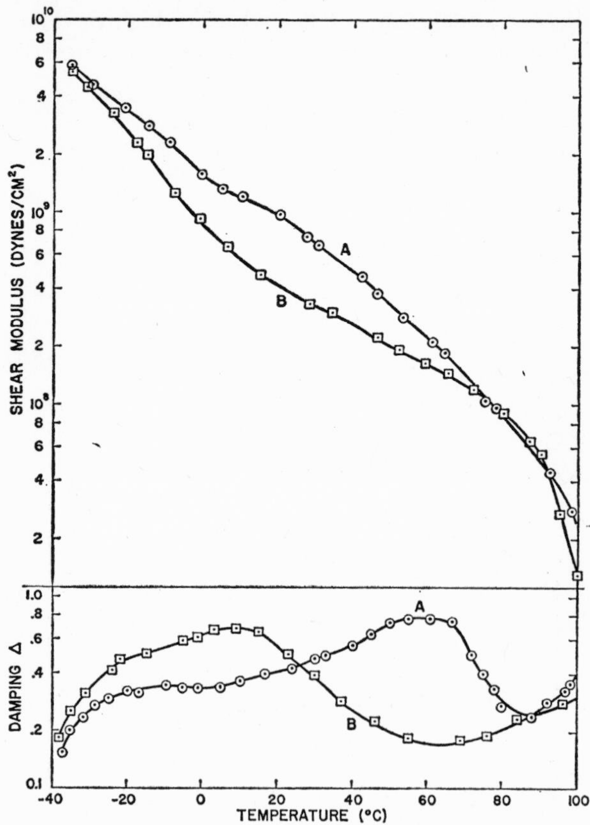

Figure 7.25. Effect of thermal treatments on the dynamic mechanical properties of polyethylene (low density). A. Slowly cooled from melt to 20°C. B. Quenched from melt at 150°C into ice water. [*Nielsen, L. E.*, *Soc. Plastics Eng. J.*, **16**, *525* (*1960*)]

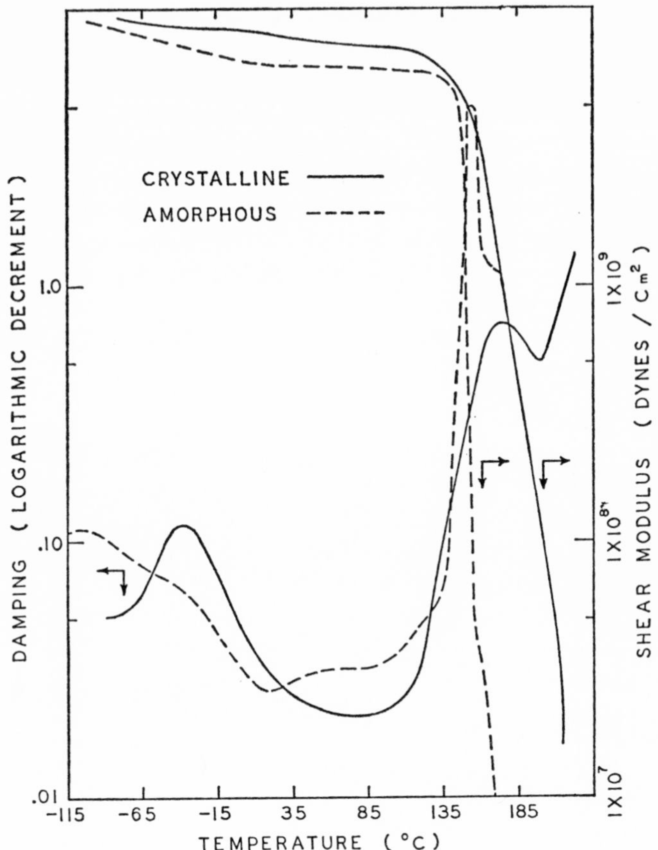

Figure 7.26. Dynamic mechanical properties of the polycarbonate of Bis Phenol-A. (*Nielsen, L. E., unpublished data of Monsanto Chemical Co.*)

Heat treatments have a greater effect on the properties of crystallizable polymers than on the properties of amorphous or atactic ones. Heat treatments may bring about changes in the degree of crystallinity, size of crystallites, and morphology of the polymer. For instance, quenching a polymer from the melt by immersion in ice water may produce an amorphous polymer or one with small and imperfect crystallites of low crystallinity. Slow cooling or annealing at a temperature slightly below the melting point tends to produce a highly crystalline polymer with large spherulites.

The effect of heat treatments on polyethylene is shown in Figure 7.25[109].

In one case the polymer was slowly cooled through the melting range while in the other case the polymer at 150°C was quenched in ice water. The slowly cooled specimen may have been slightly more crystalline, but most of the difference is due to the small size (or perfection) of the crystallites in the quenched sample. This is shown by a shift of 50°C in the alpha transition temperature of the two materials.

"Bis Phenol-A" polycarbonate is an example of a crystallizable material which remains amorphous if rapidly cooled from the melt. Exposure of this amorphous polymer to the vapors of some liquids converts the polycarbonate to a crystalline polymer. The differences between amorphous and crystalline polycarbonate are shown in Figure 7.26[102]. The main glass

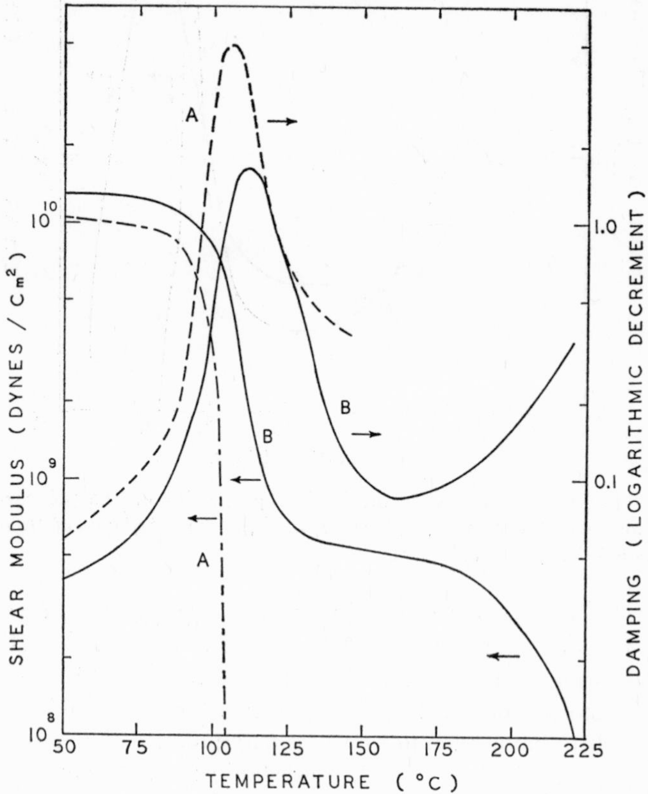

Figure 7.27. Dynamic mechanical properties of isotactic polystyrene. A. Amorphous. B. Crystalline. [*Newman, S., and Cox, W. P., J. Polymer Sci.*, **46**, *29 (1960)*]

transition at 150°C is essentially the same for both amorphous and crystalline material. The modulus of the amorphous polymer drops nearly to zero above the glass temperature. The modulus of the crystalline polymer, however, remains at about 10^8 to 10^9 dynes/cm^2 nearly to the melting point at 220°C. The amorphous polymer has a large secondary transition below −100°C; crystallization shifts this transition to −30°C when measured at one cycle per second. This secondary transition, which may be due to some motion of the carbonate group, is largely responsible for the remarkable toughness of polycarbonates.

Isotactic polystyrene is another polymer which can exist in both the amorphous and crystalline states. Figure 7.27 shows the difference in dynamic properties of the polystyrene in the two states[101, 144]. The glass temperature near 100°C is well separated from the melting point at 235°C so the crosslinking characteristics of crystallites in preventing flow are readily apparent. Even above the glass temperature the modulus of the crystalline polystyrene is so high that the material is semirigid. The modulus drops low enough to give a rubbery material only at temperatures approaching the melting point of the crystallites.

Dynamic Properties of Filled Polymers. Fillers are used in a polymeric material to increase its modulus or strength, change its coefficient of expansion, increase its toughness, improve its abrasion resistance or other properties, and to dilute the polymer to lower its price. Other fillers are used to color polymers, but in this case their concentration is so low that the mechanical properties remain nearly unchanged by the presence of the filler.

Rigid, inert fillers nearly always increase the modulus of polymers, either in the rigid or rubbery state. This might be expected since the modulus of most polymers is around 10^{10} dynes/cm^2 in their most rigid state, while common inorganic fillers generally have moduli of at least 10^{11} dynes/cm^2. In most cases the change in modulus is approximately proportional to the volume fraction of filler present. Some fillers are more efficient than others in changing the modulus even when the fillers are compared at equal volume fractions. This is illustrated in Figure 7.28[112] for different fillers in rigid polystyrene. Mica is especially efficient in increasing the modulus of polystyrene.

The modulus of a filled rigid polymer may be approximated by[112]:

$$G = G_1 v_1 + A G_2 v_2 \tag{7.67}$$

where G is the shear modulus of the filled material, G_1 and G_2 are the moduli of the pure polymer and filler, respectively. The corresponding volume

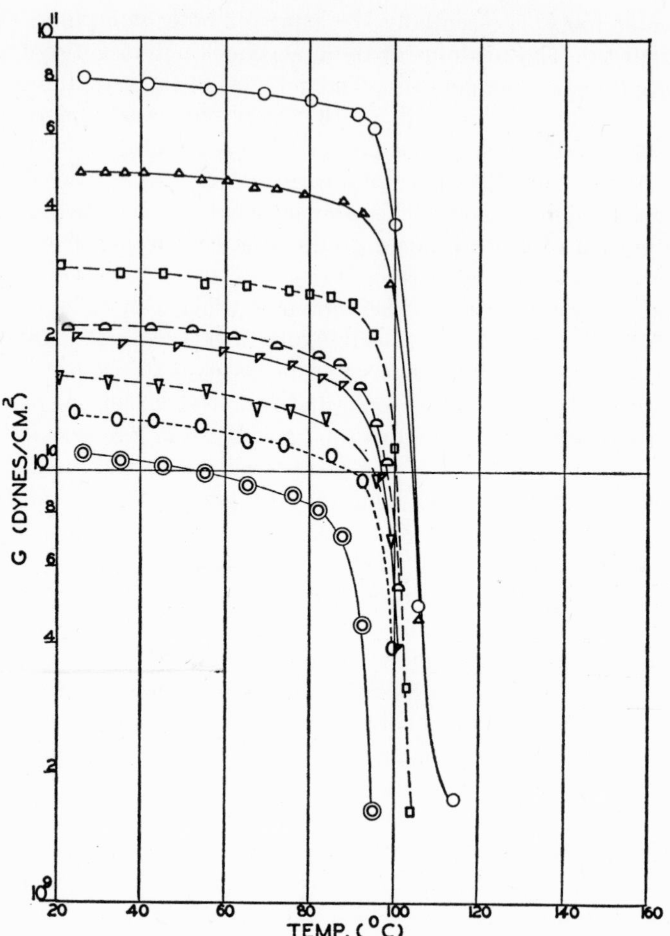

Figure 7.28. Shear modulus vs. temperature for filled polystyrene. ◎ Polystyrene control. ▽ 20% mica. △ 40% mica. 0 20% calcium carbonate. ⌓ 40% asbestos. ○ 60% mica. ▽ 20% asbestos. □ 60% asbestos. [*Nielsen, L. E., Wall, R. A., and Richmond, P. G., Soc. Plastics Eng. J.*, **11**, *22* (*1955*)]

fractions are v_1 and v_2. The constant A is called the adhesion factor and can vary between zero and one; it is an empirical constant which gives a measure of the adhesion between the polymer and the filler, and at the same time it corrects for some of the theoretical inadequacies of equation 7.67. Kerner[67] has derived a more complex equation for the modulus of filled polymers; his theoretical equation under certain conditions has the same form as equation 7.67. Kerner's equation was discussed in Chapter 6.

Fillers shift the temperature of maximum damping to higher temperatures. This shift can be deduced from Figure 7.28 where fillers raise the temperature at which polystyrene softens. Below the glass temperature, fillers may either decrease or increase the mechanical damping. Long fibrous fillers, especially those which are themselves tough or strong, tend to increase the damping when expressed either as the dissipation factor G''/G' or as the loss modulus G''. Laminar fillers such as graphite and mica also are effectve in increasing the damping of some polymers[138]. Friction develops between the thin laminas or sheets of the filler as they slip over one another when the polymer mixture is deformed.

The effect of fillers such as carbon black on the properties of rubbers has been extensively studied[4, 17, 24, 26, 45, 91]. The filler increases the modulus and generally the loss modulus also. The dissipation factor E''/E' remains approximately constant or increases slightly when carbon black is added to the rubber. Not all carbon blacks have the same effect on dynamic properties[17]. Very high concentrations of inert fillers in rubbers or plasticized polymers bring about a very pronounced broadening of the transition region with high damping over a temperature range several times greater than for the unfilled material[138]. Friction between filler particles may contribute to the damping.

Landel[76] has studied the dynamic properties of uncrosslinked polyisobutylene rubber filled with small glass beads. The Williams-Landel-Ferry[149] temperature shift treatment could be applied to this system. The glass beads raised the glass temperature approximately 0.25°C for each volume per cent of beads in the rubber. Glass beads in a urethane rubber gave similar results[5]. The beads broaden the dispersion region somewhat, but the filled materials have nearly the same dissipation factor as pure polyisobutylene as long as the volume fraction of beads is less than about 0.25. At higher concentrations the damping maximum decreases, but the damping at very high frequencies (or at temperatures below the glass temperature) is greater than for pure polyisobutylene. The beads increase the modulus; the effect is greater when the materials act like rubbers (high temperatures or low frequencies) than when the materials are rigid (low temperatures or high frequencies).

Amplitude and Stress Effects. Most dynamic mechanical tests are made at such small stresses or amplitudes of deformation that the dynamic properties are independent of the stress or amplitude. However, the dynamic behavior of rigid polymers is strongly dependent upon the stress at high values, and the behavior of rubbers becomes dependent upon the elongation at large elongations. This aspect of dynamic testing is unexplored from the standpoint of the role played by the chemical structure of polymers. However, from the practical standpoint of the design engineer, it is important to know how the properties change at large stresses or deformations.

Filled polymers are very sensitive to amplitude effects. When rubbers are filled with carbon black or other solid fillers, the modulus generally drops as the amplitude increases[17, 34, 35, 37, 45, 116, 117, 118]. Fillers raise the modulus above the value for the unfilled polymer as long as the amplitude of deformation is small, but above a fairly definite amplitude the modulus starts to decrease[118]. At high amplitudes the modulus may decrease to approximately the value for unfilled rubber. The modulus of unfilled rubbers is nearly independent of amplitude except at very large elongations.

For filled rubbers, the damping E''/E' is often nearly independent of amplitude, but in other cases, the damping gradually decreases with amplitude. As with the modulus, fillers usually increase the loss modulus E'' over the value found for the unfilled rubber[24, 26]; E''/E' may increase or decrease as the filler content increases. The amplitude effects of filled rubbers in most cases can be attributed to either a dewetting of the filler by the polymer[9, 145] or to a thixotropic breakdown of the filler agglomerates[117]. At large deformations, the rubber may pull away from the filler particles and create microscopic voids. A rest period will allow part of the bonds to re-form[45].

Dynamic moduli are sensitive to static strains as well as to the amplitude of the dynamic strains. If a material is stretched by a static load at the same time the dynamic modulus is measured, the dynamic modulus increases as the static deformation increases[49, 50, 90, 116].

The dynamic modulus of a rubber stretched 600 per cent may be a factor of ten to a hundred times greater than the unstretched value[90]. The loss modulus may also be increased by a static elongation, but the dissipation factor decreases with a static elongation. Part of these changes may be brought about by crystallization induced by molecular orientation, but some of the stiffening action at high elongations may be a result of some chain segments being so highly stretched out that they can not behave as coiled Gaussian chains. A completely stretched out chain segment has a very high elastic modulus.

At stresses comparable to the yield stress or the tensile strength of a polymer, the dynamic properties of rigid polymers vary with the applied oscillating stress[78, 79, 124, 127, 128]. The modulus decreases, and the damping increases with stress. The energy dissipated per cycle is proportional to the square of the stress if E''/E' is a constant. At very low stresses, this is generally true, but at high stresses the energy dissipated per cycle becomes proportional to a power of the stress greater than 2.0—usually between 2.2 and 3.

Resonance Dispersions. Some crystalline polymers exhibit resonance dispersions in addition to the viscoelastic relaxation dispersions discussed in previous sections. Resonance dispersions give rise to very unusual dynamic mechanical behavior[8, 31, 32]. Over very narrow frequency ranges the dynamic compliance can have both maxima and minima, and the damping can be negative. The phenomena are somewhat analogous to the anomalous refractive dispersion of light near an absorption band[63].

Typical dynamic data on a polymer showing resonance dispersion are given in Figure 7.29[32]. Most of the sharp damping peak occurs within a few per cent of the resonance frequency. This is in contrast to viscoelastic dispersions covering several decades in frequency. The real part of the compliance reaches a sharp maximum at a frequency slightly less than the frequency at which the damping J'' is a maximum. The real part of the compliance then rapidly decreases to a negative minimum at a frequency slightly higher than the frequency at which the damping maximum occurs.

Polyvinyl stearate and other crystalline materials have several resonance

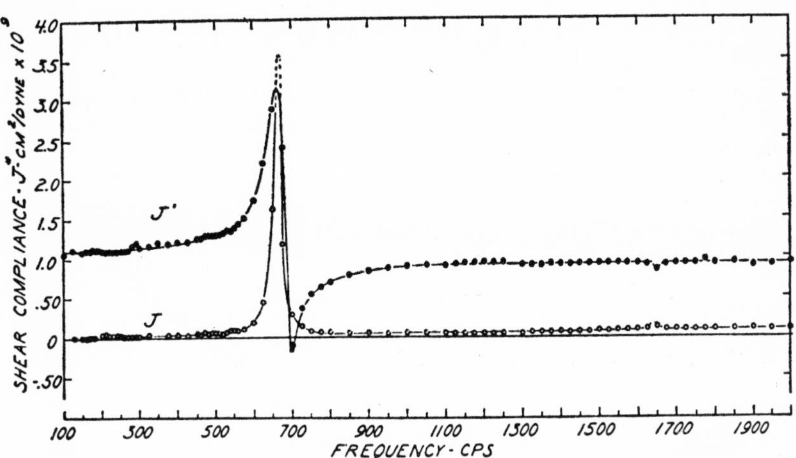

Figure 7.29. Variation of the real and imaginary parts of the complex shear compliance with frequency for polyvinyl stearate at 25°C and 0.8% static compression. Solid points, J′; open points, J″. [*Fitzgerald, E. R., J. Appl. Phys.*, **29,** *1442* (*1958*)]

dispersion regions. The intensity of these dispersion peaks and the frequency at which they occur are strongly affected by thermal treatment, cold working, clamping pressure on the specimen, time, and temperature. In some cases an increase in temperature brings about an increase in modulus in contrast to the usual behavior of polymers. Negative values of damping are observed when potential energy stored in the specimen is given up to the test apparatus. This stored energy could come from energy put into the specimen by cold working or from external stresses imposed by the specimen clamps. If this potential energy relaxes into oscillatory energy at a rate faster than energy can be dissipated by the system, a negative damping results. The whole field of resonance dispersion is poorly understood, but the phenomena appear to be due to the presence of either residual stresses in the specimen or to external stresses applied to the specimen by clamps. Since resonance dispersions have only been found with crystalline materials, they may be related to dislocations or imperfections in the crystalline phase.

Appendix A

Dynamic Mechanical Properties Measured by a Torsion Pendulum

$$I\frac{d^2\theta}{dt^2} + KG^*\theta = F(t) \qquad (7.A)$$

The angle of twist is θ, I is the moment of inertia of the oscillating system, G^* is the complex shear modulus, and K is a constant depending upon the dimensions of the specimen. The first term gives the inertial forces, the second term gives the force required to twist the specimen, and the last term $F(t)$ is the external force, which varies with time. For free vibrations, there is no external force, so $F(t) = 0$.

Since $G^* = G' + iG''$, the equation of motion for free vibrations becomes:

$$I\frac{d^2\theta}{dt^2} + K(G' + iG'')\theta = 0 \qquad (7.B)$$

The solution, when G' and G'' are assumed to be independent of frequency, is of the form

$$\theta = \theta_0 e^{-\alpha t} e^{i\omega t} = \theta_0 e^{(i\omega - \alpha)t} \qquad (7.C)$$

where α is an attenuation factor, and $e^{i\omega t}$ indicates the oscillatory nature of the motion. On substituting this solution into the equation of motion, one obtains

$$I(\alpha^2 - \omega^2 - 2i\omega\alpha) + iKG' + KG'' = 0 \qquad (7.D)$$

Separating this into real and imaginary parts results in

$$G' = \frac{I}{K}(\omega^2 - \alpha^2)$$
$$G'' = \frac{2\alpha I\omega}{K} \qquad (7.E)$$

Using the definition of logarithmic decrement Δ, and the fact that the motion is sinusoidal with a period of P, that is,

$$e^{i\omega t} = e^{i\omega(t+P)} \qquad (7.F)$$

the logarithmic decrement becomes

$$\Delta = \ln\frac{\theta_1}{\theta_2} = \ln\frac{\theta_0\, e^{-\alpha t}e^{i\omega t}}{\theta_0\, e^{-\alpha(t+P)}e^{i\omega(t+P)}} = \alpha P \qquad (7.G)$$

The period P is related to the natural angular frequency ω_n by

$$P = \frac{2\pi}{\omega_n} \qquad (7.H)$$

Substitution of equations G and H into equations E gives the dynamic properties in terms of experimentally observable quantities. Thus,

$$G' = \frac{I}{KP^2}(4\pi^2 - \Delta^2)$$
$$G'' = \frac{4\pi I\Delta}{KP^2} \qquad (7.I)$$
$$\frac{G''}{G'} = \frac{4\pi\Delta}{4\pi^2 - \Delta^2}$$

These equations are based on the assumption that G^* is independent of frequency. If the derivation had been made using the assumption that the dynamic viscosity is independent of frequency, equations I would have been changed to

$$G' = \frac{I}{KP^2}(4\pi^2 + \Delta^2)$$
$$G'' = \frac{4\pi I\Delta}{KP^2} \qquad (7.J)$$
$$\frac{G''}{G'} = \frac{4\pi\Delta}{4\pi^2 + \Delta^2}$$

In general, neither of these assumptions is accurate over a wide range of frequency for high polymers.

Appendix B

Dynamic Mechanical Behavior of a Maxwell Unit

The equation of motion of a Maxwell unit with a spring constant E and a dashpot with a viscosity η is

$$\frac{d\epsilon}{dt} = \frac{1}{E}\frac{d\sigma}{dt} + \frac{\sigma}{\eta} = \frac{1}{E}\frac{d\sigma}{dt} + \frac{\sigma}{\tau E} \tag{7.K}$$

since $\eta = \tau E$. The strain or deformation is ϵ, the stress is σ, and τ is the relaxation time.

The stress and strain are assumed to be complex oscillatory functions of the form

$$\begin{aligned} \sigma &= \sigma_0{}^* e^{i\omega t} \\ \epsilon &= \epsilon_0{}^* e^{i\omega t} \end{aligned} \tag{7.L}$$

and the complex dynamic modulus E^* is defined by

$$E^* = E' + iE'' = \frac{\sigma_0{}^*}{\epsilon_0{}^*} \tag{7.M}$$

Substituting these equations into the equation of motion gives

$$i\omega = \frac{i\omega\sigma_0{}^*}{E\epsilon_0{}^*} + \frac{\sigma_0{}^*}{\tau E\epsilon_0{}^*} = \frac{i\omega E^*}{E} + \frac{E^*}{\tau E} \tag{7.N}$$

Expanding this equation and separating it into real and imaginary parts gives

$$\begin{aligned} E' &= \omega\tau E'' \\ \omega &= \frac{\omega E'}{E} + \frac{E''}{\tau E} \end{aligned} \tag{7.O}$$

After substituting the first of these equations into the second, the final solution for the dynamic behavior of a Maxwell unit as a function of frequency becomes

$$\begin{aligned} E' &= \frac{\omega^2\tau^2 E}{1 + \omega^2\tau^2} \\ E'' &= \frac{\omega\tau E}{1 + \omega^2\tau^2} \\ \frac{E''}{E'} &= \frac{1}{\omega\tau} \end{aligned} \tag{7.P}$$

References

1. Atkinson, E. B., and Eagling, R. F., "Physical Properties of Polymers," Soc. Chem. Ind. Monograph No. 5, p. 197, New York, Macmillan Co., 1959.
2. Auberger, M., and Rinehart, J. S., *J. Appl. Phys.*, **32**, 219 (1961).

3. Ballou, J. W., and Smith, J. C., *J. Appl. Phys.*, **20,** 493 (1949).
4. Becker, G. W., and Oberst, H., *Kolloid Z.*, **148,** 6 (1956).
5. Bills, Jr., K. W., Sweeny, K. H., and Salcedo, F. S., *J. Appl. Polymer Sci.*, **4,** 259 (1960).
6. Blanchette, J. A., and Nielsen, L. E., *J. Polymer Sci.*, **20,** 317 (1956).
7. Bobalek, E. G., and Evans, R. M., *Trans. Soc. Plastics Eng. J.*, **1,** 93 (1961).
8. Bodner, S. R., *Trans. Soc. Rheology*, **4,** 141 (1960).
9. Bryant, K. C., and Bisset, D. C., *Rubber Chem. Tech.*, **30,** 610 (1957).
10. Buchdahl, R. and Nielsen, L. E., *J. Appl. Phys.*, **21,** 482 (1950).
11. Buchdahl, R. and Nielsen, L. E., *J. Polymer Sci.*, **15,** 1 (1955).
12. Bueche, F., *J. Polymer Sci.*, **22,** 113 (1956).
13. Charlesby, A. and Fukada, E., "The Rheology of Elastomers," p. 150, Mason, P. and Wookey, N., Ed., New York, Pergamon Press, Inc., 1958.
14. Cole, E. A., and Holmes, D. R., *J. Polymer Sci.*, **46,** 245 (1960).
15. Cox, W. P., Isaksen, R. A., and Merz, E. H., *J. Polymer Sci.*, **44,** 149 (1960).
16. Cramer, W. S., *J. Polymer Sci.*, **26,** 57 (1957).
17. De Mey, S., and Van Amerongen, G. J., *Kautschuk u. Gummi*, **9,** (1956) or *Rubber Chem. and Tech.*, **29,** 1215 (1956).
18. Deutsch, K., Hoff, E. A. W., and Reddish, W., *J. Polymer Sci.*, **13,** 565 (1954).
19. Dillon, J. H., and Gehman, S. D., *India Rubber World*, **115,** 61 (Oct., 1946).
20. Dillon, J. H., Prettyman, I. B., and Hall, G. L., *J. Appl. Phys.*, **15,** 309 (1944).
21. Drumm, M. F., Dodge, C. W. H., and Nielsen, L. E., *Ind. Eng. Chem.*, **48,** 76 (1956).
22. Duckwald, C. S., *Modern Plastics*, **33,** 148 (March, 1956).
23. Dunell, B. A., and Dillon, J. H., *Textile Research J.*, **21,** 393 (1951).
24. Ecker, R., *Rubber Chem. and Tech.*, **27,** 859 (1954).
25. Ecker, R., *Rubber Chem. and Tech.*, **30,** 200 (1957).
26. Enabnit, R. S., and Gehman, S. D., *Ind. Eng. Chem.*, **43,** 346 (1951).
27. Eyring, H., Alder, M. G., Rassmassler, S. A., and Christensen, C. J., *Textile Research J.*, **22,** 223 (1952).
28. Farrow, G., McIntosh, J., and Ward, I. M., *Makromol. Chem.*, **38,** 147 (1960).
29. Ferry, J. D., "Rheology," Vol. 2, Chap. 11, p. 433, Eirich, F. R., Ed., New York, Academic Press, Inc., 1958.
30. Ferry, J. D., "Viscoelastic Properties of Polymers," New York, John Wiley & Sons, Inc., 1961.
31. Fitzgerald, E. R., *J. Chem. Phys.*, **27,** 1180 (1957).
32. Fitzgerald, E. R., *J. Appl. Phys.*, **29,** 1442 (1958).
33. Fitzgerald, E. R., and Ferry, J. D., *J. Colloid Sci.*, **8,** 1 (1953).
34. Fletcher, W. P., and Gent, A., *Trans. Inst. Rubber Ind.*, **26,** 45 (1950).
35. Fletcher, W. P., and Gent, A., *Trans. Inst. Rubber Ind.*, **29,** 266 (1953).
36. Fletcher, W. P., and Gent, A., *J. Sci. Inst.*, **29,** 186 (1952).
37. Fletcher, W. P., and Gent, A., *Rubber Chem. and Tech.*, **27,** 209 (1954).
38. Flory, P. J., "Principles of Polymer Chemistry," Chap. 11, Ithaca, Cornell University Press, 1953.
39. Flory, P. J., *Trans. Faraday Soc.*, **51,** 848 (1955).
40. Fox, T. G., and Loshaek, S., *J. Polymer Sci.*, **15,** 371 (1955).
41. Fujino, K., Kawai, H., and Horino, T., *Textile Research J.*, **25,** 722 (1955).
42. Gaskins, F. H., and Philippoff, W., *Ind. Eng. Chem.*, **51,** 871 (1959).

43. Gehman, S. D., *Rubber Chem. and Tech.*, **30,** 1202 (1957).
44. Gehman, S. D., Jones, P. J., and Woodford, D. E., *Ind. Eng. Chem.*, **35,** 964 (1943).
45. Gui, K. E., Wilkinson, Jr., C. S., and Gehman, S. D., *Ind. Eng. Chem.*, **44,** 720 (1952).
46. Heijboer, J., *Kolloid Z.*, **148,** 36 (1956).
47. Heijboer, J., *Kolloid Z.*, **171,** 7 (1960).
48. Heijboer, J., Dekking, P., and Staverman, A. J., "Proceedings of the Second International Congress on Rheology," p. 123, Harrison, V. G. W., Ed., London, Butterworth's Scientific Pub., 1954.
49. Hillier, K. W., *Trans. Inst. Rubber Ind.*, **26,** 64 (1950).
50. Hillier, K. W., and Kolsky, H., *Proc. Phys. Soc. London*, **62,** 111 (1949).
51. Hoegberg, H., "International Symposium on Plastics Testing and Standardization," Spec. Tech. Publ. No. 247, p. 95, Philadelphia, Am. Soc. Testing Materials, 1958.
52. Hoegberg, H., Lovell, S. E., and Ferry, J. D., *Acta Chem. Scand.*, **14,** 1424 (1960).
53. Hoff, E. A. W., Robinson, D. W., and Willbourn, A. H., *J. Polymer Sci.*, **18,** 161 (1955).
54. Hoffman, J. D., Weeks, J. J., and Murphey, W. M., *J. Research Nat. Bur. Standards*, **63A,** 67 (1959).
55. Horio, M., and Onogi, S., *J. Appl. Phys.*, **22,** 977 (1951).
56. Horio, M., Onogi, S., Nakayama, C., and Yamamoto, K., *J. Appl. Phys.*, **22,** 966 (1951).
57. Illers, K. H., *Makromol. Chem.*, **38,** 168 (1960).
58. Illers, K. H., and Jenckel, E., *Rheol. Acta*, **1,** 322 (1958).
59. Illers, K. H., and Jenckel, E., *Kolloid Z.*, **160,** 97 (1958).
60. Illers, K. H., and Jenckel, E., *J. Polymer Sci.*, **41,** 528 (1959).
61. Jenckel, E., *Kolloid Z.*, **136,** 142 (1954).
62. Jenckel, E., and Herwig, H. U., *Kolloid Z.*, **148,** 57 (1956).
63. Jenkins, F. A., and White, H. E., "Fundamentals of Physical Optics," p. 297, New York, McGraw-Hill Book Co., 1937.
64. Jones, T. T., *Brit. Plastics*, **33,** 525 (1960).
65. Kawaguchi, T., *J. Polymer Sci.*, **32,** 417 (1958).
66. Ke, T'ing-Sui, and Ross, M., *Rev. Sci. Instr.*, **20,** 795 (1949).
67. Kerner, E. H., *Proc. Phys. Soc. London*, **69**B, 808 (1956).
68. Kimball, Jr., A. L., *Gen. Elec. Rev.*, **27,** 244 (April, 1924).
69. Kline, D. E., *J. Polymer Sci.*, **22,** 449 (1956).
70. Kline, D. E., Sauer, J. A., and Woodward, A. E., *J. Polymer Sci.*, **22,** 455 (1956).
71. Koppelmann, J., *Kolloid Z.*, **144,** 12 (1955).
72. Koppelmann, J., *Rheol. Acta*, **1,** 20 (1958).
73. Koppelmann, J., *Kolloid Z.*, **164,** 31 (1959).
74. Kuhn, W., and Kuenzle, O., *Helv. Chim. Acta*, **30,** 839 (1947).
75. Kurath, S. F., Passaglia, E., and Pariser, R., *J. Appl. Polymer Sci.*, **1,** 150 (1959).
76. Landel, R. F., *Trans. Soc. Rheology*, **2,** 53 (1958).
77. Lazan, B. J., *Modern Plastics*, **20,** 83 (Nov., 1942).
78. Lazan, B. J., *Trans. Am. Soc. Testing Materials* **65,** 87 (1943).
79. Lazan, B. J., and Yorgiadis, A., *Modern Plastics*, **21,** 119 (Aug., 1944).

80. Lazurkin, Y. S., *Rubber Chem. Tech.*, **13,** 898 (1940).
81. Leaderman, H., "Rheology," Vol. 2, Chap. 1, Eirich, F. R., Ed., New York, Academic Press, Inc., 1958.
82. Lyons, W. J., *Textile Research J.*, **19,** 123 (1949).
83. Lyons, W. J., *J. Appl. Phys.*, **29,** 1429 (1958).
84. McCrum, N. G., *J. Polymer Sci.*, **27,** 555 (1958).
85. McCrum, N. G., *ASTM Bull.* No. 242, 80 (Dec., 1959).
86. Markovitz, H., Yavorsky, P. M., Harper, Jr., R. C., Zapas, L. J., and De Witt, T. W., *Rev. Sci. Instr.*, **23,** 430 (1952).
87. Martin, G. M., and Mandelkern, L., *J. Research, Nat. Bur. Standards*, **62,** 141 (1959).
88. Marvin, R., "Viscoelasticity: Phenomenological Aspects," Chap. 2, Bergen, J. T., Ed., New York, Academic Press, Inc., 1960.
89. Marvin, R. S., Fitzgerald, E. R., and Ferry, J. D., *J. Appl. Phys.*, **21,** 197 (1950).
90. Mason, P., "Physical Properties of Polymers," Soc. Chem. Ind., Monograph No. 5, p. 262, New York, Macmillan Co., 1959.
91. Mason, P., *J. Appl. Polymer Sci.*, **4,** 212 (1960).
92. Maxwell, B., *ASTM Bull.* No. 215, 76 (July, 1956).
93. Maxwell, B., *J. Polymer Sci.*, **20,** 551 (1956).
94. Merrett, F. M., *J. Polymer Sci.*, **24,** 467 (1957).
95. Merz, E. H., Nielsen, L. E., and Buchdahl, R., *Ind. Eng. Chem.*, **43,** 1396 (1951).
96. Miller, R. L., *Polymer*, **1,** 135 (1960).
97. Morrisson, T. E., Zapas, L. J., and De Witt, T. W., *Rev. Sci. Instr.*, **26,** 357 (1955).
98. Moyal, J. E., and Fletcher, W. P., *Rubber Chem. and Technol.*, **19,** 163 (1946).
99. Muus, L. T., McCrum, N. G., and McGrew, F. C., *Soc. Plastics Eng. J.*, **15,** 368 (1959).
100. Newman, S., *J. Appl. Polymer Sci.*, **2,** 333 (1959).
101. Newman, S., and Cox, W. P., *J. Polymer Sci.*, **46,** 29 (1960).
102. Nielsen, L. E., Unpublished data of Monsanto Chemical Company.
103. Nielsen, L. E., *ASTM Bull.* No. 165, 48 (April, 1950).
104. Nielsen, L. E., *Rev. Sci. Instr.*, **22,** 690 (1951).
105. Nielsen, L. E., *J. Am. Chem. Soc.*, **75,** 1435 (1953).
106. Nielsen, L. E., *J. Appl. Phys.*, **25,** 1209 (1954).
107. Nielsen, L. E., *J. Appl. Polymer Sci.*, **2,** 351 (1959).
108. Nielsen, L. E., *J. Polymer Sci.*, **42,** 357 (1960).
109. Nielsen, L. E., *Soc. Plastics Eng. J.*, **16,** 525 (1960).
110. Nielsen, L. E., Buchdahl, R., and Levreault, R., *J. Appl. Phys.*, **21,** 607 (1950).
111. Nielsen, L. E., and Chinai, S. N., Unpublished data of Monsanto Chemical Company.
112. Nielsen, L. E., Wall, R. A., and Richmond, P. G., *Soc. Plastics Eng. J.*, **11,** 22 (Sept., 1955).
113. Nolle, A. W., *J. Appl. Phys.*, **19,** 753 (1948).
114. Oakes, W. G., and Robinson, D. W., *J. Polymer Sci.*, **14,** 505 (1954).
115. Painter, G. W., *ASTM Bull.* No. 177, 45 (October, 1951).
116. Painter, G. W., *Rubber Age*, **74,** 701 (1954).
117. Payne, A. R., "Proceedings of Third Rubber Technology Conference," p. 413, Messenger, T. H., Ed., Cambridge, Eng., W. Heffer & Sons, Ltd., 1954.

118. Payne, A. R., *J. Appl. Polymer Sci.*, **3**, 127 (1960).
119. Payne, A. R., and Scott, J. R., "Engineering Design with Rubber," New York, Interscience Publishers, Inc., 1960.
120. Philippoff, W., *J. Appl. Phys.*, **24**, 685 (1953).
121. Plazek, D. J., Vrancken, M. N., and Berge, J. W., *Trans. Soc. Rheology*, **2**, 39 (1958).
122. Ree, T., Chen, M. C., and Eyring, H., *Textile Research J.*, **21**, 789 (1951).
123. Rempel, R. C., Weaver, A. E., Sands, R. H., and Miller, R. L., *J. Appl. Phys.*, **28**, 1082 (1957).
124. Robertson, J. M., and Yorgiadis, A. J., *J. Appl. Mechanics*, **13**, A173 (Sept., 1946).
125. Robinson, D., *J. Sci. Instr.*, **32**, 2 (1955).
126. Roelig, H., *Rubber Chem. and Technol.*, **12**, 395 (1939).
127. Sauer, J. A., Marin, J., and Hsiao, C. C., *J. Appl. Phys.*, **20**, 507 (1949).
128. Sauer, J. A., and Oliphant, W. J., *Am. Soc. Testing Materials Proc.*, **49**, 1119 (1949).
129. Schmieder, K., and Wolf, K., *Kolloid Z.*, **127**, 65 (1952).
130. Schmieder, K., and Wolf, K., *Kolloid Z.*, **134**, 149 (1953).
131. Shaw, R., *Rubber Chem. and Technol.*, **22**, 1045 (1949) or *India Rubber World*, **118**, 6, 796 (1948).
132. Shinohora, Y., *J. Appl. Polymer Sci.*, **1**, 251 (1959).
133. Shoulberg, R. H., Zimmerli, F. H., and Kohler, O. E., *Trans. Soc. Rheology*, **3**, 27 (1959).
134. Sinnott, K. M., *J. Appl. Phys.*, **29**, 1433 (1958).
135. Staverman, A. J., and Schwarzl, F., "Die Physik der Hochpolymeren," Vol. 4, Chap. 1, Stuart, H. A., Ed., Berlin, Springer Verlag, 1956.
136. Strella, S., *ASTM Bull.* No. 214, 47 (1956).
137. Thompson, A. B., and Woods, D. W., *Trans. Faraday Soc.*, **52**, 1383 (1956).
138. Thurn, H., *Kunststoffe*, **50**, 606 (1960).
139. Tobolsky, A. V., "Properties and Structure of Polymers," New York, John Wiley & Sons, Inc., 1960.
140. Tokita, N., *J. Polymer Sci.*, **20**, 515 (1956).
141. Treloar, L. R. G., "Physics of Rubber Elasticity," Oxford, Clarendon Press, 1958, 2nd Edition.
142. Treloar, L. R. G., *Polymer*, **1**, 95 (1960).
143. Ueberreiter, K., and Kanig, G., *J. Chem. Phys.*, **18**, 399 (1950).
144. Wall, R. A., Sauer, J. A., and Woodward, A. E., *J. Polymer Sci.*, **35**, 281 (1959).
145. Waring, J. R. S., *Ind. Eng. Chem.*, **43**, 352 (1951).
146. Wilkinson, C. S., and Gehman, S. D., *Anal. Chem.*, **22**, 283 (1950).
147. Willbourn, A. H., *Trans. Faraday Soc.*, **54**, 717 (1958).
148. Williams, M. L., and Ferry, J. D., *J. Colloid Sci.*, **9**, 479 (1954).
149. Williams, M. L., Landel, R. F., and Ferry, J. D., *J. Am. Chem. Soc.*, **77**, 3701 (1955).
150. Witte, R. S., Mrowca, B. A., and Guth, E., *J. Appl. Phys.*, **20**, 481 (1949).
151. Wolf, K., *Kunststoffe*, **41**, 89 (1951).
152. Wolf, K., and Schmieder, K., "International Symposium on Makromol. Chem.," p. 732, Milan S.P.A. Arti Grafiche Panetto & Petrelli, Rome, 1955.

153. Woodward, A. E., Crissman, J. M., and Sauer, J. A., *J. Polymer Sci.*, **44,** 23 (1960).
154. Woodward, A. E., and Sauer, J. A., *Fortschr. Hochpolym. Forsch.*, (Adv. in Polymer Sci.), **1,** 114 (1958).
155. Woodward, A. E., and Sauer, J. A., "The Physical Properties of Polymers," Soc. Chem. Ind. Monograph No. 5, p. 245, New York, Macmillan Co., 1959.
156. Woodward, A. E., Sauer, J. A., Deeley, C. W., and Kline, D. E., *J. Colloid Sci.*, **12,** 363 (1957).
157. Wurstlin, F., *Kolloid Z.*, **113,** 18 (1949) and **120,** 84 (1951).
158. Yin, T. P., Lovell, S. E., and Ferry, J. D., *J. Phys. Chem.*, **65,** 534 (1961).

Chapter 8

INTERRELATIONS BETWEEN VARIOUS PROPERTIES

Calculations Based on Distributions of Relaxation or Retardation Times

Viscoelastic theory enables one to calculate creep, stress relaxation, or stress-strain behavior from dynamic mechanical data in many cases. Likewise, the dynamic behavior or other mechanical properties can be calculated from the other types of tests[1, 13, 19, 30, 31, 37]. The conversion of one type of data to another is generally carried out by the use of the distribution of relaxation or retardation times. Once the distribution of relaxation or retardation times is known from one type of measurement, the distribution can be used to calculate another type of mechanical behavior. Some of the equations for making such calculations have been given in previous chapters; others will be given in the first part of this chapter. The original data should cover many decades of frequency or time in order to get a good approximation to the distributions. The calculations are laborious and complex, and so they are generally not used in practical applications.

The general equations for calculating the stress-relaxation modulus $E_r(t)$ or the creep compliance $J(t)$ from the distribution of relaxation times $H(\ln \tau)$, plotted on a log τ scale, or the logarithmic retardation spectrum $L(\ln \tau)$ are[13, 30, 31, 37]:

$$E_r(t) = \int_{-\infty}^{\infty} H(\ln \tau)e^{-t/\tau}\, d \ln \tau + E_\infty \tag{8.1}$$

$$J(t) = J_0 + \int_{-\infty}^{\infty} L(\ln \tau)[1 - e^{-t/\tau}]\, d \ln \tau + t/\eta \tag{8.2}$$

where E_∞ is the long time equilibrium modulus in cases where there is no flow, η is the viscosity, and J_0 is the instantaneous glassy state compliance. If the relaxation spectrum is given in terms of linear time rather than in log time, equation 8.1 for stress relaxation becomes

$$E_r(t) = \int_0^\infty H(\tau)e^{-t/\tau}\, d\tau + E_\infty \tag{8.3}$$

An analogous equation holds for creep.

Dynamic mechanical properties may be calculated from the logarithmic relaxation or retardation spectra by:

$$E'(\omega) = \int_{-\infty}^{\infty} H(\ln \tau) \frac{\omega^2\tau^2}{1 + \omega^2\tau^2}\, d \ln \tau + E_\infty \tag{8.4}$$

$$E''(\omega) = \int_{-\infty}^{\infty} H(\ln \tau) \frac{\omega\tau}{1 + \omega^2\tau^2}\, d \ln \tau \tag{8.5}$$

$$J'(\omega) = J_0 + \int_{-\infty}^{\infty} L(\ln \tau) \frac{1}{1 + \omega^2\tau^2}\, d \ln \tau \tag{8.6}$$

$$J''(\omega) = \int_{-\infty}^{\infty} L(\ln \tau) \frac{\omega\tau}{1 + \omega^2\tau^2}\, d \ln \tau + \frac{1}{\omega\eta} \tag{8.7}$$

If the distribution of relaxation times is given in linear time instead of in log time, equation 8.4 becomes

$$E'(\omega) = \int_0^\infty \frac{H(\tau)\omega^2\tau^2}{1 + \omega^2\tau^2}\, d\tau \tag{8.8}$$

The other equations become changed in a similar manner. The viscosity η is given by:

$$\eta = \int_0^\infty H(\tau)\, d\tau \tag{8.9}$$

The stress-strain curve $\sigma(\epsilon)$ may be represented by

$$\sigma(\epsilon) = E_\infty \epsilon + K \int_{-\infty}^{\infty} \tau H(\ln \tau)\, (1 - e^{-\epsilon/K\tau})\, d \ln \tau \tag{8.10}$$

where K is the strain rate, $d\epsilon/dt$ that would be present if linear viscoelasticity theory should be valid. If no stress relaxation occurs during the time required to make the test, a stress-strain curve ought to be a straight line. Curvature of a stress-strain curve is an indication that a stress-relaxation process is taking place.

Sometimes one type of spectrum must be converted to the other type.

At any given time,

$$H(\ln \tau)L(\ln \tau) \leq 1 \tag{8.11}$$

The exact relations are:

$$L(\ln \tau) = \frac{H(\ln \tau)}{\left\{\left[E_\infty - \int_{-\infty}^{\infty} \frac{H(\ln \tau')}{1 - \tau'/\tau}\, d \ln \tau'\right]^2 + \pi^2 H^2(\ln \tau)\right\}} \tag{8.12}$$

and

$$H(\ln \tau) = \frac{L(\ln \tau)}{\left\{\left[J_0 + \int_{-\infty}^{\infty} \frac{L(\ln \tau')}{1 - \tau'/\tau}\, d \ln \tau' - \frac{\tau}{\eta}\right]^2 + \pi^2 L^2(\ln \tau)\right\}} \tag{8.13}$$

A number of approximate equations relating creep, stress relaxation, or dynamic properties to the appropriate spectrum of relaxation or retardation times have been given in Chapters 3, 4, and 7.

Calculations From Molecular Theories

The molecular theory of viscoelastic behavior has reached the stage where some estimates of mechanical properties can be made from the theory[4, 13, 29, 42]. The only experimental data required to use these theories are the steady state viscosity η_0 at zero rate of shear at a given temperature and the molecular weight M of the polymer. The dynamic mechanical properties of polymers above their glass transition temperatures, according to the modified Rouse theory, are given by:

$$G' = \frac{dRT}{M} \sum_{P=1}^{N} \frac{\omega^2 \tau_p^2}{1 + \omega^2 \tau_p^2} \tag{8.14}$$

$$G'' = \frac{dRT}{M} \sum_{P=1}^{N} \frac{\omega \tau_p}{1 + \omega^2 \tau_p^2} \tag{8.15}$$

where

$$\tau_p = \frac{6\eta_0 M}{\pi^2 dRTP^2}; \qquad \left(P = 1, 2, 3, \cdots \frac{M}{M_c}\right) \tag{8.16}$$

when P has integer values between 1 and M/M_c. For values of P greater than M/M_c, the relaxation times τ_p are given by

$$\tau_p = \frac{6\eta_0 M}{\pi^2 dRTP^2(f/f_0)}; \qquad \frac{M}{M_c} < P < N \tag{8.17}$$

where

$$f/f_0 = (M/M_c)^{2.4} \tag{8.18}$$

In these equations ω is the angular frequency of the vibrations, M is the molecular weight of the polymer, M_c is the molecular weight between molecular entanglements, d is the density at the absolute temperature T, and R is the gas constant. The average segmental friction coefficient, which determines the resistance a molecular segment experiences in moving through its surroundings in the absence of intermolecular entanglements, is f_0, while f is the segmental friction coefficient for entangled molecules. Since for most polymers of practical interest M/M_c is of the order of about ten, f/f_0 is of the order of about a hundred or a thousand. The maximum relaxation time τ_1 may be calculated by putting $P = 1$ in equation 8.16. For a typical polymer with a molecular weight of 250,000, and a steady state viscosity at low rates of shear of 10^6 poises, at 175°C, the maximum relaxation time τ_1 is about four seconds[7].

Bueche's theory[4] gives similar results for the dynamic mechanical behavior in terms of the zero rate of shear viscosity η_0. The viscosity of a molten polymer as measured in a conventional viscometer is known to decrease as the rate of shear increases. In other words, molten polymers are not Newtonian in their behavior since the ratio of the shear stress to the rate of shear is not a constant as required by the definition of viscosity of a Newtonian liquid. The variation of the melt viscosity η as a function of the rate of shear $d\epsilon s/dt = \dot{\gamma}$ is given by Bueche's theory by

$$\eta = \eta_0 \left(1 - \frac{6}{\pi^2} \sum_{n=1}^{N} \frac{\dot{\gamma}^2\tau_m^2}{n^2(n^4 + \dot{\gamma}^2\tau_m^2)} \left\{2 - \frac{\dot{\gamma}^2\tau_m^2}{n^4 + \dot{\gamma}^2\tau_m^2}\right\}\right) \tag{8.19}$$

where

$$\tau_m = \frac{12\eta_0 M}{\pi^2 dRT} \tag{8.20}$$

and N is the number of segments in a molecule.

Correlation of Melt Viscosity with Dynamic Mechanical Properties

Cox and Merz[5, 6] discovered an empirical relationship between the melt viscosity of polymers as a function of rate of shear and the complex dynamic viscosity as a function of frequency. The deviation of the melt viscosity from Newtonian behavior was shown by Cox and Merz to be due to the development of elasticity in the molten polymer. Figure 8.1 shows

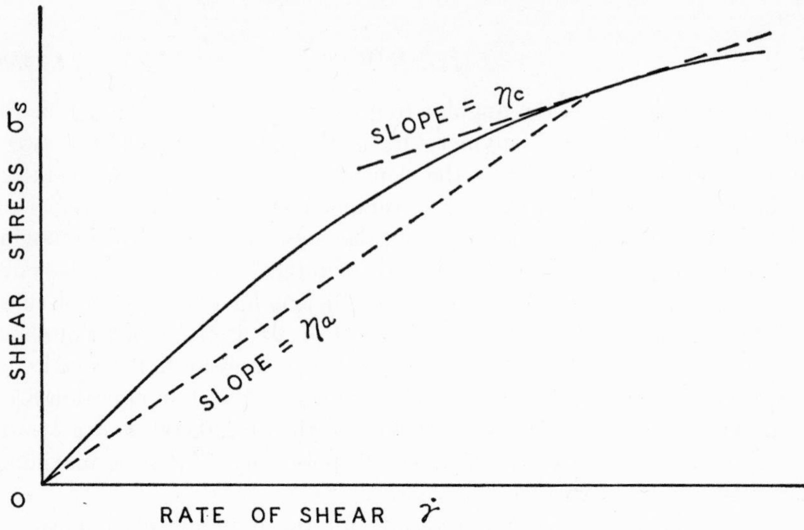

Figure 8.1. Calculation of apparent viscosity η_a and consistency η_c from a typical shear stress-rate of shear curve for a molten polymer.

the general character of data obtained from viscous polymers with a viscometer such as a capillary rheometer[22] or a rotational coaxial cylinder viscometer. To calculate a viscosity from the experimental data the shear stress σ_s is plotted against the rate of shear, $\dot{\gamma} = d\epsilon_s/dt$. The apparent viscosity is defined as

$$\eta_a = \frac{\sigma_s}{\dot{\gamma}} \tag{8.21}$$

while the consistency η_c is defined as

$$\eta_c = \frac{d\sigma_s}{d\dot{\gamma}} \tag{8.22}$$

At any rate of shear the apparent viscosity is the slope of the line passing through the origin and the experimental curve as in Figure 8.1. The consistency is the slope of the curve at any point. Extending the idea of De Witt[10] that angular frequency ω is equivalent to rate of shear $\dot{\gamma}$, Cox and Merz found that the apparent viscosity as a function of rate of shear is nearly identical to the absolute value of the complex viscosity η^* as a function of angular frequency. This correlation is illustrated in Figure 8.2[6]. Furthermore, Cox and Merz found that the consistency as a function

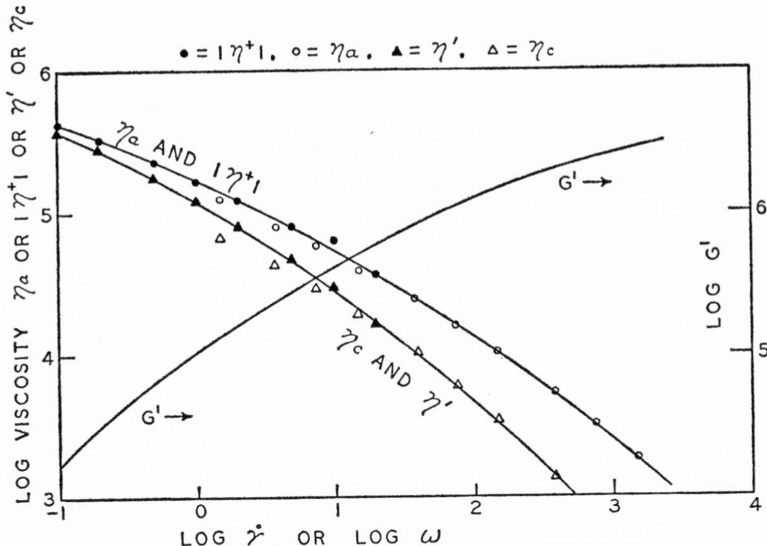

Figure 8.2. Correlation of steady flow viscosity with dynamic mechanical properties of high density polyethylene at 180°C. (*After Cox, W. P., and Merz, E. H., "Symposium on Plastics Testing and Standardization," Spec. Tech. Pub. No. 247, Am. Soc. Testing Materials, 1958*)

of rate of shear is nearly equal to the dynamic viscosity η' as a function of frequency. The polymer elasticity or shear modulus, G', can be calculated from the difference between the apparent viscosity and the consistency by

$$G' = \dot{\gamma}(\eta_a^2 - \eta_c^2)^{\frac{1}{2}} \tag{8.23}$$

An example of such a calculation from polyethylene data is shown in Figure 8.2. Recently Horio, Onogi, and Ogiwara[7] found that the dynamic viscosity η' correlates better with the apparent viscosity η_a than it does with the consistency η_c in contrast to the results of Cox and Merz. The empirical correlations of Cox and Merz are at least partially substantiated, however, by the molecular theories of viscoelasticity[6, 26, 33]. Thus, it appears that the steady flow behavior of a polymer melt can be predicted from dynamic mechanical measurements.

Correlation of Creep and Stress Relaxation with Dynamic Properties

A very simple relation exists for estimating dynamic data at a given temperature from creep data, and vice versa. If creep obeys the Nutting equation,

$$\log \epsilon(t) = \log K + \log \sigma + n \log t \tag{8.24}$$

the dynamic properties may be estimated from[3, 41]:

$$E \doteq \frac{\sigma}{\epsilon(t)} \tag{8.25}$$

$$\frac{E''}{E'} \doteq \frac{\pi}{2}\left(\frac{d \log \epsilon}{d \log t}\right) = \frac{\pi}{2} n \tag{8.26}$$

for any time. In these equations n and K are constants. These equations imply a constant damping but a modulus which increases with frequency. Time t from the creep curve is related to frequency ω of the dynamic test by $t = 1/\omega$. The constant n is calculated from the slope of the creep curve when both the elongation and time are plotted on log scales, that is:

$$n = \frac{d \log \epsilon}{d \log t}. \tag{8.27}$$

Table 8.1 compares the calculated damping from creep curves with the observed damping measured with a torsion pendulum. Although the agreement is poor in a few cases, it is amazingly good for the most part.

Ninomiya and Ferry[13, 24] have derived another relatively simple equation relating creep and dynamic properties:

$$J(t) \doteq J'(\omega) + 0.40\, J''(0.40\omega) - 0.014\, J''(10\omega) \tag{8.28}$$

TABLE 8.1. MECHANICAL DAMPING FROM CREEP BY USE OF NUTTING'S EQUATION.*

Polymer	Temp. °C	Damping E''/E' from Nutting's Eq.	Experimental Damping G''/G'
Plasticized polyvinyl chloride	40°C	0.118	0.133
Plasticized polyvinyl chloride	20	0.248	0.30
Plasticized polyvinyl chloride	0	0.418	0.44
Plasticized polyvinyl chloride	−20	0.177	0.16
Plasticized polyvinyl chloride	−30	0.141	0.15
Crosslinked butyl rubber	24	0.130	0.137
Crosslinked butyl rubber	24	0.302	0.185
Crosslinked butyl rubber	24	0.093	0.111
Styrene-butadiene copolymer	24	0.290	0.280
Styrene-butadiene copolymer	24	0.354	0.398
Polyethylene (low density)	24	0.186	0.175

* Buchdahl, R. and Nielsen, L. E., *J. Appl. Phys.*, **22,** 1344 (1951), and unpublished data of Nielsen, L. E., and Dunn, D., Monsanto Chemical Company.

$J(t)$ is the creep compliance at any time t. $J'(\omega)$ is the dynamic compliance at an angular frequency ω. If the damping is small, $J'(\omega)$ is approximately equal to the reciprocal of the dynamic modulus; more exactly it is

$$J' = \frac{E'}{(E')^2 + (E'')^2} \tag{8.29}$$

J'' (0.40ω) is the dynamic loss compliance at a frequency of 0.40ω, while $J''(10\omega)$ is the value at a frequency of 10ω radians per second. The loss compliance is related to the dynamic moduli by

$$J'' = \frac{E''}{(E')^2 + (E'')^2} \tag{8.30}$$

Frequency ω is converted to time t by $t = 1/\omega$. Plazek[28] tested this relation between creep and dynamic properties using a highly plasticized cellulose nitrate.

Dunell and Tobolsky[11, 12] developed a very simple way of estimating the loss modulus E'' from stress relaxation data. If stress-relaxation data are plotted as stress σ or relaxation modulus $E_r(t)$ against log time, the negative slope of this curve is proportional to the loss modulus at any frequency ω defined by $\omega = 1/t$:

$$E'' = \frac{-\pi}{2\epsilon_0 \log_e 10}\left(\frac{d\sigma}{d \log t}\right) = \frac{-\pi}{4.606} \frac{dE_r(t)}{d \log t} \tag{8.31}$$

The fixed strain used in the test is ϵ_0, and $E_r(t)$ is the stress-relaxation modulus as a function of time.

The stress-relaxation modulus can be calculated from dynamic data by the method of Ninomiya and Ferry[13, 24]:

$$G(t) = G'(\omega) - 0.40G''(0.40\omega) + 0.014G''(10\omega) \tag{8.32}$$

In converting from dynamic to stress relaxation behavior, the frequency ω is converted to time t by $t = 1/\omega$. This equation requires dynamic data at three frequencies for each calculation of the stress-relaxation modulus at a given time.

Miscellaneous Approximate Interrelations

The impact strength of a rigid polymer may often be roughly estimated from the value of the damping. If the dissipation factor E''/E' is below about 0.02, a rigid material is generally brittle with a low impact strength, while if the damping is over 0.10, the material usually has a high impact strength. In addition to the damping at the temperature at which the impact test is performed, the presence of secondary damping peaks can have a big effect on the impact strength. A large secondary damping peak below 0°C is often an indication of a tough polymer even though the damping at room temperature is low. Examples of high impact polymers which have low damping at room temperature but which have large secondary damping peaks at low temperatures are polystyrene-rubber polyblends and polycarbonates made from "Bis Phenol-A."

The stress-strain behavior of a polymer may often be approximated from dynamic mechanical data. The elastic modulus or initial slope of the stress-strain curve is roughly the same as the corresponding dynamic modulus obtained at the same temperature as long as the time scales of the two types of measurements are similar. If the damping of a rigid material is low, that is, if E''/E' is less than about 0.02, and if the polymer has no large secondary damping peak at low temperatures, the stress-strain curve generally is nearly a straight line without a yield point, and the elongation at break will be small (often about 2 per cent). If the dissipation factor is greater than 0.10, or if the polymer has a prominent secondary damping peak at the test temperature or below, the polymer can be expected to have a yield point and a relatively large elongation at break. It is impossible to predict yield stresses or tensile strengths from the usual types of dynamic tests. However, Boyer[2] has empirically shown that the tensile strength of some polymers can be estimated from their softening temperatures, which can be obtained from the maximum in the loss modulus E''. If the softening or heat distortion temperature is only slightly above room temperature, the tensile strength probably will be in the neighborhood of 3000 psi. Tensile strengths of about 10,000 psi can be expected if the softening temperature is around 100°C. These empirical estimates are not very accurate as the values of tensile strength depend upon so many other factors such as molecular weight and speed of testing.

Electrical Properties

The electrical properties of polymers can often be related to their mechanical behavior. The dielectric constant ϵ' and electrical loss factor ϵ'' are analogous to elastic compliance and mechanical loss factor while the resistivity is analogous to viscosity. A direct-current conductivity measurement at constant voltage is the electrical analogue of a mechanical creep test at constant load.

When a voltage is initially applied, there is no charge on a dielectric-filled condenser, so the current is large. When the condenser is fully charged, there is no current flowing in the condenser even though the voltage is a maximum. Thus, in charging a condenser filled with a low loss dielectric

TABLE 8.2. ELECTRICAL PROPERTIES OF POLYMERS AT 24°C AND 60 CYCLES/SECOND.*

Polymer	Dielectric Constant	Power Factor
Polyethylene	2.28	.0002
Polystyrene	2.5	.0001
Polytetrafluoroethylene	2.1	.0002
Polyvinyl chloride (unplasticized)	3	.01
Polyvinyl chloride (plasticized)	5–9	.05–.15
Polymethyl methacrylate	3.5	.04
Nylon 6	6.1	.4
Nylon 66	3.9–7.6	.01–.09
Cellulose acetate (plasticized)	3.5–7.5	.01–.06
Phenol-formaldehyde (mineral-filled)	4.7–5.5	.01–.06

* From various sources including, "Technical Data on Plastics," Washington, D. C., Manufacturing Chemists' Assoc., 1957.

material, the current and voltage are approximately 90° out of phase, and little heat is generated since the power factor is zero. The dielectric constant of a material in a condenser is determined largely by the number and strength of dipoles in the material and the ease with which they can respond to the applied electric field. Nonpolar polymers such as polyethylene have low dielectric constants, and the electrical properties of such materials are determined largely by impurities and dipoles introduced by oxygen during degradation processes. Polar polymers such as polyvinyl chloride, polyacrylonitrile, and nylons have higher dielectric constants as shown in Table 8.2. The dielectric constant is high when the dipoles are free to follow the electric field; it is low when the frequency is so high (or the temperature so low) that the dipoles cannot follow the field[18]. At very low and at very high frequencies, where the dipoles can either follow the field completely or not at all, the electrical loss factor is small. At intermediate frequencies the dipoles can partially follow the field, so that heat is generated as the current and voltage become more in phase.

Typical electrical data on a polar polymer are shown in Figures 8.3 and 8.4[8, 16, 17, 18, 32, 35]. At a given test frequency, the dielectric constant increases with temperature as the polymer softens. At high temperatures the dielectric constant reaches a plateau and then very gradually decreases with increasing temperature. The gradual decrease comes about from a decrease in the orientation of the dipoles as the kinetic motion of the molecules opposes the orienting effect of the electric field, and from the decreasing density. The loss factor curves go through a maximum as the temperature is changed. Curves of similar shape would have been obtained

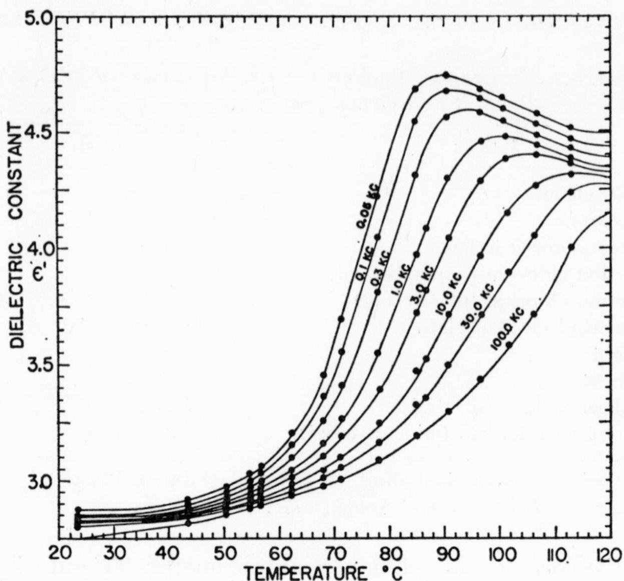

Figure 8.3. Dielectric constants of polyvinyl butyral. [*After Sutherland, T. H., and Funt, B. L., J. Polymer Sci.*, **11,** *177 (1953)*]

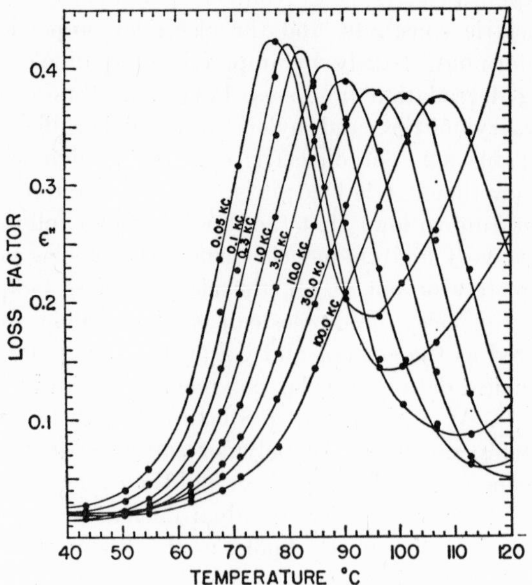

Figure 8.4. Loss factors of polyvinyl butyral. [*After Sutherland, T. H., and Funt, B. L., J. Polymer Sci.*, **11,** *177 (1953)*]

if the frequency had been varied and the temperature held constant. The curves shift with frequency (or temperature) in a manner very similar to the shifts in dynamic compliance and dissipation factor with frequency (or temperature).

The complex dielectric constant ϵ^* can be represented by

$$\epsilon^* = \epsilon' - i\epsilon'' \tag{8.33}$$

If the dipoles have a single relaxation time τ, the electrical properties can be defined by the following equations:

$$\epsilon' = \epsilon_\infty + \frac{\epsilon_0 - \epsilon_\infty}{1 + \omega^2\tau^2} \tag{8.34}$$

$$\epsilon'' = \frac{(\epsilon_0 - \epsilon_\infty)\omega\tau}{1 + \omega^2\tau^2} \tag{8.35}$$

where ϵ_0 is the dielectric constant at zero frequency and ϵ_∞ is the dielectric constant at infinite frequency. The loss factor goes through its maximum when $\omega\tau = 1$. Actual polymers have many electrical relaxation times instead of a single one just as such polymers have many mechanical relaxation times. The distribution of relaxation times spreads the loss factor curves over a wider frequency range than would have been found with a single relaxation time.

Electrical conductivity (or its reciprocal, resistivity) is another important property of polymers. Resistivity affects the alternating current dielectric properties in a manner analogous to the way in which viscosity affects the dynamic mechanical properties of a viscoelastic material. The high temperature minimum and subsequent increase in the loss factor shown in Figure 8.4 for the lower frequencies are due to conductivity. At low frequencies where the dipolar contribution to the loss factor is small, the loss factor ϵ'' is mainly due to the conductivity κ, and an equation of the following form is valid:

$$\epsilon'' = 1.8 \times 10^{12}(\kappa - \kappa_0)/f \tag{8.36}$$

where f is the alternating current frequency. The conductivity calculated from this equation extrapolates at low frequencies to the more familiar direct current conductivity, κ_0.

Correlations of electrical and mechanical properties have been attempted many times[8, 9, 14, 17, 20, 23, 25, 27, 34, 36, 40] among others. In many cases these attempts have been moderately successful. The correlation between the electrical and mechanical properties is generally best when the dipolar part of the molecule is connected directly to the backbone chain as it is in polyvinyl chloride. In this case, the phenomena related to the glass transition are responsible for the changes in both the mechanical and electrical behavior. At a fixed frequency, the peaks in the electrical dissipation factor ϵ''/ϵ' (or in the power factor) and mechanical dissipation factor occur at about the same temperature, although the electrical peak often is found at a slightly higher temperature[34, 36].

If the dipole is on a side chain, as in polymethyl methacrylate, the main peak in electrical dissipation factor does not correlate with the main mechanical damping peak[9]. In this case, the mechanical peak is associated with molecular motion of the polymer backbone while the main electrical peak is associated with motion of the side chain. Better correlation of the secondary damping peak with the main electrical peak is generally found for this type of polymer.

The method of reduced variables as developed by Williams, Landel, and Ferry[39] can be used to superpose electrical data obtained at different temperatures[14, 15, 27, 38]. The shift factor determining the temperature dependence of the relaxation times is essentially the same for both electrical and mechanical measurements. The master curves for normalized dielectric constant and electrical loss can be used to calculate distributions of relaxation times. The distribution of electrical relaxation times is generally quite similar, but not identical, to the distribution of mechanical relaxation times.

Fuoss[17] found for a series of plasticized polyvinyl chlorides that the elastic modulus was nearly constant when all samples were compared at the temperature at which the 60-cycle electrical loss factor was a maximum. The peak in the 60-cycle loss factor occurs at a temperature at which the plastic is soft and rubbery in nature. Similar correlations have been found by others.

References

1. Alfrey, T., and Doty, P., *J. Appl. Phys.*, **16,** 700 (1945).
2. Boyer, R. F., *J. Appl. Phys.*, **22,** 723 (1951).
3. Buchdahl, R., and Nielsen, L. E., *J. Appl. Phys.*, **22,** 1344 (1951).
4. Bueche, F., *J. Chem. Phys.*, **22,** 603 and 1570 (1954).
5. Cox, W. P., and Merz, E. H., *J. Polymer Sci.*, **28,** 619 (1958).
6. Cox, W. P., and Merz, E. H., "International Symposium on Plastics Testing and Standardization," Spec. Tech. Publ. No. 247, p. 178, Philadelphia, Am. Soc. Testing Materials, Oct., 1958.
7. Cox, W. P., Nielsen, L. E., and Keeney, R., *J. Polymer Sci.*, **26,** 365 (1957).
8. Davies, J. M., Miller, R. F., and Busse, W. F., *J. Am. Chem. Soc.*, **63,** 361 (1941).
9. Deutsch, K., Hoff, E. A. W., and Reddish, W., *J. Polymer Sci.*, **13,** 565 (1954).
10. De Witt, T. W., *J. Appl. Phys.*, **26,** 889 (1955).

11. Dunell, B. A., and Tobolsky, A. V., *J. Chem. Phys.*, **17**, 1001 (1949).
12. Dunell, B. A., and Tobolsky, A. V., *Textile Research J.*, **19**, 631 (1949).
13. Ferry, J. D., "Viscoelastic Properties of Polymers," New York, John Wiley & Sons, Inc., 1961.
14. Ferry, J. D. and Strella, S., *J. Colloid Sci.*, **13**, 459 (1958).
15. Fitzgerald, E. R., and Ferry, J. D., *J. Colloid Sci.*, **8**, 1 (1953).
16. Funt, B., and Sutherland, T., *Can. Chem. J.*, **30**, 940 (1952).
17. Fuoss, R. M., *J. Am. Chem. Soc.*, **63**, 369 and 378 (1941).
18. Fuoss, R. M., "The Chemistry of Large Molecules," Burk, R. E., and Grummitt, O., Ed., Chapt. 6, p. 191, New York, Intersience Publishers, Inc., 1943.
19. Gross, B., "Mathematical Structure of the Theories of Viscoelasticity," Paris, Hermann, 1953.
20. Hoff, E. A. W., Robinson, D. W., and Willbourn, A. H., *J. Polymer Sci.*, **18**, 161 (1955).
21. Horio, M., Onogi, S., and Ogiwara, S., *J. Japan Soc. Testing Materials*, **10**, 350 (1961).
22. Merz, E. H., and Colwell, R. E., *ASTM Bull.*, No. 232, 63 (1958).
23. Nielsen, L. E. Buchdahl, R., and Levreault, R., *J. Appl. Phys.*, **21**, 607 (1950).
24. Ninomiya, K., and Ferry, J. D., *J. Colloid Sci.*, **14**, 36 (1959).
25. Oakes, W. G., and Robinson, D. W., *J. Polymer Sci.*, **14**, 505, (1954).
26. Pao, Y., *J. Appl. Phys.*, **28**, 59 (1957).
27. Payne, A. R., "Physical Properties of Polymers," Soc. Chem. Ind., Monograph No. 5, p. 273, New York, Macmillan Co., 1959.
28. Plazek, D. J., *J. Colloid Sci.*, **15**, 50 (1960).
29. Rouse Jr., P. E., *J. Chem. Phys.*, **21**, 1272 (1953).
30. Smith, T. L., *Trans. Soc. Rheology*, **2**, 131 (1956).
31. Staverman, A. J., and Schwarzl, F., "Die Physik der Hochpolymeren," Vol. 4, Chap. 1, Stuart, H. A., Ed., Berlin, Springer Verlag, 1956.
32. Sutherland, T. H., and Funt, B. L., *J. Polymer Sci.*, **11**, 177 (1953).
33. Takemura, T., *J. Polymer Sci.*, **27**, 549 (1958).
34. Thurn, H., and Wolf, K., *Kolloid Z.*, **148**, 16 (1956).
35. Thurn, H., and Wuerstlin, F., *Kolloid Z.*, **145**, 133 (1956).
36. Thurn, H., and Wuerstlin, F., *Kolloid Z.*, **156**, 21 (1958).
37. Tobolsky, A. V., "Properties and Structure of Polymers," New York, John Wiley & Sons, Inc., 1960.
38. Williams, M. L., *J. Phys. Chem.*, **59**, 95 (1955).
39. Williams, M. L., Landel, R. F., and Ferry, J. D., *J. Am. Chem. Soc.*, **77**, 3701 (1955).
40. Wolf, K., *Kunststoffe*, **41**, 89 (1951).
41. Zener, C. M., "Elasticity and Anelasticity of Metals," Chicago, University of Chicago Press, 1948.
42. Zimm, B. H., *J. Chem. Phys.*, **24**, 269 (1956).

Chapter 9

MISCELLANEOUS MECHANICAL PROPERTIES

Heat Distortion Tests

The great practical importance of the heat distortion temperature or the softening temperature has led to the development of a large number of instruments. The simplest test is similar to a tensile creep test except that the temperature is increased at a uniform rate rather than being held constant[47]. The load on the specimen and the heating rate are arbitrary—typical values being of the order of 100 psi and 1°C/minute. As long as the material is rigid, it lengthens slowly because of creep and thermal expansion. At the softening or heat distortion temperature, the polymer begins to stretch at a rapid rate over a narrow temperature interval[25, 36]. This softening temperature is near the glass-transition temperature for amorphous materials, while for highly crystalline polymers, it is close to the melting point. Typical heat distortion curves are shown in Figure 9.1. The definition of the heat distortion temperature is arbitrary. It is sometimes taken as the temperature at which the elongation reaches a particular value, such as 1 per cent. The low and high temperature parts of the heat distortion curve may be approximated by two straight lines; the extrapolated intersection of these two lines is sometimes taken as the heat distortion temperature.

Other heat distortion tests, such as the common ASTM heat distortion test[1], are made in flexure. A bar is supported at two points while a load is applied at the midpoint between them. In the ASTM D648 test a load of 264 psi or 66 psi is applied to a plastic bar $5'' \times \frac{1}{2}'' \times \frac{1}{2}''$. The heat distortion temperature is taken as that temperature at which the test specimen has deformed 0.010 inch when the heating rate is 2°C per minute. As this test is normally made, much information is thrown away as only a single point on the deflection-temperature curve is recorded.

Torsional softening temperature tests are also popular[11, 19, 48]. The angular twist of a plastic bar or strip is measured as a function of tempera-

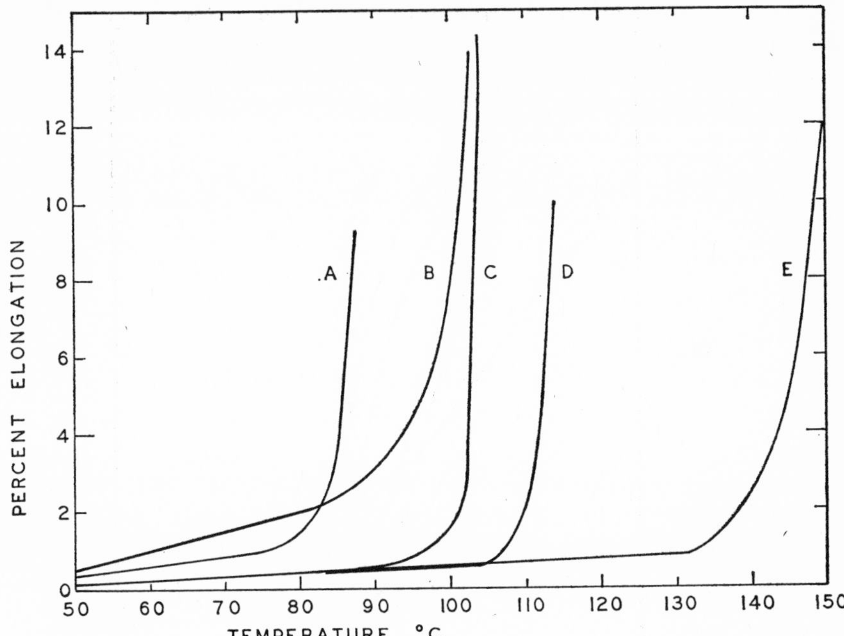

Figure 9.1. Heat distortion curves of: A. Polyvinyl chloride (50 psi load). B. Polyethylene (25 psi load). C. Polystyrene (50 psi load). D. Styrene-acrylonitrile (25%) copolymer (25 psi load). E. Plasticized cellulose acetate (25 psi load).

ture when a known torque is applied for a fixed length of time (such as ten seconds). Such a test gives the variation of the shear modulus with temperature. Typical curves obtained with a Clash-Berg torsional tester are shown in Figure 9.2[22]. Such curves are very similar to the dynamic modulus-temperature curves discussed in Chapter 7. The softening temperature is sometimes taken as the temperature of the inflection point on the Clash-Berg curve. Another softening temperature, called the flex temperature, is arbitrarily taken as the temperature at which Young's modulus is 135,000 psi or the shear modulus is 45,000 psi. The ASTM heat distortion temperature can be estimated from the Clash-Berg type of modulus-temperature curve[49]. The temperature at which the shear modulus is 10^5 psi is about the same as the ASTM heat distortion temperature when run at a stress of 264 psi. The heat distortion temperature determined at 66 psi corresponds to a shear modulus of about 3×10^4 psi.

The heat distortion curves are shifted by a change in the applied stress

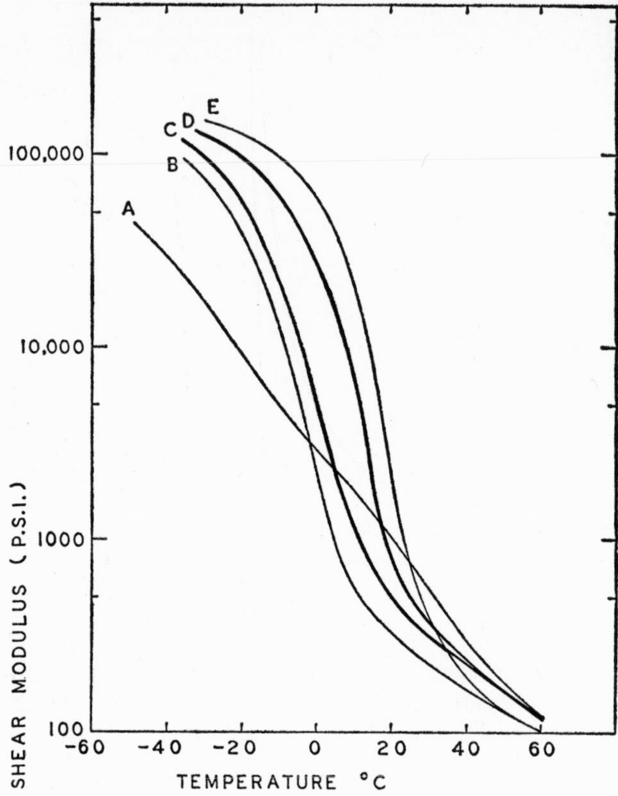

Figure 9.2. Typical Clash-Berg torsional modulus curves of polyvinyl chloride copolymer plasticized with 33.3 weight per cent of plasticizer. (*Unpublished data of Lawrence, R., and McIntyre, E., Monsanto Chemical Co.*)

A. Tri(2-ethyl hexyl)phosphate
B. Dibutyl phthalate
C. Diethoxyethyl phthalate
D. Methyl phthalyl ethyl glycollate
E. Triphenyl phosphate

as illustrated in Figure 9.3. The higher the load on the specimen the lower is the heat distortion temperature. The stress dependence of the softening temperature is greater at low stress than at high stress. For instance, the heat distortion temperature of polystyrene decreases at a rate of about 6°C/100 psi for loads near zero, while the rate is only about 2°C/100 psi for loads of 500 psi[29, 30].

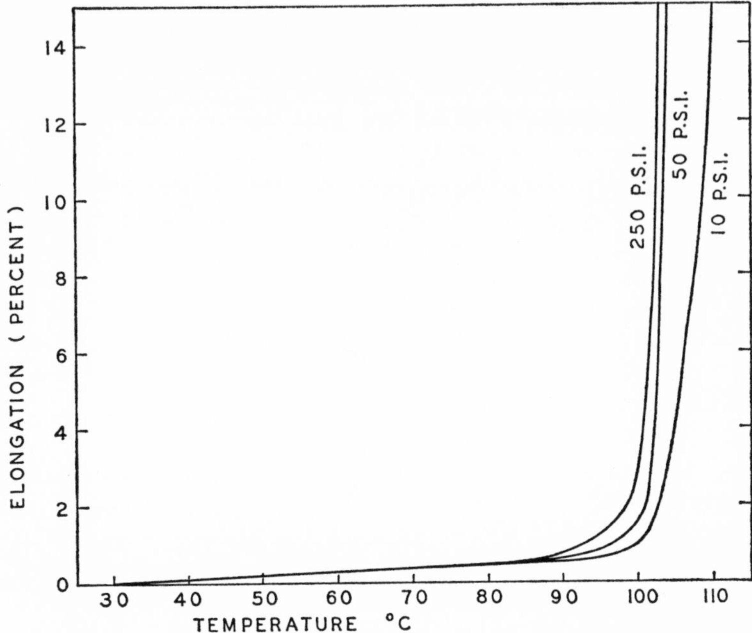

Figure 9.3. Shift of the heat distortion curves of polystyrene with tensile load.

The tensile heat distortion test is a rapid method of exploring the properties of a polymer, especially of unknown polymers where only a small amount of material may be available[47]. The slope of the elongation-temperature curve below the softening region gives the coefficient of thermal expansion if small tensile loads are used. The material rapidly elongates when the temperature reaches the glass transition region. For crystalline polymers the melting point may also be rapidly approximated. Crystalline polymers show a change in slope or a rounded step in the heat distortion curve at the glass transition; near the melting point the modulus rapidly decreases, and the specimen rapidly stretches[29, 33].

Frozen-in stresses due to molecular orientation may be measured by this technique, since oriented polymers shrink rapidly above the softening temperature. If the applied stress is less than the frozen-in stress, the polymer shrinks when the temperature reaches the softening temperature. However, if the external stress is greater than the internal stress, the specimen will never shrink. Thus, heat distortion curves at different applied stresses are useful in studying oriented molded objects, drawn fibers, and the effect of heat treatments on crystalline polymers[47].

Hardness

A hard material is generally defined as one which is not easily indented by a rigid body or as one which is difficult to scratch. Many tests have been devised to measure hardness. The intuitive concept of hardness held by most people is similar to the Moh scale of hardness, which is based upon the ability of a material to scratch any material of lower hardness. However, this concept does not necessarily agree with the hardness tests generally used on plastics or rubbers. In fact, most people would not consider rubber as a hard material, but by some tests rubber is very hard! Some of the conventional tests used on plastics and rubbers are described in ASTM tests D314, D676, D785, D1415, D1484, and D1526[1] or in other books on testing of materials[13]. These tests do not measure basic material properties; the answers depend upon the type of apparatus, the specimen form, and the test conditions.

Since many hardness or durometer tests are based upon the penetration of the test material by a loaded sphere, this type of test will be discussed in some detail. Tests in which a metal ball or an indenter is forced into the polymeric material measure a property which is primarily determined by the elastic modulus of the material. The theory of this test was developed many years ago by Hertz and has been reviewed by Timoshenko[46]. A spherical indenter made of material 1 is pressed into a plane flat specimen of material 2. Both materials are assumed to be perfectly elastic. The sphere is generally made of a hard metal while the polymeric material is a block with a flat surface. The amount of penetration or the indentation depth h (distance of mutual approach from initial contact to final state) is given by [34, 46]:

$$h = \left[\frac{3}{4}\left(\frac{1-\nu_1^2}{E_1} + \frac{1-\nu_2^2}{E_2}\right)\right]^{\frac{2}{3}} F^{\frac{2}{3}} r^{-\frac{1}{3}} \tag{9.1}$$

In this equation E_1 and E_2 are the Young's modulus of the material making up the sphere and plane surface, respectively, while ν_1 and ν_2 are the corresponding Poisson's ratios. F is the total force (load) acting between the sphere and the specimen, and r is the radius of the sphere. If the modulus of the sphere is much greater than the modulus of the test specimen, that is, $E_1 \gg E_2$, then the above equation can be simplified to give:

$$h \doteq \left[\frac{3}{4}\left(\frac{1-\nu_2^2}{E_2}\right)\right]^{\frac{2}{3}} F^{\frac{2}{3}} r^{-\frac{1}{3}} \tag{9.2}$$

or

$$F \doteq \frac{E_2 r^{\frac{1}{2}} h^{\frac{3}{2}}}{\frac{3}{4}(1-\nu_2^2)} \tag{9.3}$$

Thus, Young's modulus can be estimated from such indentation tests.

The radius a of the circle of contact when the sphere is pressed into the specimen is

$$a = \left[\frac{3}{4}\left(\frac{1 - \nu_1^2}{E_1} + \frac{1 - \nu_2^2}{E_2}\right)\right]^{\frac{1}{3}} F^{\frac{1}{3}} r^{\frac{1}{3}} \tag{9.4}$$

The pressure P at the center of the area of contact is

$$P = \frac{3F}{2\pi a^2} \tag{9.5}$$

Thus, the maximum pressure at the bottom of the sphere is equal to one and a half times the average pressure over the area of contact. The maximum tensile stress σ_m, which occurs in the specimen at the boundary of the circle of contact, is

$$\sigma_m = \frac{1 - 2\nu_2 F}{2\pi a^2} \tag{9.6}$$

The above equations are not strictly true when used with high polymers since such materials are not perfectly elastic, and the depth of penetration is time dependent. The British Standard Hardness Test for rubber or the ASTM test D1415[1, 32] make use of the equation[42]

$$F = 0.00017\ E_2 r^{0.65} h^{1.35} \tag{9.7}$$

where the indenting force F is in kilograms, Young's modulus E_2 is in kg/cm^2, the radius of the sphere is in cm, and the depth of penetration h is given in hundredths of millimeters. This equation is very similar to, but not identical to, equation 9.3 derived from Hertz's theory. Although the relation between penetration and modulus is explicit and has a good theoretical foundation, hardness values based upon the amount of penetration are extremely arbitrary. In the standard hardness tests described above, a Young's modulus of 100 psi corresponds to a hardness of about 22, while a Young's modulus of 1000 psi corresponds to a hardness of about 75. Other hardness tests are just as arbitrary. For instance, in the Shore durometer type D test a hardness of 100 corresponds to a ten-pound load on a spherical tip of 0.004 inch in radius. In the Shore durometer type A test a hardness of zero corresponds to a load of 56 g and a modulus of 0.98 kg/cm^2, while a hardness of 100 corresponds to a modulus of infinity and a load of 822 g on a circular indenter with a flat end of 0.031 inch in diameter[28]. In addition, an arbitrary time interval for the test must be chosen since the penetration increases with time for a viscoelastic material.

Rockwell hardness tests using R, L, M, E, and alpha scales are often

TABLE 9.1. COMPARISON OF HARDNESS VALUES MEASURED BY DIFFERENT METHODS.*

Polymer	Rockwell Hardness			Bierbaum Scratch Hardness
	α Scale	M Scale	R Scale	
Polymethyl methacrylate	102 (111)	72 (102)	125	17.5
Unsaturated polyester resin	91	72	124	13.5
Polyvinyl chloride (Rigid)	105	60 (66)	123	10.1
Polystyrene	109 (99)	66 (88)	124	10.3
Melamine resin	130	—	129	32.4
Melamine-cellulose laminate	115	123	—	—
Phenolic (mineral-filled)	128	—	124	21.2
Phenolic (Wood flour-filled)	120	116	—	—
Nylon 66	102 (92)	70	120	11.1
Cellulose nitrate	78	23	112	9.8
Cellulose acetate	68	25	115	11.3
Vinylidene chloride	38	—	92	8.3
Polyethylene	−151	−25	—	—

* Boor, L., Ryan , J., Marks, M., and Bartoe, W., *ASTM Bull.*, No. 145, 68 (March, 1947).

Maxwell, B., *Modern Plastics*, **32**, 125 (May, 1955).

used for rigid plastics. The standard tests are designated ASTM number D785[1]. The alpha scale is an indentation test in which a reading of 150 corresponds to an infinite modulus, a reading of 100 corresponds to 2.9×10^4 kg/cm^2, a reading of zero corresponds to 5.6×10^3 kg/cm^2, while a reading of -30 corresponds to a modulus of 4.3×10^3 kg/cm^2 [28]. The Rockwell scales *R*, *L*, *M*, and *E* are not measures of total indentation, but instead are a measure of the nonrecoverable deformation after a sphere has been pressed into the plastic and then the load released. Thus, it is not surprising that Ito[20] finds that Rockwell hardness (*R* scale) as a function of temperature gives curves which look very similar to resilience versus temperature curves and not modulus-temperature curves. Crosslinked rubbers, which retain very little permanent deformation, can give high hardness readings by such tests.

Table 9.1 illustrates how several hardness tests give different answers on a given polymer and how different tests rank polymers in different orders.

Friction and Abrasion

Frictional Properties of Polymers. The frictional behavior of polymers is important in a number of practical applications. For instance, it is desirable to have a high coefficient of friction between a rubber automobile tire and the road surface, but one wants a low value of friction in a plastic bearing.

The coefficient of friction μ is defined as the ratio of the tangential force F to the normal load W, when the surface of one material is moved relative to another surface:

$$\mu = F/W \tag{9.8}$$

The coefficient of friction is not necessarily constant for the materials making up an interface but may depend upon a number of variables such as the load, contact area, velocity of sliding, temperature, lubricants, geometry of specimens, and type of apparatus in addition to the chemical and physical properties of the materials. For convenience, coefficients of friction may be divided into three types: static coefficients, kinetic coefficients, and coefficients of rolling friction. Frictional behavior has been reviewed in detail by Bowden and Tabor[8], and more recently the friction of rubbers has been reviewed by Conant and Liska[12].

Many types of instruments have been used to measure friction. These vary in complexity from a simple inclined plane to the complex instruments of Bowden and Leben[7] and Flom[16, 17]. The agreement between different instruments is generally very poor, partly because of the very complex nature of frictional phenomena. Even when different workers use the same type of apparatus, their results often do not agree for the same materials because of the difficulty in obtaining reproducible surfaces and comparable test conditions.

There are several generalizations that can be made about sliding friction, but like most such generalizations they are not always strictly true. These so-called laws of friction are: (1) The tangential frictional force required to produce sliding of one surface over another is directly proportional to the load normal to the surfaces; (2) Frictional force is independent of the area of contact for a constant load; (3) The coefficient of friction is independent of the velocity of sliding. Most work on friction attempts to study the deviations from these laws or to clarify the mechanism of friction.

In frictional phenomena one surface is always in contact with another surface. For this reason, the absolute properties of the two materials are not as important as their relative properties[8]. The relative hardness and softening temperatures of the two materials are especially important. Molecular adhesion is another important factor. Friction tends to be great when molecular adhesion is high; this is one of the reasons why friction of a material against itself is generally higher than when measured against a dissimilar material. For the same reason, nonpolar materials tend to have lower coefficients of friction against metals than do polar materials.

The total frictional force is a complex summation of several factors including: (1) internal friction or mechanical damping; (2) shearing of junctions where the two surfaces are in intimate contact; (3) a ploughing process in which the harder material displaces the softer material in front of it to produce a friction track or scratch. The internal friction part is especially important in rolling friction and in automobile tires. If polymers were perfectly elastic, a ball or cylinder should experience no frictional force as it rolls down a smooth plastic surface. As a ball rolls, it depresses the polymer in front of it, and the polymer snaps back again and pushes the ball at the rear. If the materials are perfectly elastic, the energy recovered at the back of the ball is exactly equal to the energy expended in front. However, because of mechanical damping and delayed recovery in polymeric materials, the material depressed in front of the ball does not spring back rapidly enough behind the ball to give it a push from the rear. Because of this damping or hysteresis, energy is dissipated and work must be performed on the ball to keep it rolling[9, 16, 17]. As a result, excellent correlations are found between rolling friction and dynamic mechanical properties[2, 9, 16, 17, 27]. As expected, the coefficient of rolling friction behaves as a function of temperature or rolling velocity in the same manner that mechanical damping does as a function of temperature or frequency. The coefficient of rolling friction μ_r is related to the dynamic mechanical properties by[17, 18]:

$$\mu_r = K \frac{G''}{G'} \left(\frac{W}{G'r^2} \right)^{\frac{1}{3}} \tag{9.9}$$

where W is the load on the ball of radius r, G' is the shear modulus of the plastic on which the ball is rolling, G''/G' is the mechanical dissipation factor, and K is a characteristic of the polymer which varies from 0.120 to 0.107 as Poisson's ratio of the polymer goes from 0.3 to 0.5. For a given value of damping, the coefficient of rolling friction decreases as the modulus increases since the deformation of the polymer decreases.

On a submicroscopic scale even smooth surfaces are rough, so that surfaces which appear to be in contact are actually touching each other in only a few points. At these contact points very large forces are encountered so that the contact points are deformed, plastic flow occurs, and the two surfaces are welded together at these points. When sliding of one surface over another takes place, these junctions or contact points must be sheared. If the junctions are weak, the shearing takes place at the actual interface.

However, in many cases the junctions are welded together so strongly that the shearing takes place below the surface of the softer material. This shearing action gives rise to one of the factors making up the total frictional force. If this shearing term is the largest factor in determining the frictional force, the coefficient of friction is roughly approximated by[8, 43]

$$\mu = \frac{\sigma_B}{P_y} \tag{9.10}$$

where σ_B is the shear strength of the softer material and P_y is the yield pressure of the softer material. The yield pressure might be expected to be roughly proportional to $J^{\frac{2}{3}}$ where J is the absolute value of the complex compliance. James, Norman, and Payne[21] attempted to test this relation for plasticized polyvinyl chlorides. Although the coefficient of friction increased with the absolute value of the complex compliance for these materials, the quantitative agreement with the theoretical equation was poor.

In most cases where plastic flow can occur at the contact points, it appears that the real area of contact is proportional to the load, so that the first law of friction holds, and the tangential frictional force is proportional to the normal load. For elastic materials such as rubber, the actual area of contact should be proportional to about the $\frac{2}{3}$ power of the load since Hertz's equation should hold; in this case the frictional force should not be directly proportional to the load[8]. As expected on the basis of this dependence of the true contact area on load, the coefficient of friction of most rubbers decreases somewhat as the load increases[12].

If one surface is harder than the other, the asperities of the harder material plough out grooves or scratches in the softer material. This ploughing action makes up the third term in the frictional force and in many cases is a big factor in abrasion and wear. Since polymers are soft compared to most metals, the contribution to friction of the ploughing term might be expected to be important in many cases.

The Bowden-Leben apparatus[7] shows that under many conditions the sliding between surfaces is not a continuous process but proceeds in a series of jerks or "stick-slip" movements. "Stick-slip" motion is a result of static friction being greater than kinetic friction. The real area of contact increases gradually during the "stick" stage as the surfaces are pulled into more intimate contact by the increasing tangential force. "Slip" occurs when the forces become great enough to shear and plough the material. During the "slip" stage the area of contact and the friction rapidly decrease.

Typical values of the coefficient of friction are given in Table 9.2. These

TABLE 9.2. COEFFICIENTS OF FRICTION OF POLYMERS.*

Polymer	Metal Against Polymer	Polymer Against Polymer
Polyvinyl chloride	0.4–.9	0.45–.55
Polystyrene	0.4–.5	0.4–.5
Polystyrene polyblend	0.38	
Polymethyl methacrylate	0.25	0.4
	0.4–.5	0.4–.6
Nylon 66	0.3 (0.36)	
Nylon 6	0.39	
Polyethylene (low density)	0.33–.6	0.33–.6
	0.6–.8	0.1
Polyethylene (high density)	0.23	
Polyvinylidene chloride	0.68–1.8	0.8–2.0
Polyvinyl fluoride		0.1–.3
Polytrifluorochloroethylene	0.56	
Polytetrafluoroethylene	0.04–.10	.04
	0.10–.15	
Phenol-formaldehyde resin	0.61	
Rubber	0.3–2.5	

* Bowden, F. P., *Endeavor*, **16,** 5 (1957).
Bowers, R. C., Clinton, W. C., and Zisman, W. A., *Modern Plastics*, **31,** 131 (Feb., 1954).
Conant, F. S. and Liska, J. W., *Rubber Chem. and Technol.*, **33,** 1218 (1960).
Marcucci, M. A., *Soc. Plastics Eng. J.*, **14,** 30 (Feb., 1958).
Shooter, K. V. and Thomas, P. H., *Research*, **2,** 533 (1949).

values have been collected from various sources, and since the experimental techniques differed, accurate comparisons of different polymers is not possible. Coefficients of friction are notoriously variable. The shearing component of friction is believed to be the most important factor for most of the polymers, but the rolling friction and ploughing components must be more or less important in some of the materials. Polytetrafluoroethylene has an especially low coefficient of friction. This is probably related to its low molecular cohesion and its low surface energy. Rubber has a high coefficient of friction compared to most rigid polymers.

The variation of the coefficient of friction for rubbers and for rigid polymers as the load and the velocity of sliding are changed is illustrated in a general way by Figure 9.4. The coefficient is not independent of load but gradually decreases as the load increases for both rubbers and rigid plastics[6, 12, 31, 38, 40]. For rubbers an equation of the form[14]

$$\frac{1}{k\mu} = 1 + \frac{15W}{E} \tag{9.11}$$

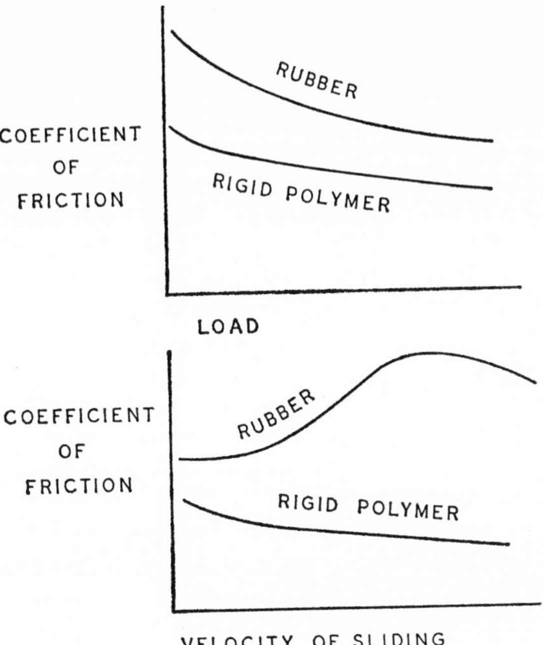

Figure 9.4. Typical variations of the coefficient of friction with load and with velocity of sliding for rubbers and rigid polymers.

holds. The coefficient of friction μ decreases as the load W increases while μ increases as the modulus E of the rubber increases. In this equation k is a constant. For rubber μ increases and then remains constant or decreases again as the velocity of sliding increases[12, 35]. With rigid plastics, however, the coefficient of friction often decreases as the velocity of sliding increases. As the velocity increases, very high temperatures are developed at the points of contact between the surfaces. For this reason it is sometimes difficult to separate the effects of velocity and temperature. At extremely high velocities a lubricating layer of molten plastic can form between the surfaces so that the friction remains low instead of increasing as one would expect on the basis that rolling friction is proportional to mechanical damping. In such cases, the velocity dependence of friction is not the same for sliding friction as for rolling friction.

For rubber the coefficient of friction decreases with temperature[39]. While the coefficient of rolling friction correlates well with mechanical damping as a function of temperature, the correlation in the case of sliding friction is not so clear. As long as the polymer is rigid, the coefficient of sliding friction generally increases gradually as the temperature is raised[8, 17, 18, 44].

Abrasion. The abrasion of rubber has been extensively studied because of the economic importance of wear of tires[4, 12, 37, 39, 41]. Much less is known about the abrasion of rigid polymers although the abrasion resistance of such materials is important too. For instance, since most plastics are relatively soft materials, their surfaces are easily marred and scratched.

Abrasion is closely related to friction in that a frictional force must be involved in any process of abrasion or wear, although friction is not necessarily accompanied by wear. The ploughing component of frictional force is intimately related to abrasion. This is especially true if one material is much harder than the other so that the asperities on the surface of the harder material can plough out grooves or scratches to an appreciable depth in the softer material. Thus, the relative hardness of rigid materials can be important[8]. In addition to physical damage of surfaces, abrasion is often accompanied by chemical attack. Local high temperatures are built up during the friction or abrasion process, so that oxidation can occur readily in some cases.

Abrasion is another mechanical property which is difficult to define and to measure adequately. Many instruments have been developed to measure abrasion, but few of them really measure the same thing. Thus, it is not surprising that different test methods generally do not agree with each other or with practical experience. Tests are useful primarily to rank materials in a certain order under a given set of carefully specified conditions with the hope that a correlation can be found with practical experience for a specific application.

When a rubber is moved over a hard surface, large deformations can occur where the rubber contacts asperities on the hard surface. These local deformations can be large enough to break or tear the rubber. Abrasion is then due to the subsequent tearing out of small pieces of rubber from the damaged surface. A mathematical theory of rubber abrasion has been developed along these lines by Schallamach[39]. His theory predicts that abrasion is proportional to the normal load and independent of particle size of the abrasive if the particles are polyhedral; abrasion, however, is proportional to the radius of curvature of the particles of abrasive if the particles are hemispherical. Abrasion is proportional to the work done on the rubber. In another theoretical paper, Schallamach[41] shows that with some types of abrasion testers, wear should decrease as the mechanical damping or hysteresis increases. Wear should be determined by the following factors:

$$\text{Wear} \propto (\text{Resilience})(\text{Slip})^2(\text{Stiffness})(\text{Contact area}^2) \tag{9.12}$$

Boggs[4] has also developed a theory of rubber abrasion in which the amount of slip between the rubber and abrasive surfaces and the modulus and hysteresis of the rubber are important variables. Zapp[50] believes the important variables in determining abrasion loss are related by an equation of the form:

$$\text{Abrasion loss} = \frac{\text{Dynamic Modulus} \times \text{Friction}}{\text{Strength of Rubber}} \tag{9.13}$$

Marcucci[26] has measured the weight loss due to abrasion for a number of rigid plastics. His results are given in Table 9.3. He found that there was much less wear on polyethylene than on a polystyrene polyblend. There was a general trend that wear increased with the coefficient of friction. Possibly with different test conditions or with a different type of apparatus the materials would not be ranked in the same order. Several accepted methods of measuring abrasion are described in the publications of the American Society for Testing Materials[1]. These tests include ASTM tests D394, D1044, D1242, and D1526.

Scratch resistance of rigid polymers is closely related to abrasion. Bernhardt[3] has reviewed the work on scratch resistance. The Bierbaum scratch hardness has been compared with a number of hardness and abrasion tests[5]. Melamine and filled phenol-formaldehyde resins have high scratch resistance, nylon and polystyrene have moderate scratch resistance, while polyethylene has a low scratch resistance. Although polyethylene is listed as having a low scratch resistance, Marcucci[26] found it to have very good abrasion resistance as measured by his test method.

TABLE 9.3. FRICTION AND RELATIVE WEAR OF PLASTICS.*

Plastic	Kinetic Coefficient of Friction	Abrasion Loss (grams)
General-purpose phenolic	0.61	0.057
Caprolactam	.39	.015
Polytrifluorochloroethylene	.56	.159
Polystyrene polyblend	.38	.64
High-density polyethylene	.23	.0016
Nylon 66	.36	.025

* Marcucci, M. A., *Soc. Plastics Eng. J.*, **14**, 30 (Feb., 1958).

Fatigue

The properties of a material change when subjected to a large number of deformations. The failure or decay of mechanical properties after repeated applications of stress or strain is known as fatigue. Fatigue life is defined as the number of cycles of deformaion required to bring about failure of the test specimen under a given set of oscillating conditions. Fatigue tests give information on the ability of a plastic to resist the development of cracks (which eventually bring about failure), as a result of a large number of cycles.

Many types of fatigue testers have been developed[1, 15]. One type of tester repeatedly flexes a cantilever or other type of beam. The rotating beam apparatus is another type that has been widely used; in this instrument the specimen, in the form of a rod with a circular cross section, is deflected from the axis of rotation by an applied force as the specimen is rotated. Different testers usually do not give the same results. Tests have been carried out under a variety of conditions. These include the following: (1) The amplitude of the cyclic stress is held constant during the test; (2) The amplitude of the cyclic strain is held constant. (3) In any of these types of tests the oscillating stresses or strains may be superimposed upon a constant static (or slowly relaxing) stress or strain. The actual stress may be a tension, a compression, or alternately tension and compression during the course of one oscillation. (4) The amplitude of the cyclic stress or strain increases with time[24]. This last type of test has the advantage of decreasing the time required to make a fatigue test. Fatigue tests may take many millions of cycles before failure occurs, so they are time-consuming. Constant deflection or strain testers have the disadvantage that once a large crack develops the stress level in the specimen drops so much that the test may continue for some time rather than have sample failure occur in a short time. In constant stress testers as soon as a crack develops, the amplitude of the deformation increases, and failure occurs in a few cycles. Constant strain testers have another disadvantage in some cases as they penalize the stiffer materials by subjecting them to greater stresses than the softer or lower modulus materials.

Fatigue data are generally reported as the number of cycles to fail at a given maximum stress level. The greater the imposed stress the fewer cycles needed to break the test specimen[10, 15, 23]. As shown in Figure 9.5, a plot of the breaking stress or logarithm of the stress against the logarithm of the number of cycles to failure gives a straight line with a negative slope[23]. For some materials it appears that at low enough stresses the material will never break. This limiting stress below which the material will

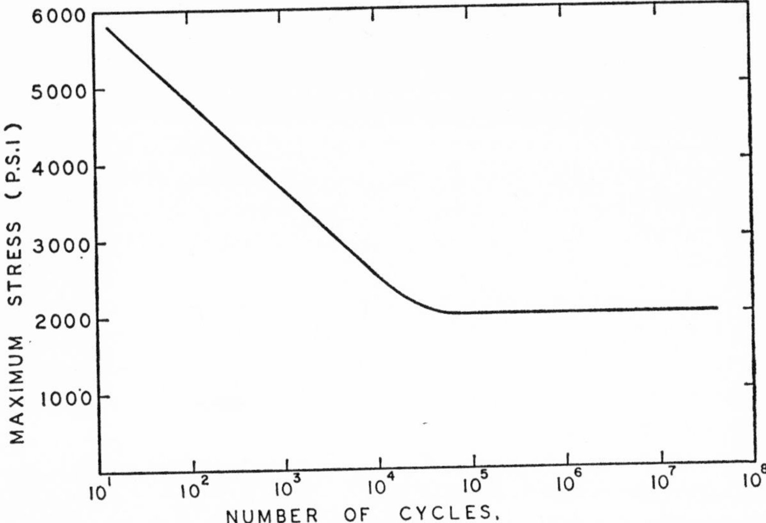

Figure 9.5. A typical fatigue-life curve of the number of cycles to fail as a function of the maximum cyclic load.

never fail is called the fatigue or endurance limit; the fatigue limit shows up as a break in the curve of Figure 9.5, to give a horizontal line. For many polymers the fatigue limit is between 20 and 35 per cent of the static tensile strength[23]. Thus, in designing structural units subjected to vibrations it is important to design them so that the maximum stresses to which they are subjected are below the fatigue limit rather than the usual tensile strength.

The fatigue life of a polymer is generally reduced by an increase in temperature. The temperature dependence can usually be expressed by an equation of the form[15]:

$$\text{Log fatigue life} = A + B/T \tag{9.14}$$

where A and B are constants. The fatigue life of a polymethyl methacrylate decreased by 58 per cent in going from −30°F to 80°F[23]. For a fabric laminated phenolic the fatigue life decreased by 25 per cent over the same temperature interval. The temperature of the specimen may not be the ambient temperature. Considerable heat is often generated by the damping or hysteresis of the material. Thus, mechanical damping is important in determining the fatigue life of a material. For polymers in which the strength decreases rapidly with temperature, high damping can be largely responsible for their fatigue failure. The heat buildup increases with damping, stress on the specimen, speed of testing, and increased specimen size. Although high damping is detrimental to fatigue life, reasonably high damping is important in a structural member in order to cut down the amplitude of resonance vibrations. If resonance vibrations are not rapidly damped out, their amplitude can become so great that failure occurs in a very short time.

Other variables affecting fatigue life are speed of testing and stress concentrators such as notches in the specimen. Fatigue life usually decreases somewhat as the speed of testing increases. However, the effect of speed of testing is small unless appreciable heat buildup occurs because of high damping or high stresses. A notch in a test specimen reduces the load-carrying capacity; the effect may be even more pronounced with alternating stresses than with static stresses.

Little is known about the effect of molecular structure on fatigue life. Dillon[15] lists the following factors which are believed to be important in determining fatigue behavior: (1) molecular flow and secondary bond rupture; (2) physical rupture of polymer chains. It is known that large external forces are capable of breaking some chains so that a decrease in molecular weight can occur. (3) Chemical scission of chains or crosslinking reactions brought about by such processes as oxidative aging. (4) Orientaion of chains. (5) Change in the degree of crystallinity. (6) Change in crystal morphology. (7) Glass-transition temperature. Damping and other mechanical properties depend upon the difference between the test temperature and the glass temperature.

Generally, undercured rubbers have better fatigue life than overcured rubbers. This observation correlates with the greater elongation and tensile strength of undercured rubbers. If the crosslinking reaction is carried too far, some of the crosslinks become very closely spaced so that even relatively small elongations put large stresses on some chain segments and stretch them to the breaking point. In addition, undesirable degradation reactions may occur if the crosslinking reaction is carried too far.

Sookne and Harris[45] found that one type of fatigue test correlated with the ultimate elongation of cellulose acetate fractions. Above a certain molecular weight very little improvement was found. Lazan and Yorgiadis[23] have compiled a large table of fatigue data on plastics. Relations of fatigue life to structure are not readily apparent from these data, however.

References

1. "ASTM Standards, 1958," Part 9, Philadelphia, Am. Soc. Testing Materials, 1958.

2. Atack, D., and Tabor, D., *Proc. Royal Soc. London,* **246A,** 539 (1958).
3. Bernhardt, E. C., *Modern Plastics,* **26,** 123 (Oct., 1948).
4. Boggs, F. W., "Proceedings International Rubber Conference," p. 149, Washington, D. C., (Nov., 1959).
5. Boor, L., Ryan, J. D., Marks, M. E., and Bartoe, W. F., *ASTM Bull.* No. 145, 68 (March, 1947).
6. Bowden, F. P., *Endeavor,* **16,** 5 (1957).
7. Bowden, F. P., and Leben, L., *Proc. Royal Soc. London,* **169A,** 371 (1939).
8. Bowden, F. P., and Tabor, D., "The Friction and Lubrication of Solids," Oxford, Clarendon Press, 1954.
9. Bueche, A. M., and Flom, D. G., *Wear,* **2,** 168 (1959).
10. Carey, R. H., *ASTM Bull.* No. 206, 52 (May, 1955).
11. Clash, Jr., R. F., and Berg, R. M., *Ind. Eng. Chem.,* **34,** 1218 (1942).
12. Conant, F. S., and Liska, J. W., *Rubber Chem. and Technol.,* **33,** 1218 (1960).
13. Davis, H. E., Troxell, G. E., and Wiskocil, C. T., "The Testing and Inspection of Engineering Materials," New York, McGraw-Hill Book Co., Inc., 1941.
14. Denny, D. F., *Proc. Phys. Soc. London,* **66B,** 721 (1953).
15. Dillon, J. H., "Advances In Colloid Science," Vol. 3, Chap. 3, p. 219, Mark, H., and Verwey, E. J. W., Ed., New York, Interscience Publishers, Inc., 1950.
16. Flom, D. G., *J. Appl. Phys.,* **31,** 306 (1960).
17. Flom, D. G., *Anal. Chem.,* **32,** 1550 (1960).
18. Flom, D. G., *J. Appl. Phys.,* **32,** 1426 (1961).
19. Gehman, S. D., Woodford, D. E., and Wilkinson, Jr., C. S., *Ind. Enq. Chem.,* **39,** 1108 (1947).
20. Ito, K., *Modern Plastics,* **35,** 167 (Nov., 1957).
21. James, D. I., Norman, R. H., and Payne, A. R., "Physical Properties of Polymers," Soc. Chem. Ind. Monograph No. 5, p. 233, New York, Macmillan Co., 1959.
22. Lawrence, R. R., and McIntyre, E. B., *Ind. Eng. Chem.,* **41,** 689 (1949).
23. Lazan, B. J., and Yorgiadis, A., "Symposium on Plastics," Spec. Tech. Pub. No. 59, p. 66, Philadelphia, Am. Soc. Testing Materials Feb. 1944.
24. Lazar, L. S., *ASTM Bull.* No. 220, p. 67 (Feb., 1957).
25. Liska, J. W., *Ind. Eng. Chem.,* **36,** 40 (1944).
26. Marcucci, M. A., *Soc. Plastics Eng. J.,* **14,** 30 (Feb., 1958).
27. May, W. D., Morris, E. L., and Atack, D., *J. Appl. Phys.,* **30,** 1713 (1959).
28. Meskat, W., Rosenberg, O., Schwarzl, F., and Staverman, A. J., "Die Physik Der Hochpolymeren," Stuart, H. A., Ed., Chap. 4, Berlin, Springer Verlag, 1956.
29. Newman, S., and Cox, W. P., *J. Polymer Sci.,* **46,** 29 (1960).
30. Nielsen, L. E., and Buchdahl, R., *J. Appl. Phys.,* **21,** 488 (1950).
31. Pascoe, M. W., and Tabor, D., *Proc. Royal Soc. London,* **235,** 210 (1956).
32. Payne, A. R., and Scott, J. R., "Engineering Design with Rubber," Chap. 5, New York, Interscience Publishers, Inc., 1960.
33. Riser, G. R., Port, W. S., and Witnauer, L. P., *J. Polymer Sci.,* **36,** 543 (1959).
34. Roesler, F. C., *Proc. Phys. Soc. London,* **69B,** 55 (1956).
35. Roth, F. L., Driscoll, R. L., and Holt, W. L., *J. Research Nat. Bur. Standards,* **28,** 439 (1942).
36. Sauer, J. A., Schwertz, F. A., and Worf, D. L., *Modern Plastics,* **22,** 153 (March, 1945).

37. Schallamach, A., *J. Polymer Sci.*, **9,** 385 (1952).
38. Schallamach, A., *Proc. Phys. Soc. London,* **65B,** 657 (1952).
39. Schallamach, A., *Rubber Chem. and Technol.*, **28,** 906 (1955), or *Proc. Phys. Soc. London,* **67B,** 883 (1954).
40. Schallamach, A., *Kolloid Z.*, **141,** 165 (1955).
41. Schallamach, A., "Proceedings International Rubber Conference," p. 142, Washington, D. C., 1959.
42. Scott, J. R., *Trans. Inst. Rubber Ind.*, **11,** 224 (1935).
43. Shooter, K. V., *Proc. Roy. Soc. London,* **212A,** 488 (1952).
44. Shooter, K. V., and Thomas, P. H., *Research London,* **2,** 533 (1949).
45. Sookne, A. M., and Harris, M., *Ind. Eng. Chem.*, **37,** 478 (1945).
46. Timoshenko, S., "Theory of Elasticity," New York, McGraw-Hill Book Co., Inc., 1934.
47. Watson, M. T., Armstrong, G. M., and Kennedy, W. D., *Modern Plastics,* **34,** 169 (Nov. 1956).
48. Williamson, I., *Brit. Plastics,* **23,** 87 (1950).
49. Witnauer, L. P., and Palm, W. E., *J. Appl. Polymer Sci.*, **2,** 371 (1959).
50. Zapp, R. L., *Rubber World,* **133,** 59 (1955).

Chapter 10

EFFECTS OF ORIENTATION AND THERMAL TREATMENTS ON MECHANICAL PROPERTIES

Molecular Orientation

Long-chain polymer molecules are believed to be randomly coiled into a loose ball which on the average has a spherical shape. Segments of one molecule entangle and intermingle with segments of other polymer chains. There are as many monomeric units or chain sections pointing in one direction as there are in any other direction for an unoriented material. In oriented polymers there are more chain segments pointing in some directions than in other directions. Orientation is generally accomplished in amorphous polymers by deforming a polymer at a temperature above its glass temperature. If the stretched polymer then is cooled to below its glass-transition temperature before the molecules have had a chance to relax back to their random coiled configuration, the orientation can be retained permanently. The mechanical properties of an oriented material are not the same as those of the unoriented isotropic material. Oriented plastics possess properties which are different in different directions; that is, they are anisotropic.

Oriented materials can generally be divided into two classes—uniaxially oriented and biaxially oriented—although crystalline polymers may require a more complex classification[35]. Uniaxial orientation is most easily accomplished by stretching a plastic bar or long strip in one direction at a temperature at which the polymer behaves as a rubber or very viscous liquid. The polymer chains or sections of the chains tend to line up parallel to the direction of stretching. In practice only a small fraction of the chain segments become perfectly oriented. Ideal uniaxial orientation of an amorphous polymer is illustrated in Figure 10.1 A.

Biaxial orientation results when a plastic sheet is stretched in two directions at right angles to each other so that the area of the sheet increases and its thickness decreases. The chain segments tend to line up parallel

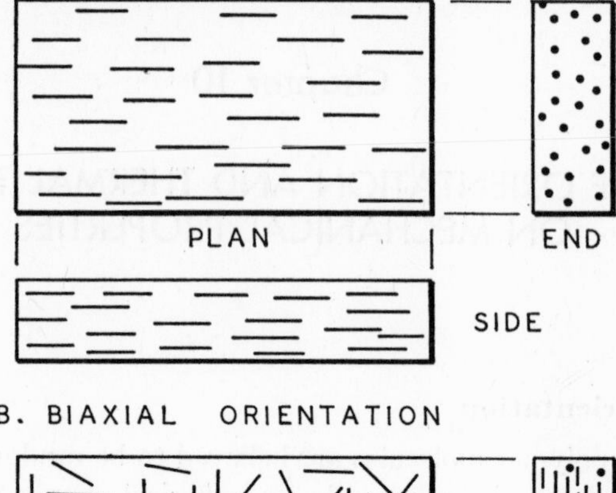

B. BIAXIAL ORIENTATION

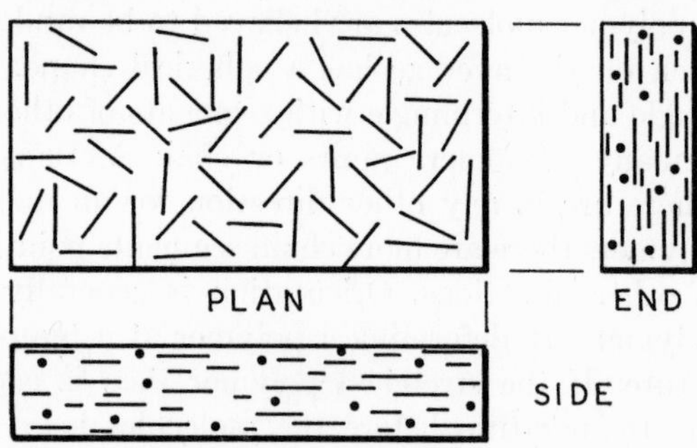

Figure 10.1. Schematic diagram of oriented polymeric materials.

to the plane of the sheet but in a random direction in this plane. Ideal biaxial orientation is illustrated in Figure 10.1 B.

Nearly all injection-molded objects are more or less oriented. The molecules are oriented during the viscous flow of the molten polymer, and part of this orientation is retained in the molded object as it cools. The orientation can be predominantly either uniaxial or biaxial, but in general the orientation appears to be a combination of the two. Factors in the injection-molding process which affect the orientation have been studied by various workers[18, 44, 46, 52, 57, 96].

Orientation can be measured by a number of methods. Birefringence or double refraction is often the easiest and most rapid measurement that can be made to estimate the extent and kind of orientation[7, 33, 95, 100, 104, 118]. Birefringence measures the difference in refractive indices in two mutually perpendicular directions, and since the refractive index (or polarizability) parallel to a polymer chain usually is different from the refractive index perpendicular to a chain, birefringence is a sensitive indicator of molecular orientation. The birefringence may be expressed in a number of ways; some of these ways are related by the equation[26]

$$(n_{\parallel} - n_{\perp}) = B\lambda = \frac{R_0}{D} = \frac{\lambda\delta}{2\pi D} \tag{10.1}$$

where $(n_{\parallel} - n_{\perp})$ is the difference in refractive indices parallel and perpendicular to the molecular alignment, B is the optical path difference in wavelengths of light per centimeter thickness of the sample, R_0 is the retardation of the light, λ is the wavelength of the light in vacuo in centimeters, δ is the phase difference in radians in the two directions, and D is the thickness of the sample.

Figure 10.1 A shows that the greatest birefrigence is observed when one looks through the thickness of the sheet perpendicular to its plane for uniaxial orientation. An ideal biaxial sheet shows no birefringence when observed through the sheet; this would be expected from Figure 10.1 B. Biaxial oriented sheets show birefringence when observed with polarized light through the edge of the sheet or at an angle to the sheet other than vertically through the sheet[100]. The amount of birefringence is proportional to the degree of orientation.

When an oriented sheet or amorphous plastic object is heated to above its softening temperature, it shrinks back to the approximate shape it had before being oriented. If it is restrained from shrinking, an oriented sheet exerts a retractive force when heated above its glass temperature. The greater the retractive force the greater the degree of orientation. The retractive force is one of the few methods of measuring orientation that is applicable to opaque plastic materials[34]. For uncrosslinked polymers the retractive force depends to some extent on the rate of heating and the test temperature because of relaxation during the heating cycle[34].

Some of the infrared absorption bands of oriented polymers show dichroism. That is, they absorb different amounts of polarized infrared radiation when the plane of vibration of the radiation is parallel or perpendicular to the direction of the oriented molecules[30, 103, 106]. Dyed oriented polymers often show dichroism to visible light. The dye molecules apparently become oriented at the same time as the polymer molecules[21, 82].

In crystalline polymers the orientation of the crystallites can be measured by x-ray diffraction. In crystalline polymers birefringence measures the orientation of both the crystalline and amorphous phases[21, 82, 103]. Thus, by a combination of various experimental techniques it is possible to independently determine degree of orientation of the crystalline and amorphous phases. For crystalline polymers, such as polyethylene and nylon, the crystalline phase becomes much more oriented than the amorphous phase when the polymer is stretched or cold-drawn[2, 3, 21, 103].

For polymers above their glass transition temperature—crosslinked rubbers and molten polymers—the retractive stress or the stress-resisting deformation is directly proportional to the degree of orientation. The orientation in turn is directly proportional to the birefringence. These results are predicted by the kinetic theory of rubber elasticity since orientation and retractive stresses are both due to entropy effects in ideal rubbers[89, 90, 91, 92, 111, 112]. Thus, for uniaxial tensile tests, the birefringence and the retractive stress are related by the simple equation

$$(n_{\parallel} - n_{\perp}) = K\sigma \tag{10.2}$$

The birefringence $(n_{\parallel} - n_{\perp})$ is the difference in refractive indices in the directions parallel and perpendicular to the direction of stretching. The constant K is called the stress-optical coefficient. Its value is dependent upon the chemical structure of the polymer, and it decreases slowly as the temperature is raised. For materials which obey the kinetic theory of rubber the stress-optical coefficient is defined by[89, 90, 91, 92, 111, 112]:

$$K = \frac{2\pi(n^2 + 2)^2(\alpha_{\parallel} - \alpha_{\perp})}{45nkT} \tag{10.3}$$

where n is the refractive index of the unoriented polymer, k is Boltzmann's constant, T is the absolute temperature, and $(\alpha_{\parallel} - \alpha_{\perp})$ is the difference in polarizability of a polymer segment parallel and perpendicular to the direction of the chain segment. A segment is generally several monomer units long. The stress-optical coefficient K is usually expressed in Brewsters, which is equal to 10^{-13} cm^2/dyne.

The kinetic theory predicts that the birefringence/stress ratio for a given material is independent of the degree of crosslinking. This is true for many rubbers and molten polymers. However, there are some materials, such as crosslinked polyethylene above its melting point, which have stress-optical coefficients which vary somewhat with the degree of crosslinking; this behavior is attributed to the non-Gaussian behavior of these polymer chains[90, 92].

For crosslinked rubbers there is a nonlinear dependence of the birefringence on the elongation. For uncrosslinked polymers and rubbery materials in which stress relaxation can occur, there is no unique relation between birefringence and elongation. However, in these cases the birefringence is directly proportional to the tensile stress on the polymer. Thus, during a stress relaxation test the birefringence will decrease along with the stress so that their ratio remains constant[101, 104, 105]. During a creep test the birefringence/stress ratio remains constant with time even though the elongation of the specimen increases with time[77, 78]. This is illustrated in Figure 10.2 for polystyrene at 110°C.

Stein and Tobolsky[104] have shown that in a stress-relaxation experiment the birefringence/stress ratio should remain constant above the glass transition temperature for the following mechanisms of stress relaxation: (1) chemical scission of network bonds, (2) reactions involving chemical interchange of bonds, (3) viscous flow, or, (4) molecular diffusion.

The relations between birefringence, orientation, and stress become much more complicated for crystalline polymers or for polymers in which there is an energy contribution to the stress in addition to the entropy contribution giving rise to rubber elasticity[4, 5, 102, 104, 105]. For instance, in stress-relaxation experiments the birefringence/stress ratio increases with time

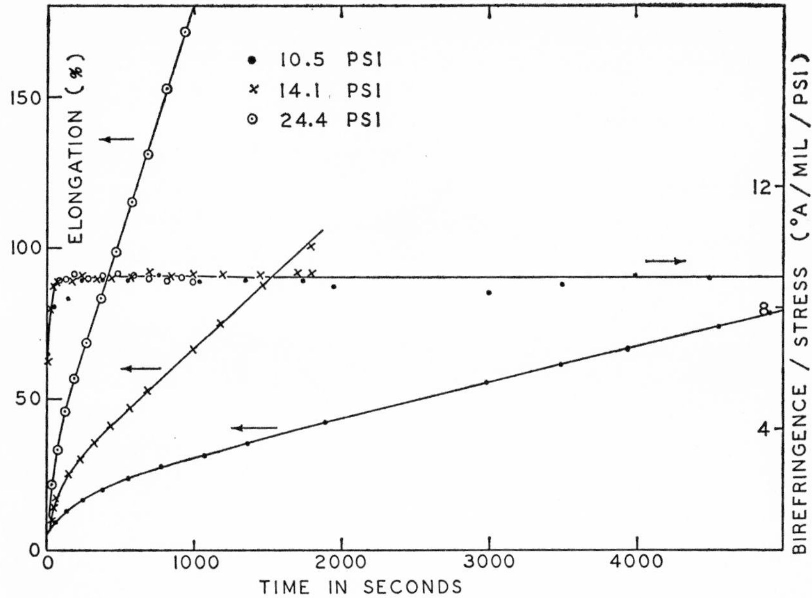

Figure 10.2. Creep and birefringence/stress ratio of polystyrene at 110°C at loads of 10.5, 14.1, and 24.4 psi. The stress-optical coefficient in Å/mil/psi can be converted to Brewsters by multiplying by 572. [*From Nielsen, L. E., and Buchdahl, R., J. Colloid Sci.*, **5**, *282* (*1950*)]

in the following cases: (1) An amorphous rubber crystallizes during the course of the stress-relaxation test; (2) The orientation of crystallites increases during the test with a crystalline polymer; (3) Distorted crystals reorganize to form undistorted crystals. Many experimental investigations support these conclusions[3, 4, 105].

Polymers, which have yield points or can be cold-drawn, become highly oriented on stretching, yet they have small retractive forces unless heated to near the glass temperature or melting point. In such cases the orientation is generally roughly proportional to the elongation rather than to the stress[28, 29, 36]. The ratio of birefringence to strain is then nearly constant.

Rigid amorphous polymers, as well as rubbery polymers, become birefringent when a stress is applied to them. Generally, a much greater stress is required to produce a given value of birefringence with a rigid polymer than with a rubber. Thus, the stress-optical coefficient usually changes rapidly with temperature in the neighborhood of the glass-transition temperature. The birefringence or stress-optical coefficient even changes sign in going through the transition region for some polymers[59, 102]. For instance, the stress-optical coefficient of polystyrene is positive at room temperature, but above 100°C. the coefficient is negative[86]. Birefringence is considered positive when the refractive index parallel to the polymer chain is greater than the refractive index perpendicular to the chain. Table 10.1 lists the stress-optical coefficients of a few polymers.

Stress-optical coefficients below the glass temperature generally are not a measure of molecular segment orientation. The coefficients in this case are a manifestation of energy rather than entropy effects. Below T_g molecular backbone motion is mostly frozen in so molecular orientation can not readily take place. In the glassy state, a stress makes a material become birefringent because of changes in polarizability brought about by mechanisms such as deformation of bond angles, changes in bond lengths, and orientation of side groups such as the phenyl group in polystyrene. Stress-optical coefficients of rigid polymers depend upon the chemical structure, temperature, and even the degree of molecular orientation put in the test specimen by a previous hot-stretching treatment[8, 85].

Effect of Orientation on the Stress-Strain Properties of Rigid Polymers

Rigid polymers which have been oriented by stretching while heated above their softening temperature have mechanical properties which vary in different directions. Uniaxially oriented materials have Young's moduli greater in the direction parallel to the orientation than in the direction

TABLE 10.1. STRESS-OPTICAL COEFFICIENTS OF POLYMERS IN BREWSTERS.*

Polymer	Coefficient Below the Glass Temperature	Coefficient Above the Glass Temperature
Polystyrene	+10 (24°C)	−5200 (110°C)
Polystyrene	+17 (−195°C)	
Poly-α-methyl styrene	−2.0 (27°C)	
Polyvinyl toluene	+15.5 (27°C)	
Poly-*p*-tertiary butyl styrene	+11.0 (27°C)	
Poly-*p*-chloro styrene	+23.7 (27°C)	
Poly-2,5-dichlorostyrene	+7.2 (27°C)	
Polymethyl methacrylate	−4.5 (18°C)	−45 (93°C)(?)
Polymethyl methacrylate	−3.8 (27°C)	
Polyphenyl methacrylate	+39.8 (27°C)	
Polycyclohexyl methacrylate	+5.9 (27°C)	
Polychloroethyl methacrylate	+5.6 (27°C)	
Poly-*o*-nitrophenyl methacrylate	+22 (27°C)	
Polybenzyl methacrylate	+45 (27°C)	
Natural rubber		+1900 (20°C)
Gutta percha		+3000 (85°C)
Polyethylene		+2000 (130°C)

* Rudd, J. F., and Andrews R. D., *J. Appl. Phys.*, **29,** 1421 (1958).
Rudd, J. F., and Andrews R. D., *J. Appl. Phys.*, **31,** 818 (1960).
Lamble, J. H., and Dahmouch, E. S., *British J. Appl. Phys.*, **9,** 388 (1958).
Saunders, D. W., *Trans. Faraday Soc.*, **52,** 1414 (1956).

perpendicular to the orientation. The effect is not dramatic at ordinary degrees of orientation; high orientation is required to give a Young's modulus parallel to the orientation which is twice the modulus of unoriented amorphous polymer[23, 24, 79]. Orientation has a much greater effect on tensile strength and elongation to break. Parallel to the orientation the tensile strength is easily increased by a factor of at least 200 or even 500 per cent[12, 23, 24, 52, 70, 79]. However, perpendicular to the orientation the tensile strength may be only a half or a third the tensile strength of an unoriented specimen. These effects are to be expected since parallel to the orientation, stresses are exerted largely on the primary bonds of the polymer chains, while in the direction perpendicular to the orientation, forces act to a large extent on the weak secondary bonds between polymer chains. Another factor which may be important comes from the orientation of any stress concentrators at the same time the polymer chains are oriented. The stress concentrators will be oriented parallel to the chains so that they are effective in concentrating stresses only in the direction perpendicular to the chains.

Orientation can convert some brittle polymers such as polystyrene or polymethyl methacrylate into ductile materials if the stresses are applied to the specimen in the direction of orientation. For stresses at right angles to the polymer chains, the polymer has less elongation to break than unoriented material. However, in the chain direction the stress-strain curve often shows a yield point, and the elongation to break can be much greater than for the unoriented material[23, 24, 79]. These phenomena are most pronounced with carefully prepared uniaxially oriented specimens, but they also are found with specimens prepared by injection molding as illustrated in Table 10.2. This table shows the improvement of tensile and impact properties of polystyrene when tested parallel to the molecular alignment. Part of the scattering of the data is due to factors in the injection-molding process other than the total birefringence as measured through the plane of the sheet. The biaxial component of the orientation is overlooked in such measurements. In addition, the orientation is not uniform throughout the thickness of injection-molded objects; there is often a highly oriented "skin"[13].

Since the tensile strength and elongation parallel to the polymer chains increases with the degree of orientation, the impact strength or energy to break a test specimen should also increase in the same direction. Although the energy to break may be increased by a factor of about ten parallel to the direction of hot stretching, the energy to break in the perpendicular direction is less than for an unoriented specimen. In only a few practical applications can advantage be taken of the high impact strength in one direction; in most cases stresses are applied to a plastic object in several directions, so the object breaks in the direction in which it is weakest[1, 41, 52].

TABLE 10.2. MECHANICAL PROPERTIES OF ORIENTED POLYSTYRENE.*

Birefringence $\Delta n \times 10^4$	Tensile Strength (psi.)		Elongation to Break (%)		Izod Impact Strength	
	‖	⊥	‖	⊥	‖	⊥
1.1	3940	3440	2.4	1.8	.24	.22
4.3	5340	4240	3.1	2.1	.32	.21
9.1	6320	4110	3.9	2.6	.36	.20
16.3	7550	4140	4.2	1.9	.65	.21
25.4	7640	3710	5.0	1.8	1.36	.18
30.9	7590	2630	6.8	1.3	—	—
41.4	8660	3440	5.2	2.1	1.54	.23
51.8	10,170	4550	4.4	2.5	1.58	.18
53.7	8440	1290	7.0	0.7	—	—

* Jackson, G. B., and Ballman, R. L., *Soc. Plastics Eng. J.*, **16**, No. 10, 1147 (1960).
‖ Stress applied parallel to chain orientation.
⊥ Stress applied perpendicular to direction of orientation.

Uniaxial orientation generally does not improve the shear or torsional properties of a plastic. The shear modulus is nearly independent of orientation, and the torsional strength may decrease[23].

The mechanical properties of oriented crystalline polymers with low glass-transition temperatures or of ductile amorphous polymers are somewhat different from the properties discussed above for brittle amorphous polymers. These differences are often emphasized by some biaxial orientation as in many commercial films which are stretched more in one direction than in another. These ductile polymers generally have greater elongations to break in the direction perpendicular to the direction of orientation. In ductile materials when the stress is applied perpendicular to the orientation, the molecules first deorient, and then they become oriented parallel to the new stretching direction. Thus, in the perpendicular direction the material has the elongation to break characteristic of the parallel direction plus the elongation required to deorient the molecules and reorient them again. It is this possibility for reorientation which gives rise to the differences between ductile and brittle polymers. Brittle polymers break before the reorientation process gets started. The modulus and tensile strength, however, even for ductile materials are generally greater parallel than perpendicular to the orientation[65].

These effects are shown for polyethylene films in Table 10.3[6]. These stress-strain data were obtained at an elongation rate of 0.336 inch/second. Polyethylene is very ductile at temperatures above −15°C, but at −60°C it has become nearly brittle in behavior so that its elongation becomes small, especially perpendicular to the orientation. As the temperature is lowered, the tensile strength increases and the elongation decreases. Although Table 10.3 is used to illustrate the behavior of ductile polymers in general with uniaxial orientation, the orientation in polyethylene films is actually

Table 10.3. Stress-Strain Behavior of Oriented Polyethylene Films.*

Temperature (°C)	Parallel Direction		Perpendicular Direction	
	Tensile strength (psi)	Elongation to break (%)	Tensile strength (psi)	Elongation to break (%)
30	3870	509	3740	789
15	4330	487	4140	765
0	4830	450	3940	661
−15	5970	454	4550	589
−30	6550	431	3730	310
−60	6930	223	7310 (?)	9

* Anderson, A. A., and Moffitt, G. L., *Modern Plastics*, **35**, 139 (Apr., 1958).

more complex[2, 3]. Other ductile polymers such as cellulose acetate, however, also show the expected behavior as outlined here. In the direction of molecular orientation the tensile strength increases and the elongation to break decreases as the degree of hot stretching and orientation increases [70]. Krassig and Kitchen[58] found that both orientation and crystallinity affect the tensile strength of cellulose fibers, but orientation is the more important variable.

Biaxial orientation of brittle polymers eliminates the poor strength properties which these materials have in the perpendicular direction when uniaxially oriented. Biaxially oriented sheets tend to have the desirable properties of uniaxial orientation in both the length and width directions. This would be expected on the basis of the ideal case shown in Figure 10.1 B. A stress in any direction in the plane of the sheet acts upon the strong primary bonds of many polymer chains. Biaxial sheets are weak in the direction perpendicular to the plane of the sheet, so the film sheets tend to split into a number of thinner sheets. Uniaxial materials, on the other hand, tend to break up into bundles of fibers running parallel to the direction of hot stretching[12].

Compared to unoriented materials, biaxially oriented sheets have higher tensile strengths and greater ultimate elongations[9, 10, 12, 31, 119]. They are also much tougher and have high impact strengths compared to unoriented sheets or films[31, 48]. Typical comparative data are given in Table 10.4 for polystyrene and polymethyl methacrylate. There is an optimum value of the amount of biaxial orientation for the best mechanical properties. If the sheet is stretched too much while in the molten state, properties such as the ultimate elongation decrease.

TABLE 10.4. COMPARISON OF BIAXIALLY ORIENTED WITH UNORIENTED SHEETS.*

Property	Polystyrene		Polymethyl Methacrylate	
	Unoriented	Biaxial Oriented	Unoriented	Biaxial Oriented
Tensile Strength (psi)	5000–9000	7000–12000	7500–10000	8000–11000
Elongation to Break (%)	1–3.6	8–18	5–10	25–50
Impact Strength	.25–.5	>3	4	15

* From various sources including:

Fortner, C., *Rubber World*, **129**, 493 (1954).

Axilrod, B. M., Sherman, M. A., Cohen, V., and Wolock, I., *Modern Plastics*, **30**, 117 (December 1952).

Hurst, D. A., *Soc. Plastics Eng. J.*, **12**, 18 (May 1956).

Effect of Orientation on the Dynamic Properties of Polymers

Very few data are available on the dynamic mechanical properties of oriented rigid amorphous polymers. If the oscillating stresses are parallel to the direction of molecular orientation, the Young's modulus of the oriented material is greater than that of the unoriented material. Nielsen and Buchdahl[79] found that the damping, E''/E', was slightly greater for oriented polystyrene than for isotropic annealed polystyrene. Huff and Mueller[47] compared the electrical properties of stretched and unstretched polyvinyl chloride. At low temperatures the electrical dissipation factor ϵ''/ϵ' increased in the order: stretched < unstretched < redrawn material. At temperatures approaching the softening temperature of the polyvinyl chloride the order was: unstretched < stretched < redrawn polymer. Because of the close analogy between electrical and mechanical dissipation factors, it can be assumed that the mechanical damping would behave in the same manner as the electrical dissipation factor. In general it appears that orientation increases both E' and E'' when the stress is applied parallel to the direction of molecular alignment; E''/E' can either increase or decrease.

In order to measure the effect of orientation on the dynamic properties of rubbery polymers, the rubber must be stretched and held in this stretched state while the measurments are being made. This is often accomplished by measuring the velocity and attenuation of high frequency waves along a thin strip of the rubber during the course of a stress-strain test[39, 40, 62, 63, 64].

The dynamic mechanical properties of rubbers change dramatically when the molecules become oriented. The Young's modulus increases rapidly with an increase in strain or orientation. Typical values are an increase in the modulus equal to a hundred times the unoriented modulus for a tensile strain of six[39, 40, 62]. As the modulus increases on stretching, the damping, E''/E', decreases somewhat so that the loss modulus E'' remains relatively constant or increases slowly. Typical values for a rubber are illustrated in Figure 10.3[64]. Mason[62] found that orientation drastically reduces the size of the peak in the damping-temperature curve, especially at high elongations such as 600 per cent. The temperature of maximum damping, however, is nearly independent of the extent of stretching.

A number of oriented crystalline polymers have been studied. In nearly all cases Young's modulus increases with orientation if the tensile stress is applied parallel to the direction of molecular alignment[14, 22, 37, 38, 40, 71, 74, 110, 115]. If the tensile stress is applied perpendicular to the direction of orientation, the modulus is lower than that for an unoriented material[74].

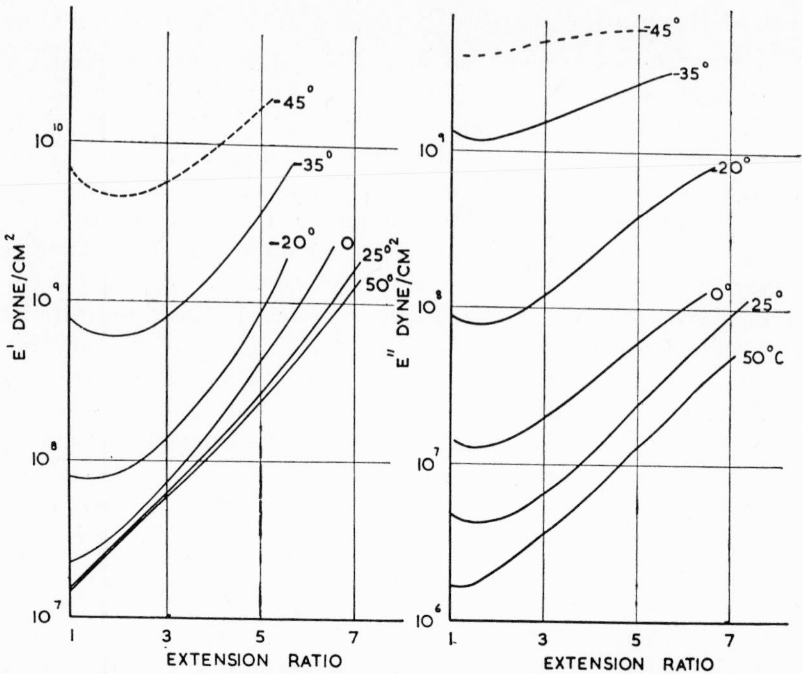

Figure 10.3. Dynamic Young's moduli of rubber as a function of the elongation at 1 kc/sec. [*After Mason, P., J. Appl. Polymer Sci.*, **5**, *428* (*1961*)]

These results can be explained on the basis that tensile stresses parallel to the direction of orientation act largely against the covalent bonds of the long chain molecules to deform bond angles and atomic distances. Stresses perpendicular to the direction of orientation act against the weak van der Waal's forces between molecules.

Orientation by cold-drawing increased the dynamic Young's modulus by a factor of 3.5 for nylon 6-6 and by a factor of 5.8 for polyethylene terephthalate; the draw ratio or ratio of stretched to unstretched lengths was six for both polymers[113]. Table 10.5 illustrates typical values for the changes in Young's modulus parallel and perpendicular to the direction of chain alignment. The modulus of these very highly oriented, crystalline polymers is approximately ten times greater than the modulus of the isotropic material. The relative decrease in the modulus perpendicular to the chains is much less. Moseley[71] predicts by a simple theory that the Young's modulus perpendicular to the chains should be two-thirds of the modulus of the unoriented polymer. Moseley's theory also suggests that the degree

TABLE 10.5. RELATIVE CHANGES IN YOUNG'S MODULI FOR HIGHLY ORIENTED POLYMERS.*

Polymer	Modulus Parallel to Chains / Modulus of unoriented polymer	Modulus Perpendicular to Chains / Modulus of unoriented polymer
Polyethylene Terephthalate	17.8	0.67
Nylon 66	19.2	0.57
Viscose Rayon	9.3	0.67
Polyacrylonitrile	5.8	0.67

* Calculated from data of Moseley, W. W., *J. Appl. Polymer Sci.*, **3**, 266 (1960).

of orientation of the crystallites in polymers can be predicted by the simple equation:

$$\text{Degree of Orientation} = 1 - \frac{E_u}{E_{\parallel}}. \tag{10.4}$$

In this equation E_u is the Young's modulus of the unoriented polymer and $E_{\parallel}$ is the modulus measured parallel to the direction of the oriented polymer molecules. The moduli should be measured at a high frequency of the order of ten thousand cycles per second so as to minimize relaxation effects. Figure 10.4 shows how the degree of orientation changes with elongation during the course of a stress-strain test on nylon 6-6. The rate of orientation is greatest near the yield point where necking and cold-drawing take place.

Very little information is available on the variation of the dynamic shear modulus with orientation. In general orientation appears to have very little effect on the shear modulus, but in some cases orientation produces a small increase[38, 113]. The dynamic shear behavior of oriented polymers has been discussed in some detail by Hellwege, Kaiser, and Kuphal[38].

The effect of orientation on the damping of a crystalline polymer is often complex so that generalizations are not so readily apparent. However, in many cases the damping, E''/E', increases with orientation. However, there are exceptions; for crystalline, oriented polystyrene the damping decreases with orientation if the dynamic tensile stress is parallel to the direction of molecular alignment. The damping in the perpendicular direction for this polymer, however, is greater than for crystalline, unoriented material[74]. The loss modulus E'' is approximately the same when tested in either the parallel or perpendicular directions. The large differences in E''/E' in the two directions is a reflection of the large differences in E'. Part of the complexity with crystalline polymers undoubtedly arises from

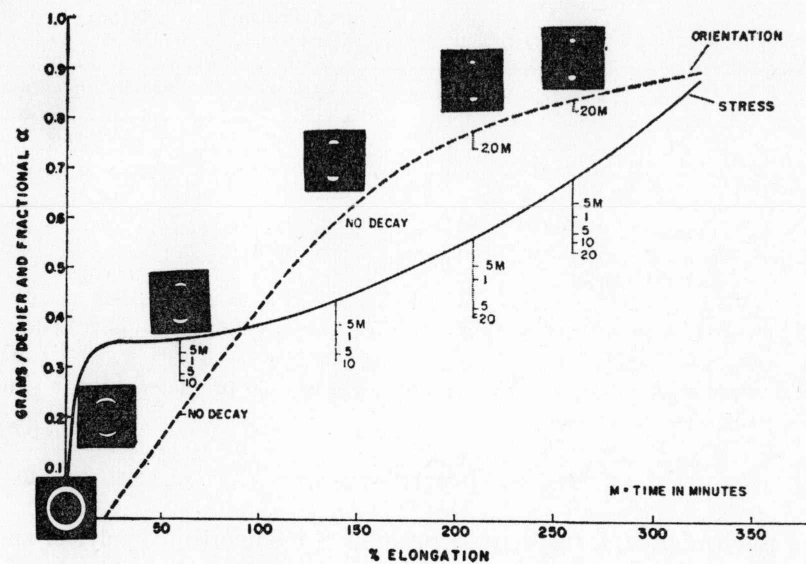

Figure 10.4. The stress-strain curve and orientation as a function of elongation for nylon 66. Ten per cent/minute elongation rate. [*After Charch, W. H., and Moseley, Jr., W. W., Textile Research J.*, **29**, *525* (*1959*)]

the inability to separate the contributions of the amorphous and crystallite orientations to the damping processes. In addition, it is not uncommon for the degree of crystallinity to change with orientation. Both crystallinity and orientation tend to shift the dispersion regions to longer times[110].

For crystalline polystyrene[74] and crystalline polyethylene terephthalate [108, 114, 121] the glass-transition temperature (or temperature of maximum damping) increases with the degree of orientation. The glass temperature of these polymers is higher for the crystalline material than for the amorphous material, but an even larger shift to higher temperatures results when the polymers are both crystalline and oriented. This same general behavior holds for many other polymers with moderate to high degrees of crystallinity. Increases in the glass temperature of roughly 25°C are typical for high degrees of orientation and crystallinity.

Orientation can bring about shifts or changes in the intensity of secondary transitions in crystalline polymers[38, 72, 73]. So little work has been done on these effects, however, that very little is known about them. The alpha transition, which normally occurs in polyethylene in the range from 50 to 100°C, can be lowered to about 0°C by orientation brought about by cold-drawing the polymer[38]. Since the alpha transition can generally be correlated with crystallite size or perfection, the shift in this transition with orientation might be an indication that the crystal size decreases on cold-drawing.

Effect of Orientation on Other Properties

Very little work is published on the effect of orientation on the creep and stress-relaxation behavior of rigid polymers. Since orientation increases the modulus in the direction of chain alignment, the total creep of an oriented material should be less than for the isotropic material. The decrease in creep and stress relaxation with orientation has been found for several polymers, including cellulose filaments[81]. Jackson and Cohen[53] found that orientation decreases the total creep in directions both parallel and perpendicular to the molecular alignment for polystyrene polymers. However, since their test specimens were not truly uniaxial but also contained a large biaxial component of orientation, the decrease in creep in the perpendicular direction might be due to the beneficial effect of the biaxial orientation.

Although orientation generally decreases the total creep, at least at temperatures well below the glass transition temperature, it can increase the rate of creep or stress relaxation. For instance, Cheatham and Dietz[23, 24] found that uniaxial orientation increases the rate of stress relaxation in polymethyl methacrylate. Pomeroy[83] reports that at elevated temperatures nylon creeps at a faster rate when oriented. It is not surprising that orientation can in some cases increase the creep rate in spite of the increase in modulus. As pointed out in the previous section, orientation often increases the mechanical damping. Thus, relations such as Nutting's equation would predict an increase in creep rate with orientation if the mechanical damping also increased. Although the exact mechanism of the increased creep or stress-relaxation rate is not known, it appears that slip between oriented chain segments is easier in some respects than slip between entangled molecular segments oriented at random. Possibly the same mechanisms are operating that enable brittle polymers to be cold-drawn after being oriented by hot stretching.

The effect of orientation on creep can be confused by at least two factors. First, parallel orientation and biaxial orientation decrease the ease of forming craze cracks, which can weaken rigid polymers. Second, oriented objects are often quench-cooled so that they have a larger free volume than slowly cooled isotropic objects. The mechanical properties of polymers below their glass temperature are strongly dependent upon the amount of free volume. These two factors are discussed in more detail later in this chapter.

Orientation lowers the temperature at which a rigid plastic object will maintain its dimensional stability[25, 79]. Orientation produces an internal stress which in many respects acts the same as an external load. In the previous chapter it was shown how the softening temperature of a polymer decreases as the external load increases. In the same manner the temperature at which shrinkage takes place with an oriented polymer decreases as the orientation increases. When an oriented material is heated, it attempts to shrink back to the same shape it had before being oriented. At a constant temperature the speed of retraction or shrinkage is proportional to the orientation for an amorphous polymer, but if enough time is allowed, it is possible that a slightly oriented material can have nearly the same total shrinkage as a highly oriented one. The reason for this is that the retractive force for rubbers and heated amorphous polymers is proportional to the orientation, but there is no unique relation between orientation and the extent of stretching.

The linear coefficient of expansion is less parallel to the direction of orientation than it is perpendicular to that direction[16, 109]. This effect is very apparent also from the thermal distortion curves on oriented crystalline polystyrene published by Newman and Cox[74]. The coefficient of expansion in this case is about 300 per cent greater in the perpendicular direction than it is in the parallel direction. Generally, the effect is not so great except in the case of very high orientation. The coefficient of expansion would be expected to decrease as molecular forces increase in roughly an inverse proportion to the change in Young's modulus. The covalent forces parallel to the polymer chains are much greater than the intermolecular forces perpendicular to the chains.

The volume coefficient of expansion of an oriented polymer is about the same as that for the isotropic material[109]. For uniaxial orientation the volume coefficient is related to the linear coefficients, $\beta_{\parallel}$ and $\beta_{\perp}$, in the directions parallel and perpendicular to the chain alignment by:

$$\text{Volume Coefficient of Expansion} = \beta_{\parallel} + 2\beta_{\perp} . \qquad (10.5)$$

Rigid polymers such as polystyrene tend to craze when subject to large loads[9, 10, 45, 66, 88, 120]. Such materials can also be made to craze by certain treatments with liquids or vapors even in the absence of any external load[11, 76]. Crazing is the result of the formation of many small cracks on the surface or in the interior of the polymer. Crazing not only results in a poor appearance, but the mechanical strength of the plastic object is weakened also.

Uniaxial orientation increases the resistance to crazing by external loads acting parallel to the direction of orientation. Unfortunately, crazing becomes more easily produced in the perpendicular direction. This phenomenon can be used to quickly make visible the orientation and flow pattern in injection-molded objects[76]. If an object molded from transparent polystyrene is soaked for some time in warm methanol and then exposed to hexane in either the liquid or vapor state, the flow pattern of the molten polymer during the injection-molding process instantly becomes visible.

Biaxially oriented films and sheets are resistant to crazing when compared to unoriented or uniaxially oriented sheets[9, 10, 48, 119, 120]. A tensile stress applied in any direction in the plane of a biaxially oriented sheet acts in the chain direction of a large percentage of the molecules. This is readily seen in Figure 10.1 B. Biaxial orientation gives in all directions in the plane of the sheet some of the desirable properties possessed by uniaxially oriented material in the direction of chain alignment.

Dependence of Mechanical Behavior on Thermal Treatment

Thermal treatments can modify the properties of polymers by bringing about the following changes in structure or morphology: (1) Rapid cooling from the melt incorporates more free volume in a material than does slow cooling. Thus, quenched materials are less dense than slow cooled or annealed ones. The Williams, Landel, Ferry[117] relations enable one to predict many of the effects due to changes in free volume. (2) Heat treatments are capable of changing the degree of crystallinity. (3) The perfection of crystallites and the morphological structure such as spherulites can be modified by thermal treatments. (4) Thermal treatments can also bring about chemical reactions such as crosslinking or degradation, but such reactions will not be included in this discussion. (5) Temperature gradients in a material while it is cooling through the softening range give rise to frozen-in stresses.

With isotropic rigid amorphous polymers the main effect of heat treatments is to change the density or free volume, which in turn affects the mechanical properties. The smaller the density the smaller is the internal viscosity and the lower is the glass transition temperature. As a result, a polymer quenched from the molten state has a higher creep rate than a slowly cooled sample. Likewise, a quenched specimen has a greater rate of stress relaxation and smaller average relaxation time than a slowly cooled or annealed sample. These phenomena are beautifully illustrated by the stress relaxation results of McLoughlin and Tobolsky[61] on polymethyl methacrylate. As the rate of cooling from the melt increases, the inflection point in the stress relaxation ratio σ/σ_0 versus log time curve shifts to lower temperatures.

Since the glass-transition temperature is intimately related to the free volume, the softening or heat distortion temperature should decrease as the rate of cooling from the melt increases. Shifts in heat distortion temperature of roughly 10°C are easily brought about. Typical data on the raising of the heat distortion temperature of polystyrene by annealing have been published by Melchore and Mark[67]. Small increases in mechanical damping of polystyrene occur as the rate of cooling increases[79]. There is a greater tendency for amorphous polymers to have yield points and to cold-draw if they are quenched rather than slowly cooled[79]. This tendency for greater elongation and increased toughness is enhanced by even a small amount of orientation.

Heat treatments generally have a greater effect on crystallizable polymers than on amorphous ones because of the additional possibilities of changing the degree of crystallinity or the crystal size or morphology. With most such polymers the degree of crystallinity decreases, the crystallite size decreases, and there is less spherulitic structure as the rate of cooling from the melt increases.

Treatments which change the degree of crystallinity produce a number of general changes in mechanical properties. For instance, the elastic moduli increase with the crystallinity at temperatures between the main glass temperature and the melting point[75]. For most polymers, crystallinity has only a small effect on the shear and Young's moduli at temperatures below the glass transition. Brittleness increases and impact strength decreases with crystallinity, especially if the increase in crystallinity is accompanied by an increase in spherulitic structure. If the polymer has a glass temperature near the test temperature or below, the tensile strength generally increases and the elongation to break decreases as the crystallinity increases. However, if the polymer tends to become very brittle, the tensile strength may actually decrease with crystallinity. The yield strength nearly always increases with crystallinity, however. There is a distinct reduction in creep with an increase in crystallinity at temperatures above the glass transition. Stress relaxation decreases and the distribution of relaxation times is extended to longer times by increases in crystallinity. Most of these effects appear reasonable if one assumes that crystallites act as stress concentrators but at the same time they behave as crosslinks in reducing the movement of molecular segments. In many cases it is difficult to differentiate changes due to slight increases in crystallinity from changes due to an increase in spherulitic structure since the two factors often go together.

The effects of heat treatments on the mechanical properties of polyethylene have been intensively studied. Changes in the degree of crystallinity can be brought about with high density, linear polyethylene[27]. However, only slight changes in total crystallinity can be produced in low density, branched polyethylene; even quenched samples have nearly the same crystallinity as slow-cooled or annealed samples. Although the degree of crystallinity of low density polyethylene can not be drastically changed, the crystallite size and perfection, length of chain folds, and the spherulitic structure can be modified. It is known that in single crystals of polyethylene the folding length increases with an increase in crystallization temperature [56, 84, 99]. It is probable that a similar phenomenon occurs in the bulk polymer; at least changes occur which can be correlated with some crystallite dimension or size.

Thermal treatments can produce large changes in the alpha transition of polyethylene. See, for instance, Figure 7.25. Quenching easily shifts this transition as much as 50°C downward. The other transitions are relatively unchanged by heat treatments. The modulus of quenched polyethylene is greater than that of slowly cooled polymer if the polymers are compared, not at equal temperatures, but at equal degrees of crystallinities as determined by density measurements. This is apparently a fairly general phenomenon as it has been observed for a number of crystalline polymers. A large number of small crystallites imposes more restrictions on the amorphous phase than what a smaller number of larger crystallites are capable of doing. The amorphous sequences between crystallites are shorter in the quenched polymer; and if one assumes that the concepts of the kinetic theory of rubber can be extended to highly crystalline polymers, then the quenched polymer should have the higher modulus. The same result is predicted by Bueche's theory[20]. Annealing treatments often produce changes in mechanical properties most rapidly in the neighborhood of the alpha transition temperature. Recrystallization apparently occurs readily at the alpha transition temperature. If polyethylene is annealed near the alpha transition temperature such as at 40°C, the total creep and the creep rate decrease[42].

The modification of the properties of polypropylene by heat treatments can be found in the papers of Miller[69], Wijga[116], and Shearer, Guillet, and Coover[94]. The results are what would be expected on the basis of the previous discussion on the change of properties with crystallinity and heat treatment. The dependence of the properties of nylon 6-6 on crystallinity and treatments is described in papers by Bobalek, Lacson, and Dawson[15], Starkweather, Moore, Hansen, Roder, and Brooks[98], and Starkweather and Brooks[97].

Effects Due to Treatments with Liquids and Sintering

Solvents and liquids are often capable of producing changes in mechanical properties. One type of liquid (plasticizers) lowers the glass transition of polymers; the effect of such liquids has been discussed in previous chapters and will not be reviewed here. Some liquids, however, produce effects which are different from the usual plasticization.

Often the properties of films cast from solution depend upon the solvent even though all or nearly all of the solvent is removed from the films before tests are made. Jones and Miles[55] found that the stress-strain properties of cellulose nitrate are strongly dependent upon the solvent used to prepare the film. At least some of the effects in this case can be attributed to changes in crystallinity or crystal morphology. Merz, Nielsen, and Buchdahl[68] found that polystyrene films cast from benzene had a lower softening temperature and greater creep than films cast from methyl ethyl ketone solutions. The results might be due to trace amounts of solvents, but they could also be explained on the basis that polystyrene molecules are less tightly coiled in benzene solutions and that equilibrium molecular configuration was not attained by the drying schedule used in preparing the films. Novikov, Dorokhina, and Zubov[80] found that the tensile strength of rubber depends upon the solvent from which the polymer was cast. They attributed the changes in tensile strength to differences in molecular shape, which in turn depends upon whether the liquid was a good or bad solvent for the rubber. Sandomirskii and Gagina[87] found that rubber films made from latex can be stronger than films cast from solutions.

Plasticizers in polyvinyl chloride often produce effects which are not associated with the usual behavior of plasticizers. Greenhoe[32] found that the the tensile strength of films made by heating polyvinyl chloride plastisols goes through a pronounced maximum as the fusion temperature is increased. At low fusion temperatures apparently the polyvinyl chloride emulsion particles are not completely fused together, and differences exist between the centers of the particles and their boundaries. The reason for the drop-off in tensile strength again at much higher temperatures is not clear; possibly the tensile strength decreases because of an increase in crystallinity or crosslinking.

Small amounts of plasticizers (about 5 to 10 per cent) allow polyvinyl chloride to crystallize much more rapidly than if no plasticizer were present[43]. This increase in crystallinity produces some changes in mechanical properties which are exactly opposite to what would be expected for a plasticizer. For instance, the impact strength first decreases and then increases as the plasticizer content increases, and the tensile strength and

Young's modulus first increase with plasticizer concentration before decreasing as expected.

Some liquids, which act as plasticizers in lowering the main glass-transition temperature, also produce changes in the seconary transitions or give rise to new transitions as measured by low frequency dynamic mechanical tests. For instance, Illers[50], among others, found that water gives rise to a secondary transition at about −75°C at one cycle per second in nylons such as the 6-12 polyamide. The transition is attributed to motion of the water molecule bound to the amide groups by hydrogen bonding. The dry polyamide has its main glass transition at 50°C and another transition at about −140°C when measured at one cycle per second. As the water content increases, the main transition is lowered, the temperature of the lowest transition remains relatively constant, and the new transition remains at about −75°C while its intensity increases. A similar phenomenon has been reported for the semi-crystalline polyurethane made from 1,4-butanediol and 1,6-hexamethylene diisocyanate[54]. Liquids such as water and alcohols lower the glass transition from 40°C. However, at the same time, a new damping peak develops at −70°C, while the intensity of the transition at −135°C decreases with concentration of liquid. Polystyrene has only very weak secondary transitions, but some plasticizers give rise to two fairly prominent low temperature transitions[51]. The lowest of these transitions is unusual in that it shifts to higher temperatures as the plasticizer concentration increases. The cause of these transitions is not clear, but they may be related to movements of the phenyl group or to imperfections in the chain structure such as occasional head-to-head arrangements of monomer units or to changes in tacticity.

Sintering and cold pressing are not widely used as fabrication techniques for high polymers. Polytetrafluoroethylene is probably the only polymer which is normally fabricated by a sintering process, although formation of films from latices might also be considered as sintering[17]. If the sintering process is not complete, voids will be left in the polymer so that its apparent density is decreased. Also, the boundary between particles will not be completely destroyed if sintering is not perfect. A void space of 6 per cent in polytetrafluoroethylene has the following effects on mechanical properties[107]: (1) the flex or fatigue life is decreased by a thousand fold. (2) The tensile modulus is decreased slightly—about 30 per cent. (3) The tensile strength is decreased about 50 per cent while the elongation to break is decreased by 80 per cent. (4) The impact strength is decreased by 80 per cent. McCrum[60] found that the dynamic shear modulus is nearly independent of void space if the voids occupy less than 4 per cent of the volume, but the shear modulus does depend upon the degree of crystallinity. Thus, by a density measurement and a shear modulus measurement both the void content and the crystallinity of polytetrafluoroethylene can be determined.

Powders of such polymers as rigid polyvinyl chloride or polyacrylonitrile can be cold-pressed at room temperature under high pressure to give transparent specimens[19]. These cold-pressed polymers are very brittle and have very little mechanical strength. Apparently very few polymer chains have diffused from one powder particle to another so as to securely tie the particles together. Diffusion and cohesion between particles takes place readily only at temperatures equal to the glass temperature or above[49]. Data on the temperature and pressure conditions to bring about self-adhesion have been published for polyvinyl chloride, polystyrene, and polymethyl methacrylate[49]. If too much pressure is applied, good sintering or self-adhesion will not take place because of the increase in glass temperature by pressure. Thus, at a given temperature above the glass transition, there is both a lower and an upper limit to the pressure that can be used to produce strong transparent specimens in a reasonable time from powdered polymers. Schilling[93] has measured the transparency and dynamic shear modulus of a number of cold-pressed polymers. Both the modulus and transparency increase with the pressure used to form the specimens. The modulus of polyacrylonitrile can be varied by a factor of about two over the extreme range of pressures used to form the specimens. The low modulus values are probably due to some microscopic voids and to imperfections in continuity at the boundaries between former particles.

References

1. Adams, C. H., Jackson, G. B., and McCarthy, R. A., *Soc. Plastics Eng. J.*, **12**, 13 (March, 1956).
2. Aggarwal, S. L., Tilley, G. P., and Sweeting, O. J., *J. Appl. Polymer Sci.*, **1**, 91 (1959).
3. Aggarwal, S. L., Tilley, G. P., and Sweeting, O. J., *J. Polymer Sci.*, **51**, 551 (1961).
4. Alfrey, Jr., T., Wiederhorn, N., Stein, R., and Tobolsky, A., *J. Colloid Sci.*, **4**, 211 (1949).
5. Alfrey, Jr., T., Wiederhorn, N., Stein, R., and Tobolsky, A., *Ind. Eng. Chem.*, **41**, 701 (1949).
6. Anderson, A. A., and Moffitt, G. L., *Modern Plastics*, **35**, 139 (Apr., 1958).
7. Andrews, R. D., *J. Appl. Phys.*, **25**, 1223 (1954).
8. Andrews, R. D., and Rudd, J. F., *J. Appl. Phys.*, **28**, 1091 (1957).
9. Axilrod, B. M., Sherman, M. A., Cohen, V., and Wolock, I., *J. Research Nat. Bur. Standards* **49**, 331 (1952).

10. Axilrod, B. M., Sherman, M. A., Cohen, V., and Wolock, I., *Modern Plastics*, **30**, 117 (Dec., 1952).
11. Bailey, J., *Modern Plastics*, **24**, 127 (Oct., 1946).
12. Bailey, J., *India Rubber World*, **118**, 225 (1948).
13. Ballman, R. L., and Toor, H. L., *Modern Plastics*, **38**, 113 (Oct., 1960).
14. Ballou, J. W., and Smith, J. C., *J. Appl. Phys.*, **20**, 493 (1949).
15. Bobalek, E. G., Lacson, J., and Dawson, W. R., *J. Appl. Polymer Sci.*, **3**, 113 (1960).
16. Boyer, R. F., and Spencer, R. S., *J. Appl. Phys.*, **16**, 594 (1945).
17. Brown, G. L., *J. Polymer Sci.*, **22**, 423 (1956).
18. Bryant, K. C., and Hulse, G., "Plastics Progress, 1955," p. 227, Morgan, P., Ed., London, Iliffe and Sons, Ltd., 1956.
19. Buchdahl, R., and Nielsen, L. E., Unpublished data of Monsanto Chemical Company.
20. Bueche, F., *J. Polymer Sci.*, **22**, 113 (1956).
21. Chappel, F. P., *Polymer*, **1**, 409 (1960).
22. Charch, W. H., and Moseley, Jr., W. W., *Textile Research J.*, **29**, 525 (1959).
23. Cheatham, R. G., and Dietz, A. G. H., *Modern Plastics*, **29**, 113 (Sept., 1951).
24. Cheatham, R. G., and Dietz, A. G. H., *Trans. Am. Soc. Mech. Eng.*, **74**, 31 (1952).
25. Cleereman, K. J., Karam, H. J., and Williams, J. L., *Modern Plastics*, **30**, 119 (May, 1953).
26. Coker, E. G., and Filon, L. N. G., "Treatise on Photoelasticity," p. 185, Cambridge, University Press, 1931.
27. Collins, R. L., *J. Polymer Sci.*, **27**, 75 (1958).
28. Crawford, S. M., *Proc. Phys. Soc. London*, **66**, 884 (1953).
29. Crawford, S. M., and Kolsky, H., *Proc. Phys. Soc. London*, **64**, 119 (1951).
30. Elliott, A., Ambrose, E. J., and Temple, R. B., *J. Chem. Phys.*, **16**, 877 (1948).
31. Fortner, C. P., *Rubber World*, **129**, 493 (1954).
32. Greenhoe, J. A., *Plastic Tech.*, **6**, No. 10, 43 (Oct., 1960).
33. Gurnee, E. F., Patterson, L. T., and Andrews, R. D., *J. Appl. Phys.*, **26**, 1106 (1955).
34. Hathaway, C. T., *Soc. Plastics Eng. J.*, **17**, 567 (June, 1961).
35. Heffelfinger, C. J., and Burton, R. L., *J. Polymer Sci.*, **47**, 289 (1960).
36. Heller, W., and Oppenheimer, H., *J. Colloid Sci.*, **3**, 33 (1948).
37. Hellwege, K. H., Kaiser, R., and Kuphal, K., *Kolloid Z.*, **147**, 155 (1956).
38. Hellwege, K. H., Kaiser, R., and Kuphal, K., *Kolloid Z.*, **157**, 27 (1958).
39. Hillier, K. W., *Trans. Inst. Rubber Ind.*, **26**, 64 (1950).
40. Hillier, K. W., and Kolsky, H., *Proc. Phys. Soc. London*, **62**, 111 (1949).
41. Hoegberg, H., "International Symposium on Plastics Testing and Standardization," Spec. Tech. Publ. No. 247, p. 95, Philadelphia, Am. Soc. Testing Materials, Oct., 1958.
42. Hoff, E. A. W., Clegg, P. L., and Sherrard-Smith, K., *Brit. Plastics*, **31**, 384 (1958).
43. Horsley, R. A., "Plastics Progress, 1957," p. 77, Morgan, P., Ed., London, Iliffe and Sons, Ltd., 1958.
44. Horsley, R. A., Lee, D. J. A., and Wright, P. B., "Physical Properties of Polymers," Soc. Chem. Ind. Monograph No. 5, p. 63, New York, Macmillan Co., 1959.

45. Hsiao, C. C., and Sauer, J. A., *J. Appl. Phys.*, **21**, 1071 (1950).
46. Huck, N. D., and Clegg, P. L., *Soc. Plastics Eng. Trans.*, **1**, 121 (1961).
47. Huff, K., and Mueller, F. H., *Kolloid Z.*, **153**, 5 (1957).
48. Hurst, D. A., *Soc. Plastics Eng. J.*, **12**, 18 (May, 1956).
49. Igonin, L. A., Ovchinnikov, Y. V., and Arzhakov, S. A., *Doklady Akad. Nauk. S.S.S.R.*, **120**, 1062 (1958); *Rubber Chem. and Technol.*, **32**, 527 (1959).
50. Illers, K. H., *Makromol. Chem.*, **38**, 168 (1960).
51. Illers, K. H., and Jenckel, E., *Rheol. Acta*, **1**, 322 (1958).
52. Jackson, G. B., and Ballman, R. L., *Soc. Plastics Eng. J.*, **16**, No. 10, 1147 (1960).
53. Jackson, G. B., and Cohen, L., Unpublished data of Monsanto Chemical Co.
54. Jacobs, H., and Jenckel, E., *Makromol. Chem.*, **47**, 72 (1961).
55. Jones, G. G., and Miles, F. D., *J. Soc. Chem. Ind.*, **52**, 251T (1933).
56. Keller, A., *Kolloid Z.*, **165**, 15 (1959).
57. Keskkula, H., and Norton, Jr., J. W., *J. Appl. Polymer Sci.*, **2**, 289 (1959).
58. Krassig, H., and Kitchen, W., *J. Polymer Sci.*, **51**, 123 (1961).
59. Lamble, J. H., and Dahmouch, E. S., *British J. Appl. Phys.*, **9**, 388 (1958).
60. McCrum, N. G., *ASTM Bull.* No. 242, 80 (Dec., 1959).
61. McLoughlin, J. R., and Tobolsky, A. V., *J. Polymer Sci.*, **7**, 658 (1951).
62. Mason, P., "Physical Properties of Polymers," Soc. Chem. Ind. Monograph No. 5, p. 262, New York, Macmillan Co., 1959.
63. Mason, P., *J. Appl. Polymer Sci.*, **1**, 63 (1959).
64. Mason, P., *J. Appl. Polymer Sci.*, **5**, 428 (1961).
65. Maxwell, B., *J. Appl. Polymer Sci.*, **5**, S11 (1961).
66. Maxwell, B., and Rahm, L. F., *Ind. Eng. Chem.*, **41**, 1988 (1949).
67. Melchore, J. A., and Mark, H. F., *Modern Plastics*, **31**, 141 (Nov., 1953).
68. Merz, E., Nielsen, L., and Buchdahl, R., *J. Polymer Sci.*, **4**, 605 (1949).
69. Miller, R. L., *Polymer*, **1**, 135 (1960).
70. Morey, D. R., and Martin, E. V., *Textile Research J.*, **21**, 607 (1951).
71. Moseley, Jr., W. W., *J. Appl. Polymer Sci.*, **3**, 266 (1960).
72. Mueller, F. H., and Huff, K., *Kolloid Z.*, **145**, 157 (1956).
73. Mueller, F. H., and Huff, K., *Kolloid Z.*, **164**, 34 (1959).
74. Newman, S., and Cox, W. P., *J. Polymer Sci.*, **46**, 29 (1960).
75. Nielsen, L. E., *J. Appl. Polymer Sci.*, **2**, 351 (1959).
76. Nielsen, L. E., *J. Appl. Polymer Sci.*, **1**, 24 (1959).
77. Nielsen, L. E., and Buchdahl, R., *J. Chem. Phys.*, **17**, 839 (1949).
78. Nielsen, L. E., and Buchdahl, R., *J. Colloid Sci.*, **5**, 282 (1950).
79. Nielsen, L. E., and Buchdahl, R., *J. Appl. Phys.*, **21**, 488 (1950).
80. Novikov, A. S., Dorokhina, T. V., and Zubov, P. I., *Rubber Chem. and Technol.*, **31**, 27 (1958).
81. Passaglia, E., and Koppehele, H. P., *J. Polymer Sci.*, **33**, 281 (1958).
82. Patterson, D., and Ward, I. M., *Trans. Faraday Soc.*, **53**, 1516 (1957).
83. Pomeroy, C. D., *Brit. J. Appl. Phys.*, **12**, 3 (1961).
84. Ranby, B. G., and Brumberger, H., *Polymer*, **1**, 399 (1960).
85. Rudd, J. F., and Andrews, R. D., *J. Appl. Phys.*, **31**, 818 (1960).
86. Rudd, J. F., and Gurnee, E. F., *J. Appl. Phys.*, **28**, 1096 (1957).
87. Sandomirskii, D. M., and Gagina, K., *Rubber Chem. and Technol.*, **28**, 527 (1955).
88. Sauer, J. A., and Hsiao, C. C., *Trans. Am. Soc. Mech. Eng.*, **75**, 895 (1953).
89. Saunders, D. W., *Trans. Faraday Soc.*, **52**, 1414 (1956).

90. Saunders, D. W., *Trans. Faraday Soc.*, **53**, 860 (1957).
91. Saunders, D. W., "Rheology of Elastomers," Mason, P., and Wookey, N., Ed., Chap. 3, p. 30, New York, Pergamon Press, 1958.
92. Saunders, D. W., "Physical Properties of Polymers," Soc. Chem. Ind. Monograph No. 5, p. 15, New York, Macmillan Co., 1959.
93. Schilling, H., *Kolloid Z.*, **175**, 110 (1961).
94. Shearer, N. H., Guillet, J. E., and Coover, H. W., *Soc. Plastics Eng. J.*, **17**, 83 (1961).
95. Spence, J., *J. Phys. Chem.*, **43**, 865 (1939).
96. Spencer, R. S., and Gilmore, G. D., *Modern Plastics*, **28**, 97 (December, 1950).
97. Starkweather, Jr., H. W., and Brooks, R. E., *J. Appl. Polymer Sci.*, **1**, 236 (1959).
98. Starkweather, Jr., H. W., Moore, G. E., Hansen, J. E., Roder, T. M., and Brooks, R. E., *J. Polymer Sci.*, **21**, 189 (1956).
99. Statton, W. O., and Geil, P. H., *J. Appl. Polymer Sci.*, **3**, 357 (1960).
100. Stein, R. S., *J. Polymer Sci.*, **24**, 383 (1957).
101. Stein, R. S., Holmes, F. H., and Tobolsky, A. V., *J. Polymer Sci.*, **14**, 443 (1954).
102. Stein, R. S., Krimm, S., and Tobolsky, A. V., *Textile Research J.*, **19**, 8 (1949).
103. Stein, R. S., and Norris, F. H., *J. Polymer Sci.*, **21**, 381 (1956).
104. Stein, R. S., and Tobolsky, A. V., *Textile Research J.*, **18**, 201 (1948).
105. Stein, R. S., and Tobolsky, A. V., *Textile Research J.*, **18**, 302 (1948).
106. Stuart, H. A., "Die Physik der Hochpolymeren," Vol. 3, Chap. 5, p. 336, Berlin, Springer Verlag,
107. Thomas, P. E., Lontz, J. F., Sperati, C. A., and McPherson, J. L., *Soc. Plastics Eng. J.*, **12**, 89 (June, 1956).
108. Thompson, A. B., and Woods, D. W., *Trans. Faraday Soc.*, **52**, 1383 (1956).
109. Tjader, T. C., and Protzman, T. F., *J. Polymer Sci.*, **20**, 591 (1956).
110. Tokita, N., *J. Polymer Sci.*, **20**, 515 (1956).
111. Treloar, L. R. G., *Trans. Faraday Soc.*, **50**, 881 (1954).
112. Treloar, L. R. G., "The Physics of Rubber Elasticity," Oxford, Clarendon Press, 1958.
113. Wakelin, J. H., Voong, E. T. L., Montgomery, D. J., and Dusenbury, J. H., *J. Appl. Phys.*, **26**, 786 (1955).
114. Ward, I. M., *Textile Research J.*, **31**, 650 (1961).
115. Weyland, H. G., *Textile Research J.*, **31**, 629 (1961).
116. Wijga, P. W. O., "Physical Properties of Polymers," Soc. Chem. Ind. Monograph No. 5, p. 35, New York, Macmillan Co., 1959.
117. Williams, M. L., Landel, R. F., Ferry, J. D., *J. Am. Chem. Soc.*, **77**, 3701 (1955).
118. Winogradoff, N. N., and Bisset, D. C., *J. Polymer Sci.*, **26**, 187 (1957).
119. Wolock, I., Axilrod, B. M., and Sherman, M. A., *Modern Plastics*, **31**, 128 (September 1953).
120. Wolock, I., and George, D., *Soc. Plastics Eng. J.*, **12**, 20 (Feb., 1956).
121. Woods, D. W., *Nature*, **174**, 753 (1954).

SYMBOLS

a	Half axis length of an ellipse perpendicular to direction of stress (Chap. 6)
a	Length of a crack (Chap. 6).
a	Radius of circle of contact (Chap. 9).
A	Cross-sectional area.
A	A constant.
A_i	Amplitude of the ith oscillation (Chap. 7).
A_T	Williams-Landel-Ferry shift factor.
b	Half axis length of an ellipse parallel to direction of stress (Chap. 6).
B	Bulk modulus.
B	A constant.
B	Optical path difference for light vibrating parallel and perpendicular to direction of orientation (Chap. 10).
C	Width of test specimen.
d	Density.
D	Thickness of test specimen.
DB	Decibel (Chap. 7).
E	Young's modulus.
$E_r(t)$	Stress relaxation modulus.
E^*	Complex Young's modulus.
E'	Real part of complex Young's modulus.
E''	Imaginary part of complex Young's modulus.
E''/E'	Dissipation factor, a damping term.
$E_{\parallel}$	Young's modulus measured parallel to direction of chain alignment (Chap. 10).
f	Free volume fraction (Chap. 2).
f	Frequency, cycles/second.
f	Segmental friction coefficient (Chap. 8).
f_0	Segmental coefficient in absence of intermolecular entanglements (Chap. 8).
f_r	Resonance frequency.
F	Force.
F	Tangential force (Chap. 9).
F	A vibrating reed damping factor (Chap. 7).
g	Acceleration of gravity.
G	Shear modulus.
G_0	Shear modulus of two-phase systems.
G_1	Shear modulus of continuous phase in two-phase systems.
G_2	Shear modulus of dispersed phase (filler) in two-phase systems.
G^*	Complex shear modulus.
G'	Real part of complex shear modulus.
G''	Imaginary part of complex shear modulus.
G''/G'	Dissipation factor, a damping term.

h	Depth of penetration or indentation.
H	Heat energy dissipated per unit volume of material (Chap. 7).
$H(\tau)$ or $H(\ln \tau)$	Distribution of relaxation times.
I	Polar moment of inertia.
J	Compliance.
J'	Real part of complex compliance.
J''	Imaginary part of complex compliance.
k	Boltzmann's constant (Chap. 10).
K	A constant.
K	A geometric constant (Chap. 7).
K	Rate of strain or rate of elongation (Chap. 5).
L	Length of test specimen.
L_0	Original length.
$L(\tau)$ or $L(\ln \tau)$	Distribution of retardation times.
M	Molecular weight.
M	Ratio of amplitudes of free and clamped ends of a vibrating reed (Chap. 7).
M_0	Molecular weight of monomeric unit.
M_c	Molecular weight between crosslinks or between interchain entanglements.
$\bar{M}_n$	Number average molecular weight.
$\bar{M}_w$	Weight average molecular weight.
n	A constant.
n	A constant in Nutting equation (Chap. 8).
n	Number of monomeric units of same kind in a sequence in a copolymer (Chap. 2).
n	Refractive index of unoriented material (Chap. 10).
$(n_\parallel - n_\perp)$	Birefringence, the difference between refractive indices parallel and perpendicular to direction of molecular orientation.
N	Number of segments in a molecule (Chap. 4).
$N_A(n)$	Mole fraction of sequences of material A in a copolymer that are of length n units (Chap. 2).
$N(t)$	Number of network chains carrying a load at any time t (Chap. 4).
p	Plastic work or fracture energy (Chap. 6).
P	Hydrostatic pressure.
P	Period of oscillations (Chap. 7).
q	Swelling ratio.
Q	Q-factor, E'/E'' (Chap. 7).
r	Radius.
r	Radius of curvature at tip of a crack (Chap. 6).
R	Gas constant.
R	Resilience (Chap. 7).
R_0	Retardation of light (Chap. 10).
S	Shear displacement.
t	Time.
t_B	Time to break.
T	Temperature (Generally °K).
T	Torque (Chap. 1).

T_g	Glass transition temperature.
T_m	Melting point.
T_m°	Melting point of pure homopolymer of infinite molecular weight.
v	Velocity.
v_i	Volume fraction of component i.
v_1	Volume fraction of solvent (Chap. 2).
v_1	Volume fraction of material in the continuous phase of two-phase systems (Chap. 6).
v_2	Volume fraction of polymer in a swollen gel (Chap. 3).
v_2	Volume fraction of material in the dispersed phase of two-phase systems (Chap. 6).
$\bar{v}$	Specific volume of a multicomponent system.
$\bar{v}_i$	Specific volume of component i.
$\bar{v}_2$	Specific volume of polymer (Chap. 3).
V	Volume.
V_0	Original volume.
V_1	Molar volume of solvent.
V_u	Molar volume of polymer repeat unit.
W	Tensile load or weight used to deform a beam.
W_c	Degree of crystallinity.
W_i	Weight fraction of component i.
$W_A(n)$	Weight fraction of material A in a copolymer which is in sequences containing n units of monomeric type A.
X_A	Mole fraction of component A.
Y	Deflection or displacement of a beam by an applied force or load W.
Z	Number of atoms in the backbone of a polymer chain.
α (alpha)	Extension ratio L/L_0 .
α	Attentuation factor (Chap. 7).
$(\alpha_\parallel - \alpha_\perp)$	Difference in polarizability of a polymer segment parallel and perpendicular to direction of chain segment.
$\beta_\parallel$	Coefficient of thermal expansion parallel to direction of molecular orientation.
$\beta_\perp$	Coefficient of thermal expansion perpendicular to direction of molecular orientation.
γ (Gamma)	Surface free energy per unit of area (Chap. 6).
$\dot{\gamma}$	Rate of shear.
δ (delta)	A constant (Chap. 6).
δ	Phase difference in radians for light vibrating parallel and perpendicular to direction of orientation (Chap. 10).
$\tan \delta$	Dissipation factor.
Δ	Logarithmic decrement.
ΔH	Energy of activation, or heat of reaction.
ΔH_u	Heat of fusion per mole of crystalline polymer repeating unit.
ϵ (epsilon)	Strain.
ϵ_s	Shear strain.
ϵ_y	Elongation or strain at yield.
ϵ_B	Elongation or strain at break (ultimate elongation).
ϵ'	Dielectric constant (Chap. 8).

ϵ''	Electrical loss factor (Chap. 8).
η (eta)	Viscosity.
η^*	Complex viscosity.
η'	Real part of complex viscosity.
η''	Imaginary part of complex viscosity.
η_a	Apparent melt viscosity.
η_c	Consistency.
θ (theta)	Shear angle (Chap. 1).
θ	Angle of twist (Chap. 7).
κ (kappa)	Electrical conductivity (Chap. 8).
λ (lambda)	Wavelength of a sound wave.
λ_i	Ratio of number average molecular weight of blend to number average molecular weight of component i (Chap. 4).
μ (mu)	Geometric shape factor.
μ	Coefficient of friction (Chap. 9).
μ_r	Coefficient of rolling friction (Chap. 9).
ν (nu)	Poisson's ratio.
σ (sigma)	Stress.
σ_s	Shear stress.
σ_y	Yield stress.
σ_B	Tensile strength.
τ (tau)	Relaxation time, or retardation time.
ϕ (phi)	Angle of twist in radians (Chap. 1).
χ_1 (chi)	First neighbor interaction parameter (Chap. 2).
ψ (psi)	Specific damping capacity.
ω (omega)	Angular frequency in radians per second.

AUTHOR INDEX

SUBJECT INDEX